MEDITERRANEAN
HOMESICK
BLUES

By Ben Chatfield

With Enzo Cilenti

It's been quoted many times before, but that's because it is perfect...

"Twenty years from now you will be more disappointed by the things that you didn't do than by the ones you did do. So throw off the bowlines. Sail away from the safe harbour. Catch the trade winds in your sails. Explore. Dream. Discover."

MARK 'You can quote me on that' TWAIN

First published in 2012 by
LYC Publishing
24 Endell Street
London
WC2H 9HQ

A CIP catalogue record for this book is available from the British Library

ISBN 978-0-9574103-0-5

Brand and product names are trademarks or registered trademarks of their respective owners.

Lovingly created by Infinite Authors
Printed in Great Britain

Quotes
Page 26 from The Rolling Stones' 'Tumbling Dice'
Page 42 from F. Scott Fitzgerald's *Tender Is The Night*
Page 60 & Page 206 from Brigitte Bardot's 'Nue Au Soleil'
Page 62 from Gerry Rafferty's 'Baker Street'
Page 147 from The Rolling Stones' 'Sympathy For The Devil'
Page 158 from DJ Shadow's 'Lost & Found'
Page 223 from Primal Scream's 'Jailbird'
Page 229 from Radiohead's 'Fake Plastic Trees'
Page 272 from Manu Chao's 'Bongo Bong'
Page 296 from Rupert Everett's *Red Carpets and Other Banana Skins*
Page 316 from Edna St Vincent Millay's 'Recuerdo'

La table des matières

Prologue 11
University of Warwick, Coventry. 19
A semi-detached house, Sutton, London 20

L'Automne 23
1 Old golfers 24
2 Balade Niçoise. 26
   Des bouches des bébés 34
3 Ritchie Canningham. 36
4 Yes, I Cannes. 40
   Le Petit Guide Cannois (Partie 1). 43
5 Ma bande à part 45
   Le croissant. 47
6 Mind that child! 55
7 Ma Madrague 59
8 Baby, let's play house 61
   Le Petit Guide Cannois (Partie 2). 63
9 For crying out loud 65
10 Cui Bono?. 68
   Les 19 livres que je dois lire cette année, et leurs
   argumentaires éclaires. 72
11 Cannes 90210. 74
   Ne prenez pas infraction: des actions et des gestes
   des gens du midi. 79
12 Charlotte's Web. 80
   Le Petit Guide Cannois (Partie 3). 87
13 Waiting for Enzo 89
   Comprendre pourquoi Serge est si important
   pour les français 93
14 The Paving Stone Roses. 95

L'Hiver 99

15 The staff room 100
16 Corsica starts on England, France steps in 108
    La Corse 110
    Jean-Paul Sartre (dans le cas où vous l'auriez manqué) . . . 117
17 Play the way you're facing 119
18 londres 125
19 Sapphic Christmas 127
20 What do you do for money, honey? 133
21 Absinthe makes the heart grow fonder 138
    Le guide existential du foot français 144
    Les Îles Cannoises 152
22 Je m'appelle Paul Newman 153
23 Le hard stuff 160
24 A la recherche du temps gâché 167

Le Printemps 169

    Claude MC et la montée de hip hop Français 170
25 Another one bites the dust 172
    Le supermarche Français: tout ce que vous
    devez savoir 177
    Trente-cinq mots français que vous avez oublie
    qu'on utilise en anglais 181
26 Nu 183
27 Going bananes in Cannes 190
    Monaco ou Monte-Carlo? 191
    Planète Marseille: Partie 1 195
    Planète Marseille: Partie 2 la bagarre, le foot et
    les fascistes. Et Bernard Tapie 198
28 The girl with the cappuccino tresses 204
29 Pass the hemlock 220
30 Before you slip into unconciousness... 225
31 What fresh Hell is this? 228
32 Odi et amo 230

L'Eté 239

33 Pampelonne Babylonne......................... 240
    Pampelonne: la vie à la plage 243
34 The Master and Large Margarita 248
35 "Never confuse charisma with a loud voice" 251
    St.Tropez: Cause Célèb........................... 258
36 Cabane 260
    B.B. – Brigitte Bardot Et Dieu Créa la Femme......... 264
37 The Glimmer Twins............................... 266
38 L'année des Méduses............................. 272
    **Phrases familières et parfois impolies que je
    n'aurais jamais appris ailleurs qu'au restau** 277
39 Living dolls..................................... 280
40 You got the client you always wanted.................. 285
41 Le cri.. 289
42 In the club...................................... 296
43 From Queer to Eternity............................ 303
44 Tigers play too rough.............................. 306
    Voici Johnny!!!!! 308
45 Salut, Pierrot.................................... 313
46 Three men and a little scooter 314
    **Un an plus tard: des actions et des gestes charmants
    des gens du midi**................................ 317
47 And in the end... 318
48 Hi honey, I'm home!.............................. 324
49 University of Warwick, Coventry, October 1995........ 328

University of Warwick, Coventry, December 1995......... 331
Outro... 332

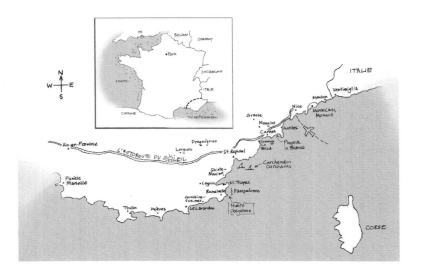

Acknowledgements

I would like to thank lots of people; Victoria, Mum, Dad, Sod. And those that were there; Alistair and Pollyanna particularly (and for the longevity), Charlotte, Andreas, Jason Priestley, Taba, Fabressa, Patrick and Bernard, Ines, Monsieur Guy Rufin, Lee, Adam. Dr Oliver Davis at the University of Warwick. And also Sarah Rogers. The British Council, particularly Daniel Lovelock and Talin Chakmakjian for their early support and championing.

Enzo would like to thank Sienna, Lucia and Valentina.

Everything you read in this book happened. Though not necessarily in that order.

None of the characters are fictitious and each person does, to the author's knowledge, still exist.

Their names have been changed to protect the innocent, the feeble minded and so as not to upset some of the more criminally inclined people the author may have got drunk with.

Thank you.

Front cover designed with Mark Petty at ParkGrande.

Prologue

"It was the best of times, it was the worst of times."

"My name is Charles Highway, but you wouldn't think it to look at me."

"Lolita, light of my life, fire of my loins."

"It was a bright cold day in April, and the clocks were striking thirteen."

"In my younger and more vulnerable years my father gave me some advice that I've been turning over in my mind ever since."

"Somewhere in la Mancha, in a place whose name I do not care to remember, a gentleman lived not long ago, one of those who has a lance and ancient shield on a shelf and keeps a skinny nag and a greyhound for racing."

"If you really want to hear about it, the first thing you'll probably want to know is where I was born, and what my lousy childhood was like, and how my parents were occupied and all before they had me, and all that David Copperfield kind of crap, but I don't feel like going into it, if you want to know the truth."[1]

The course tutor dramatically opened the day by reading out classic openings to stories. It was inspiring. The creative writing course was

1 *A Tale of Two Cities* by Charles Dickens, *The Rachel Papers* by Martin Amis, *Lolita* by Vladimir Nabokov, *1984* by George Orwell, *The Great Gastby* by F.Scott Fitzgerald, *Don Quixote* by Miguel de Cervantes and *The Catcher In The Rye* by J.D. Salinger.

called 'Autobiography into Fiction' and we were to start our programme by writing our own. As a class we were then asked to write a paragraph on something that happened to us once. It was a broad brief. Rather pathetically I sat there struggling for five long minutes. Everyone else scribbled frenziedly. I could not think of a single thing that had ever happened to me, ever. I began to get hot under the collar and started feeling like I was sitting in a Biology exam at school having mistakenly revised Physics. The tutor came round and somewhat condescendingly tried to help me. I am thirty-five. I was told to try and remember one interesting year of my life. As the flop sweat gathered I couldn't only not remember one interesting year of my life, I couldn't remember any years. I became the amazing man with no past.

Breathing deeply I came to the conclusion that I don't have a stand-out year. Not on a writing-about-it scale. I pored over my life for tragedy, celebrity, infamy...nothing...shark attack. Ooooh. Shark attack. I had recently watched the only known footage of a shark attack on YouTube in order to feed my irrational fear of nature's perfect predators and decided to make up a story about that. My story actually contained the line, "I learned that I had almost drowned as my body struggled to remain buoyant without the use of my non-existent legs."

We went around the class reading out our short œuvres and I listened to wonderfully crafted travel stories about arriving in Belize for the first time and the smell of the night air in Belmopan (there were two). I decided not to read out my infantile, voyeuristic and slightly disturbing shark tale. Our homework was to continue our opening and develop it into a draft of a story, loosely titled 'My Defining Year'. I shelved the shark and started to write this, the entirely autobiographical-into-fictional story-cum-diary-cum-scrapbook of a year in the life of someone you have never heard of. Entirely based on work I started fifteen years ago.

I have read that among screenwriters there is an old metaphor for crafting stories in films. Act I, send a man up a tree; Act II, throw rocks at him; Act III, get him down again. That was my basis for this story. I needed a tree.

I started my higher education on the first branch up a big posh tree at the University of Nottingham in 1992, which I hated with a passion. I hated university in general because it intimidated me and I didn't feel like I belonged there. I loved London and should have stayed put. I needed the distant sound of police sirens to get me to sleep. I hated all the public school kids walking around with airs and graces, all posh hair and with a social confidence I could only dream of. I had set this out in my head early on. I went there with a closed mind and a very balanced aspiring working class into lower-middle class view of things – I had a chip on each shoulder. Not the best bedrock on which to be making the biggest decision of my life. And yet inside I desperately wanted to like it. Or just be liked.

Against the odds on the first day I made friends with a cheery Aston Villa fan called Tom. I was relieved more than words can say when he agreed to knock for me that night, so I would at least have someone to attend the first night toga party (what?) with at the Hall's own Students' Union. Somewhat disappointingly he never knocked and I lacked the intestinal fortitude to venture out of my room on my own. I spent the night listening to the sounds of seven hundred people getting more and more pissed about twenty metres away and making merry as I nursed my pathetic and fragile ego in my increasingly tiny space (the walls were moving in) in the red-brick courtyard, paralysed by shyness.

Day Two, a significant one in university terms, and I had no friends at all. Due to my failure to read the prospectus properly with the course sign-up dates, I then missed all the slots that morning to go and sign up for what I had actually gone there to study. I ended up stuck with French Language and History twinned with the last-puppy-in-the-window courses of Theology and Political Geography in my first 'semester'. This double-header of social leprosy (self-perceived) and academic uselessness (evident, as I had not envisaged a career as a priest living in a left-wing mountain community in the Massif Central) dovetailed beautifully with my immature self and forced a decision to leave university and return to my chosen career of garden clearance, creosoting and lawn mowing.

BEN CHATFIELD

GARDENING
ANY OUTDOOR WORK UNDERTAKEN
GARDEN CLEARANCES
PAINTING AND CREOSOTING

telephone 081 644 8131

My state of the art Letraset business card

After much self-analysis and chatting with parents I was convinced that this did seem a little like throwing the baby (me) out with the bathwater (Nottingham). I had worked hard through grammar school, an industrious if non-gifted student, and repeated visits to see my best friend, Sod, at the University of Warwick (where I had been offered a place initially, and might have gone if the IRA had not called in a warning the morning of my open day thus shutting down London Transport) convinced me that there was a lot of fun to be had if you were in the right place for you. Warwick had been described in an article in *The Telegraph* as looking like "a child run amok with LEGO in the middle of the countryside". I instantly liked it. Despite their similar standings I also found it amusing that alumni at Nottingham included D.H. Lawrence and Warwick's included Timmy Mallett. This led to an application for an unheard-of transfer mid-term, something akin to signing for someone in football's January transfer window when no such thing existed.

The transfer was declined but the hospitable French department at Warwick, plus a kindly girl with a philanthropic streak in Sod's halls, saw to it that all was not lost. After much help from the irascible, yet substantial, deputy head of my secondary school, an end of year transfer was agreed. This meant that I just had to spend my first year in leafy Nottingham and attain a 2:1 overall to get my dream move. Tick, tick, tick, tick.... Boom! Varsity heaven was just round the corner.

During those bleak and lonely eight months in Nottingham I visited Warwick on an almost weekly basis using my National Express coachcard for enormous trans-Midlands savings and incredibly long journeys (once we clocked up six hours on the 30-mile trip) and managed to:

- make one solitary friend called Dominic, who wore a Bon Jovi denim jacket (BAD MEDICINE World Tour) to lectures, and was so small he walked on tiptoes;
- join the windsurfing association as a novice, attending a session once, at which I learned that urinating in a wetsuit keeps you warm and that windsurfing is very much as hard as it looks;
- be the first person in the hall's history to breakfast on my own every single day of Term One at 7.30 am in the oak-panelled dining room (my own perceived record);
- be the only person all year to be rejected from a 'formal dinner' (I didn't own a tie);
- watch a phenomenal amount of MTV in the Junior Common Room (hence it followed that I developed a taste for new jack swing music like Jodeci, WrecksNEffect, Teddy Riley and Guy), and my own company;
- cement both of these tastes when I got a part-time job at McDonalds in the city centre.

I developed a passionate belief in the theory that jocks and prom queen-types go on to lead pedestrian and empty lives while the ones who developed problems getting laid (or getting a conversation even) went on to rule the world. I was just waiting for the universe to make its first move.

I left Nottingham on June 9th, 1993. I had packed my bags by 8 am and spent the day, as I had spent most of the previous 246, watching characters I had got to know way too intimately on 'Yo! MTV Raps' and 'The Real World'.[2] In the afternoon, while other students went on the lash to celebrate finishing exams I watched, emotionless (normally this would make me emotion-al), as England were beaten 2-0 by the USA at football and literally never looked back as my Dad and I packed up the car and we headed for London to prepare for the rest of my life.

My second university year at Warwick lived up to my dreams of clubs, drugs, tugs and jugs. And actually having some real-life, not

2 'The Real World' was an early version of Big Brother in which immature and selfish American jocks and prom queens were filmed being spiteful to each other which would later be hailed as influential in the worst possible sense.

'Real World', friends. Plus a social life that involved leaving my room. In fact I embraced that second year like a demon, attempting to make up for my disastrous first year with a new-found gusto. Aside from the obvious stuff my course had suddenly become incredible. Where once were ox-bow lakes, proportional representation and Jesus now was French cinema! It was a linear journey through the greats, starting with *Les Enfants du Paradis*[3] and taking in *La Règle du Jeu, Partie de Campagne, Tirez sur le Pianiste*, the explosion of *La Nouvelle Vague* with *L'Année Dernière à Marienbad, Les Quatre Cent Coups, A Bout de Souffle, Hiroshima Mon Amour, Bande A Part, Alphaville, Ma Nuit Chez Maud* and *Pierrot le Fou*. Then it was the 70s and 80s with *Le Genou de Claire* and Depardieu's tour de force, *Cyrano de Bergerac*. We were in the hands of an incredible tutor who brought everything to life, telling us how Tarantino had stolen a particular idea for *Reservoir Dogs* or how *Dirty Harry* had been inspired by that jump cut or extreme close-up. And now here I was, at the apex of my very own *nouvelle vague*, self-absorbed to the point of eating myself, beguiled by everything (weed-smoking a factor)... a francophilic Walter Mitty.

And then my third year as a student, to be spent in France as a language assistant, lay out in front of me. This is the story of that year.

As I had not applied for any of France's overseas *départements* (Guadeloupe, Martinique, French Guiana, La Réunion, Mayotte) I knew that I would be based somewhere on the mainland, so between about one hundred miles and eight hundred miles from my home town of London. Considering the significance I am about to attach to it I was ridiculously close to my home in London. But to me it felt like Vietnam. So this book is kind of like *Apocalypse Now* without the helicopters.

The linear story was pieced together from memories, bits of a diary,

---

3 The Children of Paradise/The Children of The Gods: If you have not seen any old French films this is the one to start with. Incredible in every respect but primarily its actual production at all, filmed as it was in a time of great penury. Filmed in Nice during the Occupation the Jewish set designer and composer both had to perform their epic work in secrecy. Set on the Boulevard du Crime in 1840s Paris the paradise of the title is a reference to the 'Gods', the highest up, cheapest seats in the house, occupied by the poorest of the poor. The story is centred around Garrance, a magnetic woman with four men in her life and is the ultimate theatre-as-life piece, whilst at the same time being tough and real and timeless.

letters to friends, lots of letters to and from Sod, stacks of anecdotes and daydreams. I have delved deeply into my personal scrapbooks of newspaper cuttings, magazines and old bits of paper, hoarded like a serial killer in shoeboxes. I have scoured thousands of magazines searching for the one in which I turned the bottom right-hand corner over to remind me that in the moment of reading it I thought it was genius and one day it would inspire 'my book'. I have written down over four thousand quotes, reread books I have loved to try and work out exactly why and listened to lyrics over and over to work out what it was I connected with in them so much. My study is a derivative one but as George Orwell said, "No-one draws water from the well when he can run the tap." Probably easier to say when you have just written *Animal Farm*. But I am agreeing with it and my tap is left running on full.

The principal function was that my tutor at Warwick suggested that I should write a diary, as it could form the bedrock of my final year language examination. This would mean that I could avoid having to learn about something like 'Third Wave Immigration in the Cities of Northern France' for that particular part of my degree. Which I saw as a real plus.

Here we go. One year. From soup to nuts. Up a big tree. A big French tree like a *Pin Parasol*. Will the meany French throw rocks at him? Will he get down again? Let's find out. As the greatest French actor of all time, and the coolest man to have walked along the *Champs-Elysées* haranguing a hot girl selling the *International Herald Tribune*,[4] Jean-Paul Belmondo, says,

"*Allons-y, Allonzo.*"

Or in English, 'Let's go, Daddy-O'…

---

4 From *A Bout de Souffle*, AKA *Breathless*.

University of Warwick, Coventry

May 10, 1994

The letters came in today with the allocated schools for the year out. They put up a notice on the French department's notice board. Chris walked up, shook his head and said, "Calais? What will I do at weekends? Get a part-time job in Eastenders[5] on an industrial estate?" Karen has been sentenced to a year in Metz, a kind of French take on Sunderland. She has taken the news like she is from the French version of Newcastle. Jake got Limoges. In his words, "I don't like football, I'm not very industrial and cognac makes me sick." He meant industrious. The twat. Impressive knee-jerk Limoges knowledge, nonetheless.

My three closest friends have, on paper, three shockers. Limoges. Calais. Metz.

But it's not all doom and gloom. Oh no. My eyes finally reach Alpes Maritimes on the map in the dreamy south...Monaco, Nice, Antibes, Cannes...Cannes. That's me. I got Cannes...

I've got Cannes.

---

5 Not the TV show. In the 90s, and before the advent of cheap booze on our shores, the 'booze cruise' was quite the big thing. People would pile into hired vans and take the ferry to these massive warehouses near Calais where you get booze for half the price. I can remember being loaded into the empty car in November and returning late at night with my head wedged between a 48 can tray of Kronenbourg and 8 crates of vin de table. 'Eastenders' was, and maybe still is, the biggest wine and beer emporium in Calais.

A semi-detached house, Sutton, London

June 16, 1994

I am supposed to be writing this diary as of now. But I am not even in France. I don't know what I am supposed to write here. Today I worked for my Uncle Max, labouring on a small building site in Epsom where he is building a garage. Now I am so tired I can barely write. That's it. This is going to be the most boring diary ever. *La Fin.*

July 7, 1994

This is going well. Today I have to write a letter to my new school. I know this because I have received a letter telling me to do it. Fortunately there is a section in the back of my Collins French dictionary, which shows you how to write formal letters. I have been using this template since I was about 14 and should really have moved on. I should also be using a French–French dictionary by now. But it seems like a ridiculous idea.

Tomorrow I am applying the second coat of varnish to Mr and Mrs Halsey's garden fence. She makes lovely cakes and he is a gent who stands with me all day talking about cricket. I don't know it like he does, but I like it when he talks.

MEDITERRANEAN HOMESICK BLUES

Monsieur Benjamin Chatfield
21 Rosehill Gardens
Sutton
Surrey
SM1 3JZ
Tel.081-644-8131

A Monsieur le Principal du Collège E.Roux   Sutton, le 8 juillet 1994

Monsieur le Principal,

Je suis étudiant à l'Université de Warwick et j'ai été nommé dans votre collège en qualité d'assistant d'Anglais pour l'année scolaire 1994-1995. Avant de prendre mes fonctions, je souhaiterais obtenir de plus amples informations en ce qui concerne mes devoirs et mes attributions. Est-il possible de m'envoyer de l'information sur votre école, l'échelle des cours Anglais et l'âge des eleves avec qui je m'occuperai.

Auriez-vous l'obligeance de me faire savoir la date à laquelle je devrais arriver? Vous serait-il également possible de me faire parvenir quelques renseignements sur les possibilités de logement dont je pourrais bénéficier? Je vous en serais très reconnaissant. En plus, est-ce qu'il y a d'autre information dont vous avez besoin d'ici en Angleterre?

Soyez assuré que j'attends la rentrée scolaire avec impatience et que je ferai tout mon possible pour vous donner entière satisfaction.

En attendant de vous rencontrer, je vous prie d'agréer, Monsieur le Principal, l'assurance de mon plus grand dévouement.

Ben Chatfield

Using a typewriter, this was my fourth attempt

L'Automne

Old golfers

September 6 – 2 pm, Heathrow Terminal 2, Gate 23

It is apparent that my Dad checks out women almost as much as I do. This is no mean feat. He actually spotted one that had gone under my US Navy-grade radar equipment. She looks like a kind of Dutch version of Blondie in 1980 meets Linsey Dawn McKenzie[6] meets (can you have a third when you do 'meets'?) Courtney Love. She is most definitely at the same boarding gate as me right here, right now.

Boeing 737, Flight BA 127

I have taken the flight to Nice from Heathrow twice before, but this time everything is very different. As I sit gazing out of the window I put on my headphones and pressed play on a track I have been planning to listen to at this very moment. It sounds like my future. The joy of listening to music as a plane waits on a runway about to take off is a new one to me, but does music ever sound better? More life-alteringly important, more poignant, more personal? There is something so incredibly filmic about this moment that it is overwhelming all my senses and making me think that I am at the start of a Tom Cruise movie. Probably flying back from the Caribbean to New York to win the heart of my gorgeous girl-next-door type, the only woman to believe in me, and, more importantly, make me believe in me. Having almost ruined everything after an affair with an inappropriate, yet very hot, woman because I made some terrible mistake I am about to make her see that I am FOR REAL. Maybe one day we will open a bar together. I am gazing out of the window and for the first time in my life I feel a thrilling sense of what might be, and what is going on around me, and the potential consequences of all my actions. I am 20, so nothing

---

6 Pneumatically-breasted porn star who featured heavily in my life at this point.

really has any long-term significance. Things just kind of happen. Fear is still quite alien to me. Excluding sharks. I was watching the golf the other day with my Dad and he explained why (I had asked) old golfers never win anything. In all logical thinking they should. They can still hit the ball as far and they have all that experience to build on, all that nous. But that is the problem. The Experience. Experience is also the knowledge of what it's like to lose, to fail. And that creates 'The Fear'. I realise therefore that I am a young golfer, I have no fear, all I can see is the green as I strike out long and hard down the fairway.

Later, Boeing 737, Flight BA 127
This is all being heightened by the fact that the Dutch-looking girl spotted in the departure lounge is somewhat brilliantly sitting at the window seat in front of my window seat, although no words have been exchanged. Soundtracked by the opening strains of The Stones' 'Tumbling Dice' (which I am pretty sure that she can hear through my headphones).

She has just ordered a tomato juice with Worcester Sauce. Oh my God, that is exactly what I was going to order.

Ten minutes later, Boeing 737, Flight BA 127
She turned round and peaked over the top of the seat. "Are you listening to the Stones?"

"Honey, got no money,
I'm all sixes and sevens, and nines."

Balade Niçoise

September 6 (still), now about 7 pm

So we were on the plane. It is quite difficult talking to someone who is sat in the window seat in front of your window seat. I stuck my face between the edge of her chair back and the window. But the similarities with the 'Here's Joooohnnnnnyyy' scene in *The Shining* were too much.

We spoke briefly about our shared love of tomato juice. She said, "tomato", I said, "tomato".[7] I established that her name was Charlotte. I told her that my name was "Benjamin". She looked weirded out. I was trying to make myself sound exotic. But managed to make myself sound about four. I said, "Ben, Benjamin, whatever." She laughed. I copied and retreated back to my headphones.

Charlotte, all ruffled blonde hair, blue eyes, green jeans (yes!) and curves, was queuing in front of me at passports when I struck again. I asked her if she was, by any chance, also a 'a language assistant with the Central Bureau programme' heading to the pre-course in the hills of Nice (why do I always think too much?). She was. I even plucked up the courage to tell her that her slightly husky voice reminded me of Anita Pallenberg in *Performance*.[8] We agreed to share a taxi. In the taxi she told me breezily about her boyfriend and her best friend who had seen her off at the airport. I hope she didn't see Dad eyeing her up.

Straight off the bat she told me that her parents were divorced. She went into massive detail about the separation, and how painful it was and how her adored Dad is British Consul to Papua New Guinea.[9]

---

7 That song, 'Let's Call the Whole Thing Off' is the biggest phoney song ever. The lines, "You like potato and I like potahto, You like tomato and I like tomahto" are totally ludicrous. Who on earth says "potahto"?

8 I am going through a slightly obsessive Stones phase here.

9 At the time I thought "Oh My God, we are so connecting!" Now I know that this is what mental people do.

Wherever/whatever that is. She is the perfect blend of troubled, yet wealthy. She described her boyfriend in detail and I created the mental picture of Michael Hutchence, but about 7 feet tall and 36, with pairs of leather maracas instead of hands. She showed me his picture and it proved eerily prescient as a KICK-era Hutchence he is indeed. Her best friend, cosied up to him in the photos, looked about sixty. She also has two children, one of whom Charlotte is Godmother to and looks about four years older than me. Am I reading too much in to this? Doth the lady protest too much?[10]

September 8

Lying on my bunk bed at the Niçois hostel. It is a strange chateau-cum-prison high up in the hills behind Nice. It is the kind of place I imagine the Nazis took quite a liking too when they occupied here, furthering my view that the CENTRAL BUREAU has some shady secrets. We are on the second day of a four-day training course. Yesterday morning we arrived and were shown to our dorm-style rooms with a third floor balcony looking out on to a breathtaking view of the bay of Nice and its unique turquoise blue sea. There are about 50 of us in total, random English students about to be scattered all over middle and secondary schools across the Alpes-Maritimes region (the 'South of France' as we know it) to teach the youth of France how to speak English and what the British are all about. The idea is that we learn a thing or two ourselves. It's an interesting cultural exchange!

The course has thus far involved lots of talks which have mostly involved various ways of telling the boys not to "date" their pupils and the girls not to "date" their teachers. One bloke asked if the male assistants were allowed to "date" their teachers as this combination had not been covered. Chance would be a fine thing. Essentially the message was, "Don't be an idiot." Which is a fairly pointless piece of advice to give to a 20-year-old. It's one of the only things I know how to do.

Last night at dinner I was pretty shocked to hear a guy from Bristol tell us about a rumour that a female assistant in his department had

---

10 Always beware people who are 20 whose boyfriends are 36 and whose best friends are 40.

slept with a whole department of eight teachers a couple of years before in Paris.

I hope I don't need to write this much every day.

Sod

What's happening brother? Listening to that album A LOT! How's Sweden? Send it my regards. Good to chat the other morning. What a dick am I, eh? I am aware you can't respond to this in real time. I don't know where to start so I am just going to write. I am high up in the hills of Nice and I have met an unfeasibly fit bird called Charlotte. Like stupid fit. Makes Pop-Mo Jan look rough. Seriously. Met her minutes after I spoke to you at the airport. Weirdly my Dad spotted her.

There are about 50 of us here and quite clear groupings amongst us already. My friendship (soon to be more? Hmmm. She has a boyfriend who is 36!!!!!) with Charlotte has kind of meant that I have had no problems getting other friends. Her interest in me, and all the other lads' interest in her, I reckon, is making me look more interesting, thus attractive. I used the word interest one too many times there. I have managed to get stuck in the opposite of a vicious circle... the circle that keeps on giving, a kind of charitable, gentle circle. Maybe a shag circle. Haha, no, who knows. This is quite rambling eh? This is where I am...

So, the real reason I write is to tell you this... the people I am spending the most time with....

Andreas Argyros is, much like you, a gentle London Cypriot. Unlike you he is from Enfield and is a giant. Like you he looks a bit like Pete Sampras. Unlike you, ok I will stop that now, it is annoying even me and I am writing it... He can blow smoke rings, which are like perfectly round donuts and he has the largest CD collection I have ever seen. One giant fold-out box is dedicated to Cypriot rock music by artists called things like Armageddon and Rotting Christ. Have you heard of them? He is intensely wary of the food served to us at the centre and seems to always have a plastic bag full of pistachios with him, like Linus' blanket. Or your Mum. He too supports Chelsea which sucks. He started properly missing home today (so after two days) which is fuckin brilliant. He is actually going back to London next weekend, which makes me feel like we are NOT ON THE ADVENTURE I THINK WE ARE. And I don't like that. Last night he danced like he was shadow boxing (I thought he was joking when he did it, then I remembered your brother) and when he has a drink he abstains from imbibing it until everyone else in the round is right near the bottom of their glasses before necking it in one hit.

Alistair Whiston-Thomas is massively my favourite of the lads here and would be yours too. He is from an incredibly different background to us, a fact which both of us seem to find fascinating. Tall and foppishly handsome (did that sound gay?), his blond hair is cut into a long-floppy public school haircut, the like of which you have to go to a proper public school to be able to get, as we have discussed before. The entirety of his limited wardrobe looks like it has been passed down from his great grandfather meaning it all looks really well-made but is also tatty and battered. This just makes it look really dandy (I have started using this word a lot) in my eyes. He has an old flight jacket which looks like it was worn in 'Memphis Belle' and he smokes Gitanes. He looks like Charles Dance. Whilst I have a new canvas suitcase he has an old battered leather doctor's bag. I expect it contains a threadbare copy of The Hobbit or The Catcher In The Rye. I hope he is not into Tolkien too much though. I think not, those Ringers tend to wear it on their pointy sleeves. He attended the same public school as Winston Churchill and plays the guitar, the drums, the piano and, most impressively, the saxophone. He has also only brought one pair of shoes with him, which I have openly marvelled at. They are an old pair of dark brown Clarks' desert boots, which I now really want to get but that is probably one step ahead from practicing signing my name as 'Ben Whiston-Thomas' and might freak him out. But

a saxophone, which he knows how to play and a guitar. (I have actually brought my tambourine here with me. I feel like I am trying desperately hard. But you know.)

Pollyanna Peters. On paper she is the archetypal Guildford girl, but Pollyanna Peters (I really like using her whole name) has hair like Polly Magoo (that super-cool French film called Qui êtes-vous, Polly Maggoo? which I saw with Virginie and is all about wankers like her in the fashion industry.) But Polly is very fit and is kind of classy in a way which makes me not want to be a dick. (I was going to write 'she is just my friend' in a really patronising way when I remembered, thank God, that I am not a complete dick) and dresses like she is in a '60s girlband from The Motor City, all fringe, striped t-shirts and hairbands. She is also from the University of Nottingham, and on meeting again 2 days ago (haha, these friendships are DEEP!) she took a while (ages) before remembering me... which is always pretty cool. I kind of had to persuade her that she did. Eventually she remembered me from that time I had been checking the level of ink in my Techpoint pen (the ones with a window in the side you always steal from me), miles away in my own world, and had held it up to the light in a massive lecture hall. (did I ever tell you this?) I had timed this brilliantly with the exact moment that the Head of the French Department had asked a particularly taxing question on Proust's A la Recherche du Temps Perdu (which I had not, and never did, read, despite getting a 2:1 for an essay on it). My bemused response to his thinking that I had been proffering an answer was of great amusement to everyone, evidently her gang of fashionistas in particular. As I turned crimson I also realised that I had my LEVI'S-emblazoned sweatshirt on back to front. I laughed nervously at her memory and acted like I had moved on. In reality, I have. Yes????? But to her I am probably still the moron with no friends who couldn't dress himself.

Rhiain Blayney is an incredibly verbose Welsh strumpet who looks a bit like Kylie and from the stories I have heard from her so far has left men (and women) littered in her wake. Wolfy would most definitely fancy her. As do I. But that statement is so obvious as to be rendered almost entirely meaningless these days. Without doubt the most fun girl here after Charlotte (who I think she is a bit scared of), particularly if fun is directly related to "always behaving as if she would soon be putting out". She seems phenomenally experienced in the sexual ways of the world. If it is true, she seems to have slept with the entire male and female population of Cardiff University. But her best bit (aside from being very agreeable to look at) is that she is actually a part-time life model! Actually really turned me on when she told me. But most things do.

You remember I told you that Pop once said that friends were not necessarily the people you like best, they are merely the people who got there first? I think he might have a point. Tonight we are going out on the lash in Nice. Let's see what happens.

Write when you can be arsed. If it involves Swedish girls then send photos. If not drawings. Or hair cuttings.

Break on through to the other side...adios

From me and 11 long-haired friends of Jesus.

PS I'm currently reading The Buddha of Suburbia. It's great. Kureshi just wrote this;

"I thought about the difference between the interesting people and the nice people. And how they can't always be identical. The interesting people you wanted to be with — their minds were unusual, you saw things freshly with them and all was not deadness and repetition...then there were the nice people who weren't interesting, and you didn't want to know what they thought of anything."

I think I am in with the interesting people. But some of them seem nice too. But that is a contradiction?

PPS I have been wearing Pop's old Ray Bans he gave me. I am thinking about wearing them all the time, like that would be my 'thing'. Like Cruise. No-one has done more for the sunglasses business than Tom Cruise....

PPPS I just learnt the word imbibing and I am planning on using it a lot. Knock yourself out.

September 9
We hit Nice hard last night. Nice, we have been told repeatedly in various talks, is the fifth largest city in France. We also learnt that the city was named by the Marseillans after 'Nike', which I never knew meant the goddess of victory, and not 'shoes' in modern Greek??!
Our coach dropped us off on the appropriately-named *Promenade des Anglais*,[11] in front of the Hotel Negresco,[12] which looks wicked. Wonder how much it is a night in there? Maybe Charlotte's dad will pay.
Vieux Nice, the old town, was where we really found our feet (bars). Most of the cave-like bars had live music on. In one, Alistair said that the keyboard player was so bad he sounded like he was playing the keyboards with his head. I wanted to write that down. Kronenbourg tastes fuckin' amazing here. And the Heineken is the 5% one which you only get in Europe.[13] We discovered a beer called 'Desperados'. Which is a kind of Mexican beer infused with tequila. I don't even know what infused means. Four beers in we were talking deep and meaninglesses. It would appear that Charlotte and Michael Hutchence have something of a chequered history and it would also appear that a 16-year age gap may not be such a great thing after all. For him! This'll be a NEW SENSATION! We all staggered back to the hostel at about four in the morning and Alistair fell asleep for the night on the table outside the breakfast hall.
The evening was also remarkable for the fact that I heard the song '7 Seconds' by Youssou N'Dour and Neneh Cherry nine times. I counted. Nine!!!! We asked a barmaid and she told us that it had been number

11 So-named as it was built by us Brits back in the late eighteenth century. The rich English settlers had come up with the idea of a regal long pathway to run behind the beach. As they were rich they did not plan to get their hands dirty so they used the materials around them. Beggars, primarily. They were all over the place in Nice and they set about the work in a way not normally synonymous with their chosen career. The local council was impressed and got involved too, creating what was first called the *Camin dei Anglès* – the English Way. This sounded too much like part of a takeover plan by the settlers so they changed it to *La Promenade des Anglais* in 1860.

12 Legend had it that the perky pink domes of the hotel were modelled on the breasts of Dutch exotic dancer and coutesan, Mata Hari. The French were fascinated by her, then they killed her by firing squad under suspicion of being a spy. But they loved her really.

13 In 2011 the United Kingdom is part of the EU. As it was in 1994.

one for weeks. Quite like it. I met Neneh Cherry once when I did work experience at *Smash Hits*. I saw up her skirt when she sat down.

DES BOUCHES DES BÉBÉS

Before you ever go to France you should learn how the children speak. Even if you are just going for a holiday and not to be a teacher. Because they speak clearly and everyone in France references how they talk all the time when they are speaking with adults. This would have been helpful to have known beforehand.

Bichounet!	Little soldier
Bichounette	Sugar plum
Le bobo	A 'hurt' or wound
J'ai bobo!	I am hurt
Le caca (faire caca)	Pooh (go for a...)
Le chat-chat	Pussy cat
Le chien-chien	Doggy
Coucou!	Coo-ee (beware, very camp for men)
Le dodo (faire dodo)	Sleep (to go to...)
Des joujoux	Toys
Faire joujou	To play
Le lolo	Milk – not to be confused with...
Les lolos	Boobs
La mamie	Grandma
La menotte	Hand – not to be confused with...
Les menottes	Handcuffs
Miam-Miam	Yum-Yum (as in nice grub)
Le minou	Pussy cat (Warren Beatty would have used this with success in French like he did in American, girls love it)
La moumouche	Little fly
Le nounours	Teddy bear
Le panpan	Spanking – not to be confused with... using that in an adult situation.
Le papi	Grandpa
Le pépète / la pépétte	Bum
Le pipi	Wee (pee-pee)
La poupoule	Chicken

Le pet	Fart
Faire sisite	Sit down
La tata/tatie	Auntie
Le tonton	Uncle
Le toto	Car
Le totoche / la totosse	Dummy
Le toutou	Doggy
Le zizie	Willy

Ritchie Canningham

September 11

There is a Chinese proverb which states that 'opportunity lies on the flip side of disaster'. This is not always the case as I think I am in the process of proving. The course ended a few hours ago and I was feeling pretty chipper. All my new mates are real finds. They are the interesting ones. And then there's Charlotte. In the final talk the course director was telling us all that this was it etc., grasp the opportunity, live the dream, shag Charlotte (I daydream a lot, *non?*). I was just about to join the small group who were due to leave for Cannes when it became apparent, and it seems vaguely incredible that this hasn't been flagged up before, that I do not in fact have anywhere to stay when I arrive in Cannes. And of course everyone else does. Why do I still have this kind of childish idea that things will be sorted out for me and that everything will just fall into place? I am such a dick. In this instance I pretty much thought that the school were going to have a little cottage in the grounds like something out of a Marçel Pagnol book[14] and I would have fresh bread and *pain au chocolat* delivered to me every morning by the baker's comely daughter, Anne-Sophie. I am a long way from my home and I don't have a new one.

Later

A strange sense of *déjà-vu* has descended on me as all of the other assistants are excitedly getting into taxis and on to buses. What was I doing all summer whilst they were reading all the fuckin' brochures and finding and renting their *apartements et chambres à louer*? Oh yeah, I was creosoting fences along the Northern Line.[15] I feel like for once

---

14 Adored, super idyllic French writer.
15 I had spent that summer with my head in the clouds, daydreaming of becoming a

in my life I've played it right. In with the in-crowd, all sorted. But no. Door slammed in my face again. Was there a letter? It's probably all my fault.

A representative of the assistant programme has taken pity on me. Theme. As the organisation does not appear to have any ready-made apartments to let in Cannes (probably in the letter I didn't read) it was decided to grab hold of the other four students who have been allocated positions in the city and see if I can crash with any of them for a few days. Two of the girls have already left the hostel, having sorted out accommodation together, a guy called Estéban has not turned up to the course and there is a girl called Michelle who has already left. Her parents own a three-bedroom apartment just off the *Croisette*, Cannes' very own promenade. She's my best bet. Just need to work out who will bring me my *pain au chocolat*.

I am now hitching in with two of the course directors who are going to drive me to Cannes in the morning. Great. Fourteen hours on my own.

I just gave myself a pep talk that at least I have got my foot in the door.

Night.

September 12

Found an ad in a magazine for NAF NAF shoes. Features hot naked woman in said shoes sort of grabbing her crotch and menacingly towering over a piglet. I think it's brilliant.

---

noble young Oliver Mellors to south London's very own Lady Constance Chatterley. The gardens of south London, some on bleak estates, some a bit leafier, required quite some leap of imagination to transform them into D.H. Lawrence's wild timberland. Some days, trying desperately to be aloof and masculine, I would disappear into the shed at the bottom of the twenty-foot garden and look longingly over my shoulder for Connie to follow me in, convinced that I was a real, 'living' man. The fact that my clients were neither nursing handicapped husbands nor sexually frustrated and in need of virility injection was an aside....And some of my customers certainly didn't look so much like Lady Chatterley as depicted in film. But I was twenty and daydreaming was what I did.

September 14

First entry for two-and-a-half days. Excuse the length. First non-writing day was a bit full-on as got lift with two mental people from 'The Bureau' here to Cannes. They forgot to mention that we would be stopping off at every single academic establishment ever constructed. It was early evening yesterday when I arrived at Michelle's flat and I bowled up alone having never met her. Had hoped the two *profs* would grease the path but *non*. Must stop using random French words in sentences as it is really irritating. Brilliantly managed to arrive here at exactly the same time as the handful of guests for a dinner party. This was not a dinner party to celebrate my arrival, just a dinner party. A dinner party to me is my Mum and Dad, some friends, a George Benson album, stuffed olives and, if I am lucky, some left over chicken chasseur and garlic bread in the morning. This was not that.

Michelle is part-Vietnamese, part-Bostonian (her parents met at Harvard, natch) and part-Oxford Uni starlet. This exotic combo was established early and made me feel woefully inadequate. I felt like a hick, compared to this lavish life of triple nationalities, multiple passports, tapenade, dessert wine (both of which were served tonight) and the whole 'having somewhere to live' thing.

Michelle is also really beautiful, but I don't actually fancy her. She is beautiful like a painting. And I don't fancy any paintings. I wonder if I will ever fancy girls like that?

The flat is in *Rue du Commandant André*, 50 metres from the *Croisette*, about ten metres from the *Rue d'Antibes* and about 200 metres from the *Palais des Festivals*. The Palais is the centre of world cinema festivals, and the mecca for any student of French film.

Carrying all my worldly possessions in two, desperately unfashionable, suitcases I struggled up the four narrow flights of stairs to Michelle's parents' apartment. I peered up the intimidating wrought-iron stairwell and I felt like I was Jean Gabin in *Le Jour se Lève*.[16] I imagined police stakeouts on the roof as I barricaded myself at the top of the building,

16 *Le Jour se Lève* (Daybreak) is a highly claustrophobic film which we studied last year. Set in a sliver building, it is the melancholic tale of François, a factory worker who commits murder, and then locks himself in the sliver block with only his memories to haunt him. Which they really do.

a prisoner of love's edict, a victim of consequence. Chain-smoking of course.

Amazingly Michelle has agreed to let me stay, or rather she had been steered by the Central Bureau to allow me to stay until I've got myself sorted. I am beyond grateful, but apprehensive, about how I am going to get on with her and her Oxford Blue rowing boyfriend, Jules. The fact that I was meeting him for the first time at this dinner party was not my dream scenario. The fact that I am here at all is probably not his.

I think I managed to piss Michelle off before I even met her by carefully placing my suitcases on top of her sleeping cat. My attempt to rectify the situation and move the bag knocked the telephone from its perch and sent a high-pitched ringtone throughout the entire building's stairwell. *Bon soir*, high society!

Walking up here I cheerfully wondered what the worst thing was that could happen, safe in the knowledge that I had not arrived yet and predicting awful scenarios before they happened meant they never would. Overheating inside and crushed by the disastrous entrance I took a seat at the table. I decided against projecting forward any further in time to some awful scenario, as I clearly have the ability to better it in reality. My heart pounding and my forehead dribbling with sweat Jules leaned in to break the ice. "So Ritchie, what are you reading at Worcester?"[17]

---

17 In 1994 Worcester did not have a university.

QUATRE

Yes, I Cannes

September 16

Things have calmed down a bit since my arrival. It is now slightly like (I imagine) staying in a high-class hotel but with no meat on the menu. Michelle and Jules are strict vegetarians. Even vegans, which I think means the vegetables have to be killed humanely. But I have a feeling he is just doing it to get in her silk Laura Ashley knickers. I know this cos I saw them on the radiator.

September 17

There is a burger place in Cannes called 'Quick' which is a bit like Burger King. I am pretty sure that I saw Jules coming out of there this evening. He would obviously say he had a 'Fish Royale' or something but I don't trust him. He smelt of horsemeat. I have also been looking for flats in the area but it would appear that no estate agents are open on Sundays, Mondays, Tuesdays or Thursday afternoons.

September 18

As part of my diary I am reading up profusely on the area I am to be living in. Provence as a whole has had a special place in my heart dating back to when we first drove down to a campsite near St Raphaël in the silver Ford Escort MkII in 1983. I actually remember the air changing as we got to early Provence. I remember the cotton-covered lavender-scented bolster pillows in the hotel, the smell of the onion soup and the mental Parisians hurtling past my car window on the brilliantly named *Autoroute du Soleil.*[18] I also remember my silver SONY Walkman struggling through the ninth straight playing of my own edits of Dire Straits' 'Alchemy' on one side, my sister's 'Street Sounds Volume 5'

---

18 'The Sunshine Motorway', which sounds like a song by The Mamas and The Papas.

(featuring Grandmaster Flash) on the other. My first memory of the Mediterranean Sea was that same holiday when my parents pulled off the motorway at Cannes and let us swim in the sea and eat ice cream.

I think Jules is sensing my mistrust of him as he is paying me even less attention than normal when he ignores me. It's like an even more negative form of ignoring. We all had dinner together (asparagus and fennel risotto) and they only spoke to each other. And that was sparse.

September 19
I have developed a theory. When Cannes is good it is very, very good. And when it is bad, it will be horrid.[19] At one end of the spectrum you have Cary Grant swimming up to Grace Kelly on the Carlton Beach in To Catch a Thief (Cary Grant is my hero). And then there's the other. I can't believe how phenomenally bourgeois this place is. It's the planet's epicentre of festivals and conferences (this week is the international market of real estate, fun fans) and home to some of the world's most expensive hotels. I think it may also be the epitome of a lot of dislikeable things. It is certainly very white. It is expensive and plastic-y and most of the people who work in public-facing roles (almost the entire population of Cannes) appear to think it is OK to be rude to your face if they think that you are either a) poor or b) not from Cannes. I am both and so everybody is being reasonably unpleasant to me, all the time.

Tonight Jules smelt of ham.

September 20
Complaining about French waiters is so boring and obvious – like talking about how big the food portions are in America – but I have to write this down or I will forget it. Today I went to what I am pretty sure is the cheapest, most low-rent café in Cannes, maybe France. I ordered an espresso, which was 6 francs. I left a 10 franc coin. Tipping 4 francs is out of the question/budget so I waited patiently. The waiter, having now served me, lost interest in my existence on planet earth. He started to chat to a friend/wipe tables/stare into mid-space/wonder whether

19 See later chapters for details.

human essence is determined through life's choices. This forced me (I think he was acutely aware of this) to swallow my pride (or my money if I now decided to over tip – unlikely, bearing in mind the service I was getting) and walk over to the lady at the till with my money in order to pay, therefore cutting the waiter out of the transaction and thereupon insulting his ability by doing one of the two things that his job description covers. This has ensured me the kind of treatment on any unlikely return reserved for enemies of France, like the Germans.

September 21

I can't find anywhere to live.

'7 Seconds' is still number one.

September 22

I am reading *Tender Is The Night* again by F. Scott Fitzgerald. There are three reasons for this.

1 It reminds me of Debbie[20]

2 It is about places down here

3 This kind of description:

> "He won everyone quickly with an exquisite consideration and a politeness that moved so fast and intuitively that it could be examined only in its effect. Then, without caution, lest the first bloom of the relation wither, he opened the gate to his amusing world. So long as they subscribed to it completely, their happiness was his preoccupation, but at the first flicker of doubt as to its all-inclusiveness he evaporated before their eyes, leaving little communicable memory of what he had said or done."

20 25 year-old American woman who was my English teacher at school. In no way dreamy but in every way masturbatory.

LE PETIT GUIDE CANNOIS (PARTIE 1)

A quick historical overview tells us that Cannes is much, much more than a film festival with attitude and France's surliest waiters (no mean feat). Far from it being some *arriviste* Riviera town, it was civilised as far back as the 2nd century BC. A Ligurian tribe (The Ligurian Sea is one of the world's coolest seas, nestling between the Italian Riviera and the islands of Corsica and Elba) settled there and established Cannes as a fishing village, which I can't imagine the locals were ecstatic about.

Everything remained pretty fishing village-y until the Middle Ages when the Cannes we see today started to take shape. The old castle, which peers out over the whole town from the corner of Le Suquet (the old bit), dates from the 10th century. It still sits there proudly now as the Castre Museum. A plague hit Cannes in the 14th century and then, on their knees, the Cannois were repeatedly attacked by pirates and bandits (there is an analogy here about the film industry and more specifically the Weinsteins).

Just about recovered from that little spat the 16th century brought another plague and a load more ambulance-chasers joined in with the looting and plundering. Recovered, they then suffered the ignominy of a Spanish attempt to nick their two islands (more on them later) in the 18th century. But the picaroons (in whatever disguise they wore) just couldn't leave Cannes alone and in the 1830s Cannes was once again ambushed by a marauding force, this time…the aristocrats!

The aristocrats arrived from all over the world, often landing with their French counterparts and wasted no time in building like mad. Every movement requires its poster boy (Daniel Cohn-Bendit, Che Guevara, Lech Walesa, Sid Vicious), and in 1834 Lord Henry Brougham, Chancellor of Great Britain, stepped forward. It is rumoured that Lord Brougham had planned on going to Nice but an outbreak of plague there forced him to try further along the coast. No matter, Lord Brougham rolled into town, liked what he saw and proudly announced that he had "discovered" Cannes, heralding the birth of winter tourism. The rest of the world sniggered, assuming that the Paris-obsessed fools had completely overlooked it. The French were livid. Lord Henry took the plaudits and set about building some infrastructure for the silly fishermen.

The railway station opened in 1863 and in 1868 the celebrated promenade, *La Croisette*, was built. Two years later Lord Brougham discovers it. This period, known as *La Belle Epoque*, brought even more wealth, this time of the Russian variety and by now Cannes was well on its way to becoming the hotspot to end all hotspots.

Ma bande à part[21]

September 23
Michelle and Jules have been scouring the markets of Cannes buying vegetables and herbs. Not Herbes de Provence, which would have been the obvious purchase. When they got home and got them out I asked them what they were called. Michelle gave me the French names, which I didn't know. She translated and I didn't know them in English either. I think we both felt the divide.

September 24
Jules went back to Oxford today. I think Michelle is secretly pleased. She is much nicer on her own.

September 25
Our first day at school in less than a week. I have started photocopying some pages from books, loosely planning some lessons. Did a fair bit before I came. So I should be alright. Don't really know what I am doing. More importantly I really need to find somewhere to live. As I have been allocated two *collèges* at opposite ends of Cannes the logical move would be to live in the middle. This is proving well beyond my means. Today I went into Azur Prestations and Cannes Immobilier, the windows of which advertised *châteaux* for sale, and asked if they had any studios on short leases. No they didn't. One lady didn't actually know what a studio was. I am learning quickly that the French people of Cannes do not spare your feelings. It seems to be assumed that once you have established that you are going to speak French with them then, sink or swim, that's what they are going to do. There is no sparing

---

21 My gang of outsiders.

you. This is one sport, like *pétanque*[22] which they rule the world at. Possibly because, like *pétanque*, no-one else is trying to be good at it.

September 26

Not a good day. All because of croissants. My Cannois kinship is feeling bruised and barely intact. I went into the café next door to the apartment today, ordered a *noisette* (these espressos with a dash of milk are all I drink as they make me look like I belong, and they are the cheapest) and started eating my croissant, which I had purchased in the boulangerie next door. This is not as foolish as it sounds. Many of the other cafés do not serve breakfast and so you can Bring Your Own. A kind of BYOP-D[23] movement.

As soon as I tucked into my buttery breakfast I saw a querulous waiter heading for my table with that querulous waiter look all over his face. He informed me in no uncertain terms that food consumed in the restaurant had to be purchased in the restaurant and that if I had wanted a croissant I should have asked for one. I tried to explain but he held his hand up as if against my face, which is comfortably one of the most childish things a human of any age has ever done to me, including children. I clearly made a mistake and would not, as a rule walk into restaurants and start eating a sandwich I had made earlier. Having never seen them serve a breakfast there I had simply drawn the wrong conclusion. I felt like a chump and he did everything he could over the next few minutes to accentuate this sentiment. His primary tool was that he appeared to be telling everyone else in the café what I had done, leading to some playground-inspired pointing and astonished gasps from his bourgeois collaborators.

Fucking hell. This diary is becoming all about waiters.

September 27

Today I am going to St Raphaël with a few of the others. Including Charlotte. I cannot wait.

---

22 *Boules*, or bowls.
23 Bring Your Own Petit-Dejeuner!

LE CROISSANT

The French are cunning in that they have made themselves known across the world as the breakfast specialists (they've done the same with desserts), especially with these light, buttery crab-shaped pastries, yet the rules when it comes to actually where you can eat it are convoluted and confusing. They are fundamentally making them up as they go along. And dependent on their mood.

The croissant has a surprisingly interesting story. In a nutshell, it's Austrian. Its great grandfather, the *kipferl*, dates back to the 13th century and was generally plain or filled with nuts. It wasn't until the mid-1800s that they had the idea of making it with puff pastry and this is most likely where the French joined in. Although Viennese croissant dissidents would no doubt argue differently. Legend seems to have decided that a Viennese boulangerie in Paris, and a kipferl specialist, first served up the French take around 1838–39 and named it *croissant*[24] for its crescent shape.

Despite an absence of croissant-related references in the annals of French history there is a general French consensus that they took a rather basic product and made it into something rather wonderful. We'd all like to write our own history. But the croissant did really begin to take off, much like the skateboard in the 1970s, and by 1872 our very own Charles Dickens was talking of the "dainty croissant" in his *All the Year Round* periodical.

But like other significant events in recent history such as the assassination of JFK, the Bermuda triangle, the birth of the Freemasons, Jewish world domination and the death of Elvis Presley, it is rife with plotting, subterfuge and conspiracy theories. Although Elvis was just a fat drug addict. Rumours abound that it was devised in Europe to celebrate the defeat of a Muslim invasion, or to celebrate the defeat of the Turks by the Polish much later (the crescent shape mocked the Turkish flag) or even that France's most famous sweet bread-referencing snooty regina, Marie Antoinette,

24 Crescent

imported them with her to Paris as a comforting reminder of her Viennese childhood. Despite her rumoured champagne-and-macaroon diet it would appear that this is nothing but historical puff pastry and about as reliable as the fact that she said, "*Qu'ils mangent de la brioche.*"[25] Apparently that one originates from an old Chinese tale about 'rice and meat' and the brioche thing came to light only when Jean-Jacques Rousseau attributed it to an unknown Princess in his *Confessions.*

So there you go. More than just a pastry. Just.

25 "Let them eat cake."

Cannes, September 28 (Cannes)

Sod
Gamodo. Gamodo. Gamodo. Gamodo.
Where to begin?
THIS IS THE BEST LETTER YOU WILL EVER READ.
We got together in St Raphaël-Fréjus where the Welsh
girl Rhiain Blayney (plus a couple of her friends from
home, Anwyn and Joanna — so much more later) was
having a few people over for a night out. Pollyanna
Peters, Alistair Whiston-Thomas, Andreas Argyros,
Charlotte Love and myself headed down on Friday night
and started on Rhiain's balcony overlooking the pretty
harbour. This isn't feeling it is going to be the worst year
of my life.
We got wasted on very cheap rosé (I think this one may
have been some kind of cost record, it might even have
been cheaper than water. I was certainly drinking it at
one point out of thirst) and ate hot dogs in French bread
with mayonnaise and mustard. Fed and roséd, we headed
out into the night, expectantly searching for adult fun in
a resort famed for its appeal to 4-year-olds, and about six
weeks after the rest of the normal world had gone back to
work/nursery school.
St. Raphael-Fréjus is the classic mainstream seaside
town. In season it is full of carousel rides, barbe à
papa[26] stalls and moules-frites menus. Out of season it is
massively forlorn, like a jilted summer love. It is a bit
like Eastbourne or Penzance or Broadstairs. It is quaint
and looks like it all dates from a bygone era. You expect
the bars to have jukeboxes and for people to still drink
Coke out of the old glass bottles. In a nutshell it is 1954.
In one bar they played a killer song by this bloke called
Johnny Hallyday called 'Do the mashed potato'. He is a bit
like the French Elvis.
We shuffled from one bar to the next, all of which were
practically empty. In autumn even the dossy seasonal boys

26 Candy floss.

and girls of summer have passed through leaving only the
hardcore locals. Despite attempts to the contrary I think we
all realised that the Raphaëlois were not about to embrace
our presence in their somnolent bars. Like that scene in
Bande A Part when they dance in the quiet bar, we felt
like a real gang, chasing down any semblance of fun to be
had, all the while remaining completely on the outside,
viewed with suspicion by the indifferent locals.

Charlotte is just getting better. She is also fascinating
in that she epitomises such a different world. Private
schools that sound like I should have heard of them, by
16 she had lived in London, Boston, Auckland, Delhi
and Papua New Guinea. Meaning she has been brought
up with a totally global view of her existence. Whilst
her 'good-times' front (and what a front, her lils are
ENORMOUS) is like her calling card she is also interesting
in a way I could never be. She is experienced and,
however you cut it, I am not. She is funny and witty and
I have never met anyone like her. I think I am becoming
vaguely obsessed by her. I demonstrated this by reverting to
extreme working class clichés and mannerisms. This plan
was due to the fact that she is posh and therefore roughing
it in any way is attractive to her being from a less-
than well-to-do background is quite in at the moment
I reckon based on how much Oasis everyone is listening
to (being posh never really goes out, you can just dial it
up or down a bit, dependent on which bands are doing
well) surrounded by interesting people who have lived in
interesting places it is kind of all I've got.

So I regaled her with stories of my family's roots in
Bethnal Green and Waterloo, of the pie and mash shop
in Tooting Indoor Market, of watching my uncle's band
play in working men's clubs where mass fights kick off, of
Saturday afternoons watching QPR at Loftus Road (one
season, who's counting?) and of Saturday mornings at the
adventure playground in Lambeth. I really got her when
I told her about Pop taking me to Petticoat Lane when I
was 8 to buy me that sheepskin coat like his one for my
Christmas present. I have to go easy though, I think she

might think I am almost a Trotter.

But Charlotte is still very much with rockstar boyfriend and I was very much drunk.

This is where it gets good...

Anwyn and Joanna are school friends of Rhiain's from somewhere near Bangor. Both really fit in the most obvious sense. In that I wanted to kiss them and have sex with them all the time they were near me. They were also (their summer dresses and lack of obvious bra clues suggested a dislike of material) clothes-haters. The very best kind of girls to be at a party with! They were not royally interested in the scholastic conversations of the evening and made no bones about the fact that they were indifferent to most of the other people there. Brilliant! Reasonably early on (let's say one litre of rosé each early) I made sure that I would be indifferent to their indifference. I started to talk exclusively to them and, like a tennis player mixing up his groundstrokes, I was trying any game plan to win this one.

I started off with a slightly short forehand landing a metre inside the baseline — the fact that I had once been abseiling in Wales (relative indifference). I followed it up with a heavily sliced-and-diced drop shot — that story I told you last year about Richard Burton, and his dislike of Marlon Brando when he found out that he had badmouthed him behind his back.[27] This was a good one. I don't think they really got it, but it got them where I wanted them. Thirty-love and a heavy serve swings out to the backhand side — a story about my love of Rupert Bear cartoons and having visited the artist Alfred Bestall's village in Wales on which he based Nutwood...... ace! They loved it. At this point I am cute and into Wales! (Haha, I am neither). Now at game point I finished with a beautiful one-handed topspin backhand down the line — the fact that Pop had once got drunk with Dylan Thomas

---

27 Burton on Brando, "He really is a smugly pompous little bastard and is cavalier about everybody except Black Panthers and Indians. That sober self-indulgent obese fart being solicitous about me. Sinatra is the same. Gods in their own mirrors. Distorted mirrors."

in New York when he docked there in the early fifties. This is a complete lie.

Every now and then Charlotte would join in but there was a kind of mutual antipathy between them and the two catty Welsh girls won out every time. Their availability/flesh-on-display blend had my almost undivided attention.

I went in for the kill at this point — really I had to, the wine was beginning to become damaging to my libido and I was so thirsty that I just could not stop drinking it. We had got back to Rhiain's balcony when Anwyn suggested a swim in the sea. It was admittedly a brilliant idea on a chilly autumnal night, after drinking like sailors for eight hours. I was astonished to hear Joanna echo her enthusiasm. The fact that the option seemed to have been only opened up to me was also a godsend, and I leapt at it. Alistair was playing his saxophone in the bathroom and Andreas was lying on the floor counting stars and eating pistachios. And the girls were not going to do anything which had been conceived by these two taffettes.

As you may be thinking, swimming in the ocean at night is not my idea of fun but I think I actually said that it was a 'genius' idea. The fact that the two minxes did not pause for swimming costumes or towels meant one thing. One of the greatest words in the English language. Skinnydipping.

We rushed down to the beach and the girls undressed in front of me as if we did this every evening. I scoured their incredibly nubile figures like I had never seen a naked 20-year-old Welsh girl before. I hadn't. Their pert bottoms disappeared in front of me and I bounded after them like a goofy King Charles Cavalier. The freezing sea water-booze axis shrank my zizi (I have just learnt this word) to the size of a thimble but I ploughed on like a horny trooper. The ocean floor shelved quickly and as I paddled in their wake I felt the rimy chill of deep water.

Thrashing around unlike skinnydipping Chrissie Watkins at the start of Jaws I reached out for Anwyn at the same time as I suddenly became paralysed by fear.

Scared but horny can obviously be great but if you have an extreme case of galeophobia[28] then this is not ideal. Admittedly this was the Med and not the Great Barrier Reef, but fear is not always rational.[29]

As John Williams' driving musical score clanged around my rosé-addled brain I joined the subjective camera view of a twenty-five foot Carcharodon Carcharias, the shark with the nickname 'White Death', as it careered towards my limp body, dramatically lit from below in silhouette form, rosé secreting from my pores and giving the water an eery pink hue around me, like a gay Ready Brek man. Unlike the film when the drunk lechy guy falls over his trousers on the beach I had made it to the dark depths and I knew for a fact that the giant killer would leave the naked nubile twins and go for me instead. I actually heard an old iron buoy clanging my imminent death knell in the icy cold water and knew that my naked body was about to be pulled under.

Joanna sunk her tongue into my mouth and I fucking screamed like a schoolgirl. When Anwyn leapt on my back I practically felt the sandpaper skin of the sharks'

28 Galeophobia, the fear of sharks, is one of the most ridiculous phobias as I cannot really imagine that any human who is not as mad as a tree would not suffer from it. It shouldn't even be a phobia.

29 If you start on about shark attacks in the Mediterranean people will poo-poo you. I know because I do this frequently. However, you need to know your facts and they are simple, and scary. There was a great white shark attack on a windsurfer in the Catalonia area of Spain in 1986 in which he lost a whole leg plus two more attacks thought to be great whites in the same stream of the Spanish Med over the next five years. In 1992 a three-metre male great white was washed up at Tossa de Mar in Catalunya. With terrifying echoes of *Jaws* it seems there was an attempt by the local authorities to cover up the incident through fear of upsetting the tourist trade. The story got out in the local media (including photos) but Catalunyan authorities swooped in the middle of the night and scooped the beast off the beach on a truck and dumped it at the local inland garbage fillsite. In between these incidents a scuba diver was killed by a great white shark in Italian waters in 1989. Just after the Tossa incident a five-metre two-tonne monster was caught in Croatia, one of the biggest great whites ever landed. Again hushed up for fear of the tourist trade. Which all leaves you wondering just who is the Euro Minister responsible for the sea? Minster Larry Vaughan?!! Like the poster said...DON'T GO IN THE WATER.

torso. Anwyn then attacked Joanna in much the same way with a sharp tongue to the mouth and as I thrashed in the shallow water it became apparent that the monstrous sea beast may have just swept by.

"Are we friends, Ben?", Anwyn said as she eased her naked body on to my shoulders and wrapped her legs around my neck, her fanny pressed against my skin. I felt the reassuring sensation of sand under my feet and realised with enormous relief that I still had legs.

"Yes we are," I might have said, as my lifeless body sank beneath the icy Mediterranean under the weight of her very naked torso. I came to the surface and struggled around in the still, shallow water, the blood in slicks across the surface.

Friends! No man is a failure who has friends!

Told you it was a good letter. I am having a peachy time.

PS Not one PS.

SIX
Mind that child!

September 29

Going into school today. The weekend's activities have left me feeling both elated and deflated.

September 30

I have been placed in two different *collèges*.[30] I visited the one called Collège Emile Roux yesterday.[31] It is situated in the leafy suburb of Le Cannet, a mile or so from the *Croisette*. If you designed your ideal school to grow up in then this is it. It looks like it has been made out of Duplo bricks and giant logs and it should have been called 'Collège le Big Fun'. It is spread across two floors and houses about 500 students. The staff room looks like it was designed by Renzo Piano.[32]

I was shown round this morning by the charming, and very proud, headmaster, Monsieur Guy Rufin, who is super cool. He looks like an ex-professional tennis player. He is pretty instantly my hero. He has it all. First off, his dress sense is immaculate. He was wearing a suit, which I could only compare to Cary Grant in *North By Northwest*. Secondly, his looks. Part Henri Leconte,[33] part Alain Delon,[34] and part General de Gaulle.[35] If I ever grow up I would like to be him.

The playground is enormous and includes a tennis court, a sand

---

30 A *collège* is a school for 12- to 15-year-olds. Apparently they can be a lot older if they don't pass their exams and they have to retake – this is called *le doublage*.

31 Pierre Paul Émile Roux was born in 1853 and he was a doctor, a bacteriologist and an immunologist. He also knocked about with one Louis Pasteur of milk and having your name made into a verb fame.

32 He designed the Pompidou Centre.

33 Louche French tennis hero from the 1980s.

34 Ice cool French actor, sometimes weirdly called the 'male Brigitte Bardot'.

35 You should know. He said, "How can you govern a country which has 246 varieties of cheese?"

volleyball court and has palm trees all around the outside. When Monsieur Guy Rufin asked me to join him for lunch and a glass of wine I assumed that we would be going out to a restaurant. No, no. Here at Collège le Big Fun they have pretty much built a proper restaurant within the school grounds. The teachers and students eat together, with the teachers' table in the middle of the space, surveying all the non-misbehaving children. He explained the system whereby I buy vouchers from the school for the grand sum of ten francs per week (about £1), which are good for four meals. Each meal includes a starter, a main course, a drink, a dessert, a coffee and a demi-carafe of wine (*rouge* or *rosé* "only"). He also advised me that it was probably best to not have a second carafe of wine if you had more lessons in the afternoon. "If you had more lessons in the afternoon"!! That was the only reason! I can't believe it. Here I am, francless, starving and always wine-willing, being given dream tickets for the whole of the next year, for what amounts to 25 pence per day! I love this school.

October 1

Three buses home and I have just got back from the other college, which is much closer to the sea, again about one mile from the *Croisette*, but west along the coast at the exotically named Cannes La Bocca. In my head I had conjured up images of a kind of tranquil pine forest set back from the sea where students would probably leave their canoe-kayaks before embarking on a day's rigorous learning. Cannes La Bocca literally means 'Cannes The Mouth'. After spending a few hours there the name seems very appropriate. It's a shithouse.

Imagine you designed your ideal beach-side school. This isn't it. A vast, imposing concrete slab of a building, it literally looks, and feels like, a prison. Cannes La Bocca seems to be a collection of railway tracks, warehouses and vast silos of gravel and grey sand. It just happens to be by the sea. The area is not the Cannes they sell to the rest of the world but a collection of run-down apartment blocks, cheap electronic stores and butchers. I am making it sound like Compton but it feels like that having come from the Provençal paradise up the road. When describing 'Le Slab' Monsieur Guy Rufin told me to look out for a school that looked like something created by Le Corbusier.[36] I pretended to know what he meant and laughed, possibly too much.

Inside Le Slab is as grim as its exterior and its surroundings, long corridors and heavy doorways, a canteen – I am used to restaurants – and a concrete playground with bikesheds all around to house moody-looking teenagers smoking blunts. The students look older and less *The Red Balloon*[37] than the kids at Collège le Big Fun.[38] But the teachers seem friendly, if tired-looking, and one big plus is that the school is handily situated right next to the AS Cannes football stadium.[39]

When I got back to Michelle's flat I discovered that she was not in. I waited for almost three hours in a café opposite, drinking one *noisette*, one sip per hour until her return. I heard '7 Seconds' four times. It is still number one. When she showed up she explained that she'd been buying fruit purées in a market near Grasse favoured by the top *nez* of the perfume industry.[40]

October 2

Back at Collège le Big Fun today. Monsieur Guy Rufin asked me if I would like to have lunch with him. Hello??? We had chicory salad with pine nuts to start, an actual steak with green beans and sautéed potatoes and a raspberry tarte with crème anglaise (classy custard).

---

36 Swiss architect beloved of the French. The views are divisive with the modern beauty of his *chaise longue* and, on a grander scale, the *Unité d'Habitation* in Marseille marvelled at. But he has also designed some right car parks. One critic called him "the Pol Pot of architecture".

37 *Le Balon Rouge* is a super cute French short film about a little boy who finds a balloon with a life of its own. Loved a bit like *The Snowman*.

38 It would later become apparent that this was because most of the kids at Collège le Big Fun were going on Club Med holidays at weekends and bathed in goats' milk each night.

39 AS Cannes are brilliantly the breeding ground for loads of legendary French players including Zinedine Zidane and Patrick Vieira. They had been recently promoted to the French first division, which meant that the big names would be coming to play all year long.

40 A *nez* is a 'nose'. This is the familiar term given to people who have a fine sense of smell and Grasse, as France's capital of smell (fine weather, great flowers, nice restaurants) produces an estimated three quarters of France's best smells. Food and perfume.

When Monsieur Guy Rufin asked me how I liked my steak cooked in front of the students I thought he was joking. He definitely was joking when he told the chef that, as I was English, I would like it "crispy". I feel this may be an oft-repeated joke. In fact the French mockery of English cuisine has already become standard, normally involving some kind of dig at fish and chips, le full-engleesh or les baked beans. Oh yeah, hit us where it hurts, France, my nation's culinary skills.

After lunch, as we sipped double espressos at his oaky desk which matched his oaky tan, he told me that there was a cinema club on Fridays, that the male teachers had a five-a-side football team, which they would love me to turn out for and that he was a member of the exclusive Tennis Club de Cannes, in case I ever wanted a hit (he'd read my CV. And my mind.)

Seizing the opportunity presented before me I asked Monsieur Guy Rufin if he happened to know of any good starters when it came to finding somewhere to live, as the Cannes estate agents were proving a shade less than helpful. Did he? Of course he did. He told me not to worry, wrote down the name and address of one "Madame Cocheteux" and gave it to me with a wink, which I laughed at even though I didn't get the joke, assuming that he is probably having an affair with her. This guy is such a dude that if he told his wife he was having an affair, "*Ma chérie, j'ai des relations sexuelles avec une autre femme*", she would probably just smile and agree that it was for the best. I assume that she will be a kind of 80s version of Sophia Loren, late 50s, dark tan skin, big sunglasses, skimpy silk baby-doll nighties and a heaving bosom. My head is in a whirl. I may not have a home quite yet but I have finally arrived in the south of France…watch out Azureans, it all begins here! As I walked down the street tonight it was like the moment when *The Wizard Of Oz* goes technicolour. In my head.

Ma Madrague

October the who cares – BEST DAY YET IN FRANCE

I was wrong. She looks more like Sophia Loren from the 70s. Her heaving bosom is bigger and her attire more revealing than even my wildest dreams. And I have had some wild ones. I knocked on the door at about 11 am and a voice called out, "*J'arrive.*" Madame Cocheteux is stunning. She was also wearing the smallest dressing gown I have ever seen which seemed to be barely covering some tiny bikini bottoms (a weird blue leopard skin print – I remember everything).

Her imagined heaving bosom is even better in real life and I could barely take my eyes off her buoyant chest as she walked me through her tropical garden and past her swimming pool, where she had so obviously been sunbathing when I knocked. I assume that she had been sunbathing *à l'intégral*,[41] such was the way her attire looked thrown on in a hurry. We went in to her dining room and she made coffee, which was the best coffee I have ever tasted. Her breasts were desperately fighting to get loose of that dumb dressing gown. She took out a leather wallet containing available properties. The first one she showed me was about one hundred metres from her house. "I'll take it", I said. We both laughed. But I was deadly serious.

She continued to show me other properties but I was sold by the proximity. A chinchilla ran over my foot, dogs and cats were running amok around the house and birds were squawking in the sub-tropical garden. I felt like I was in La Madrague.[42]

Scouring the walls I saw that there was also a Monsieur Cocheteux

---

41 Sunbathing naked. I often assumed this.

42 Brigitte Bardot's WWF-friendly home where her wildlife charity, the Fondation Brigitte Bardot is based. If there had been a 'Fondation Madame Cocheteux' I would have signed up immediately, devoting my life to the causes. Whatever she wanted those to be. I would be there. Even if it was anti-animals.

(groan), and he is certainly not a 20-year-old man-boy from south London. His hands look like chopping boards and in one photo he appears to be lifting the entire engine out of an old Renault truck as he laughs. Probably at something brilliant and witty he had just said. To his best friend, Michel Platini.

Madame Cocheteux excused herself to get dressed, oh to have been that door, came back minutes later in what looked like a variation on the same theme, but with short skirt added. We walked up the hill to the apartment block and even taking into consideration the fact that I had fallen in love with Madame Robinson, I loved the studio at first sight. It is also reasonably cheap, it is near Collège le Big Fun, and it is really close to her.

"On ne peut pas, comme ça, se promener dans la rue
On ne peut pas, même si l'on voulait vivre nu
Et pourtant sans être impudique, au fond
J'avoue franchement que c'est grisant
Nue au soleil
Complètement
Nue au soleil
Complètement."

Baby, let's play house

October 4

I have just finished moving in to my apartment. Unbelievable. Two days since I met Madame Cocheteux. It is in the very middle-class area of Le Cannet, about a kilometre directly inland from the *Croisette*. The apartment is part of a Vietnamese-inspired complex called Le Parc Penh Chaï. The Parc is a circular, futuristic, Kubrickian[43] space ring set amongst palm trees and vaguely oriental foliage with a giant kidney-shaped pool in the middle. I am pretty much in my element. I am looking forward to getting bombed and lying on the giant balcony imagining the helicopters swirling above the flat.

It costs about £200 per month (a hike on what I was paying in Maudslay Road, Earlsdon, Coventry) and consists of one room, a toilet and, bizarrely, an enormous balcony. In the one room there is a kitchenette (I love that word) off to the side and a brilliant fold-down table, which comes out of the wall. In Paris they are masters of making the most out of small space. I once went to a bar set up in a cupboard and it had about eight people in it. Half-full. The USP of my place is that you can sit on the loo and stir things in a saucepan on the hob at the same time. As a Gemini this appeals to my love of multi-tasking. There is a double and a single sofabed and a TV. From the moment I walked through the door I loved this apartment like nowhere else I have ever been. I think it is HER influence.

October 5

My local *épicerie* is open from 8 am–12 midday, and from 4 pm–7 pm. This four-hour lunch siesta requires no small amount of planning.

---

43 Just read *Heart Of Darkness* for an English course. Made *Apocalypse Now* seem even better and I already thought it was brilliant.

Essentially, it is open when you aren't there, and closed when you need it. Still, it seems to suit them.

October 6

My first house guest. Alistair Whiston-Thomas is staying with me for a couple of days as he had a massive hole in his teaching timetable. We have started by lying in my apartment and drinking all day. Constructive all round. His first day in Cannes was completed with a visit to the *Croisette* with his saxophone. Over the course of about three hours he earned four francs for effectively playing 'Baker Street' twenty-six times and a few bursts of 'I wish I knew how it felt to be free'. This worked out to about 40p, just over 10p an hour. When he had sat outside the train station with a hat in front of him he made nineteen francs in two hours.

October 7

Today Alistair was lying on the sofa watching TV (when not begging he does this all the time) and revealed an idea he has had for an advert. It is a proposed advert for electricity. It would start in a massive white sterile factory. The camera would pan in on the details of people working with their hands, putting things together, wires and circuit boards, complicated craftsmanship, different jobs, people welding, people typing formulas, people threading things. Then the view would shift as we dived into the cables and shot down them as if we were on a giant water slide, hurtling at lightning speed down cables. As the music gets louder we would get faster and faster and just before the crescendo moment we would pan ahead into the living room of a house on a hill as a woman picks up a plug (with the focus on her hand) and puts it in to the socket. Beautiful soft light fills the room and the endline appears, 'Many Hands Make Light Work.' I think it is brilliant.

> "This city desert makes you feel so cold.
> It's got so many people but it's got no soul
> And it's taking you so long
> To find out you were wrong
> When you thought it had everything."

LE PETIT GUIDE CANNOIS (PARTIE 2)

In the 1920s a new global trend was born and flourished here. It was called 'sunbathing' and involved removing the majority of one's clothes and lying in the sun. Although the bathing part was completely misleading. The rules would change over the years, eventually the French themselves leading the way in all of the clothes being removed, but it would prove a real laster. At the same time, and firmly establishing the art/nudity relationship artists have done so well to maintain, the area became a magnet for writers and painters. F. Scott Fitzgerald penned the reasonably well-received *Tender is the Night* whilst drinking himself to death in the area, Guy de Maupassant could be seen arguing with waiters in cafés and the French writer and poet Stephen Liegeard became the first person (as told in his own memoirs, handy) to coin the term, *Côte d'Azur*. The definitive rich American, Gerald Murphy, escaped the prohibition and came to stay with his buddy Cole Porter and that led to a herd of boho thrill-seekers stampeding south.

In 1931 the managers of the leading hotels in Cannes made the revelatory decision to stay open in the summer. Profits soared. They had never thought of it before. They combined it with the increasing craze of sunbathing and boom! ...you've got yourself a summer season!

But Cannes' history, since those revolutionary days, has been inextricably tied up with one thing. Film. By the 1930s Venice, the unimaginatively-nicknamed 'City Of Water', and rival in the world's affections for overpriced Euro-holiday resorts, was well under way with its own film festival when Cannes decided to join the craze. Nazi-heavies had begun to spoil Venice by 'persuading' the judges to give top prizes to their own propaganda films. This reached its nadir in 1938 when Jean Renoir's widely-considered masterpiece (still picks up all-time top five awards in the 21st century) *La Grande Illusion* was pipped at the post by the Joseph Goebbels-commissioned *Olympia*, the two-part story of Nazi success at the Berlin Olympics.[44]

44 Famous for launching most of the modern motion picture standards of technique

In addition to a load of Mussolini-sponsored fascist twaddle as well. The French, Brits and Yanks went mental. The Germans and Italians shrugged and banned *La Grande Illusion*. Goebbels cackled and, with no hint of irony, called Renoir's work "Cinematographic Enemy No.1".

But the tide was turning and those evil Nazis would regret making enemies of the free world's cinephiles. The French lobby sent their heaviest moviemakers down to the French government where they bullied them into paying for a politique-free film festival, with all costs to be underwritten by...them! Genius. This heavying of the French government by film folk to get them to pay for their artistic endeavours still continues to this day – it's why the French produce so many (bad) films. Plus the odd corker. Because they produce so many films, the odds are in their favour!

But Cannes was far from home and dry. Trendy Biarritz on the Atlantic coast was in the running too. Cannes played the Mediterranean card and also pitched itself as 'enchanted'. Biarritz was furious with itself, they had only boasted of seaside and casinos, and hadn't realised you could start making stuff up. The fact that the Cannes municipal authorities agreed to throw money at the idea by building a dedicated venue may also have been a factor. The opening night went brilliantly before the festival, and modern life in general, were somewhat rocked by the start of World War II.

So the inaugural *Festival International du Film* was planned for September 1939 in order to keep hold of these new-found summer tourists, allowing them to extend the season well into the autumn. After their earlier complete overlooking of the summer trade those tourism officials were really getting the hang of it now.

and also introducing the torch run still used as symbol of the Olympics. Infamous for it being a festival of sloppy Nazi dog wank.

NEUF

For crying out loud

October 8

Merde, merde, merde, merde.

My first ever lesson today was a big fucking disaster. It was terrible. As an assistant, and as the name would suggest, I am supposed to 'assist' an English teacher in the classroom. An established, know-what-they-are-doing, certified and licenced-to-do-it kind of a person. I am supposed to stand there and help out a bit, hold up the odd board and generally smile. Much like being one of the dollies on 'Play Your Cards Right' with Bruce Forsyth.

This morning's lessons at Le Slab started with me assisting a slightly loopy older woman called Madame Caramel with an older class of 16 to 18-year-olds. I didn't see her in the staff room (even just going in there seems weird, aged 20) and so headed for the classroom. Outside another teacher informed me that Madame Caramel was off sick, adding *"tu dois te débrouiller"*. This means 'fend for yourself'. The word 'fend' worried me immediately as it is the kind of word people use when talking about battles and swordfights.

My biggest lesson from day one at 'Let's Pretend We're Teachers' is that small sartorial decisions, such as the colour of one's socks, work in direct correlation to how your lesson might pan out – every single thing I did was pulled apart by the prying eyes.

I went in to be confronted by thirty recalcitrant teens rearing up in front of me. For a start they all looked older than me, especially the girls. Lolitas at the front, with mischief in their eyes. Added to this there were the Olympique Marseille fans at the back who looked like they all wanted to kick off. They all seemed to find me some kind of hilarious object to look at, which was unsettling. I instantly regretted my baggy checked trousers and became increasingly self-conscious of my wooden bead necklace, which was, metaphorically, beginning to tighten around my neck. The fact that I was wearing odd socks merely completed my *piche*[45]-look. I tried to start as emphatically as I could, "*Je m'appelle Ben et je suis le nouveau assistant d'anglais. Je suis très content de vous rencontrer,*" I said, disguising a gulp. Cue riotous laughter. Balls. Bollocks. Balls. Bollocks. At least it couldn't get any worse, I thought. Only work options were singalong to 'You are my Sunshine' or photocopied game of naming the famous sites of London. I was clearly not going to sing was I? The old maxim that man runs faster when he doesn't know where he is going could not have rung truer. There should be another one, 'Man's French gets worse when he is being taunted by thirty French teenagers.' Instead of explaining to them about the Queen's horses as I meant to (*les chevaux*), I made the schoolboy (I practically am a schoolboy) error of describing the Queen's *cheveux*. As I held up a picture of the Queen I enthusiastically explained that the Queen was famous for being a bit of a sourpuss but she cheered up when, "taking her hair for a ride at Balmoral". Cue riotous laughter. Trying to take the laughter as a positive I went on to explain how she was so rich that sometimes she "fed steak to her hair". Only when one of the Lolitas at the front took pity on me did my error come to light. I was nervous, stupid, weird to look at and now comical.

Finally I got them trying to match the names in English (of places they could not pronounce or had never heard of) with images of them (which they had never seen). It was bedlam. The only one they got was when I showed them an image of the Queen, to which they all neighed ear-splittingly. When I held up a picture of Prince Charles they all got up and reared, wagging their hands like hooves. I felt like an away team keeper who has just spilled a shot through his legs in front of the baying home fans.

The worst bit was that the students started to revel in the fact that they were essentially being looked after by someone who did not know what he was doing. Hands were raised to speak, not to say anything in English, but to make everyone else crack up. Talking in a kind of machine-gun French punctuated by laughing I think I was only picking up about 10% of. This is the real *Bocca. The Mouth. The Sea has Spoken.*

---

45 A French chav.

I don't even remember the lesson ending. I think they just left.

October 9
Brilliantly I am now of zero interest to anyone in the staff room. I went in today thinking that my experience yesterday would be the talk of the place but it seems no-one cares. I tried to start telling one of the men I had met but he literally started another conversation with someone else when I thought I was talking to him.

October 10
Back in the ring. Madame Caramel is in no hurry to return so, based on the incredible success of my first solo lesson I am back in with The Wild Ones. I don't know if it's that I was better dressed today (vintage adidas tracksuit top – universally cool) or just a certain persistence but as the lesson wore on, I dug deeper, they almost started to mellow out. The Olympique Marseille-tracksuited punks at the back kind of stopped sneering and the Lolitas at the front kind of stopped looking at me in a way that made me feel extremely uncomfortable. Progress! They still kept looking at my socks though, pointing and laughing, having observed the colour difference last time. I confronted a group at the front as to why it was funny and they all shrugged and said, "*Parce-que*".[46]

The 45-minute lesson (I use the word loosely) is at least over and my attempt to plug a hole has been noticed by the other teachers in the staff room. One said that it was a very "British" attitude to have held fort as I did.

"You Are My Sunshine
My only sunshine.
You make me happy
When skies are grey.
You'll never know, dear,
How much I love you.
Please don't take my sunshine away."

46 Because

DIX

Cui bono?

October 11

French bureaucracy is unbelievable.

I am in a *Catch 22* situation.[47] You can't have your *carte de séjour,* which is the ID card you need for everything, without having your assistant forms, and you can't have your assistant forms without a *carte de séjour.* Having no means of non-public transport I have to take a bus, then a train, then walk for over an hour to the administrative centre for the region which is situated handily about three miles from Nice airport in a kind of military compound.

During today's visit there was a point when the main consul, a kind of Gallic J. Edgar Hoover, looked like he was actually going to reject my application. I couldn't understand a word he was saying, all words sounded like "federal" and "collateral" and "jurisdiction". It would appear that I had no proof of existence. You are basically nothing in France unless you can produce a water bill. He actually asked me if I understood that this would lead to effective expulsion and a return to the UK. The desperate thing is that my lack of *carte de séjour* is also preventing me from getting any money in the form of salary or the

---

47 Everybody say things are a Catch 22 situation but I don't think many people have actually read the Joseph Heller book in which it appears (including me) so I am going to summarise. A US army pilot wants to be grounded from flying in the war and be found "unfit to fly". But the problem is that to be declared unfit, he must first ask for an evaluation, which is considered sufficient proof for being declared sane. It is therefore impossible to be declared unfit. The "Catch 22" is that "anyone who wants to get out of combat duty, isn't really crazy". Hence, pilots who request a fitness evaluation are sane, and therefore must fly in combat. At the same time, and this is a real punch in the gut, if an evaluation is not requested by the pilot, he will never receive one (i.e. they can never be found "insane"), meaning he must also fly in combat. Therefore, Catch 22 ensures that no pilot can ever be grounded for being insane – even if he were.

hallowed rent rebate back on my flat. I can't ask Mum and Dad again.

October 12

I am, quite literally, being forced into a life of crime.

I have paid a month's rent up-front for my apartment and I am a month away from being paid, and with mountains of paperwork to do to get that pay. I have literally no dollars. I stole loads of bread from the E. Roux canteen today and ate four yoghurts for dessert. I think you can drown by eating too much yoghurt.

I did, however, have a good teaching session this afternoon with my hand-drawn map and United Kingdom Quiz.

I had a lot of time on my hands.

October 13

I am not proud of this, but today is the day I started to steal from my local supermarket. I also understand that writing this down could send me to the slammer. Sliced *poulet* from INTERMARCHE, then crabsticks, chorizo and a little jar of *crevettes* from Le Petit Casino. The secret is to go into the supermarket and actually buy some things. I bought a lettuce. This distracts attention from my larceny and allows me to reduce the risk of getting rumbled.

It's not really a 'secret'.

October 14
I am justifying my thievery on two levels. One, the woman who runs the store is a foul human and I am pretty sure a racist and two, I really do not have any money.

October 15
Current situation is not helped by the fact that it has artistic value. I am reading *Le Voleur* in preparation for my final year (I have 19 books to read) and I have started to identify heavily with Jean Genet.[48] My criminal career is escalating as I read on. He probably started life as an assistant. As with Genet's dark voyage of self-discovery, I have begun to transcend moral law and on some days I too have begun to enjoy establishing my very own aesthetic of degradation.

October 16
Just like Jean Genet I have started hitch-hiking everywhere. But I will remain staunchly heterosexual. Other forms of vice I am open to.

October 17
My third visit to the French Pentagon. A benevolent French woman took pity on me and I think swept a few bits under the carpet. I feel like a boxer with a glass jaw as I am really letting the red tape headache get

---

48 Jean Genet's most famous work, it is a part-fact, part-fiction autobiography that charts the author's journey through Europe in the 1930s, wearing nothing but threadbare rags, quite often a lot less, and enduring a life of famishment, disdain, ennui and depravity. I feel that is exactly where I am headed. Apart from the vice, and the other countries, this is my life. Genet travels through a European terrain of Spain, Italy, Austria, Czechoslovakia, Poland, Nazi Germany, Belgium and of course, France. He ricochets between alleyways, dives, slums and flop-houses, in a whirl of robbery, jail and an overall exclusion from society. He was shunned by virtually everyone, like how I am being ignored by my bourgeois neighbours in Le Cannet. *Le Voleur* is structured around a series of homosexual love affairs between the author and various criminals, con artists, pimps, and even a detective.

me down, I live in Cannes for fuck's sake. I haven't really had to deal with anything on this level before. It sounds pathetic (because it is) but I think I have started to get a bit homesick. Things are kind of getting on top of me. And it's not helping that I have literally no money. Literally. The world is winning and Pop has always told me that in the struggle between yourself and the world, it's a good bet to back the world.

'7 Seconds' is still number one. It's really beginning to grate. Especially the bit where he sings, "there's a milleeeeeeon voices".

"Hello Muddah, hello Fadduh,
Here I am at Camp Grenada
Camp is very entertaining
and they say we'll have some fun if it stops raining."

LES 19 LIVRES QUE JE DOIS LIRE CETTE ANNÉE, ET LEURS ARGUMENTAIRES ÉCLAIRS

Rabelais *Gargantua* – Early Monty Python-esque tales of a giant's adventures in the 1500s.

Montaigne *Essais* – French Renaissance writer who hated love and would be the scourge of schoolchildren forever after popularising the notion of 'essays'.

V.E. Graham *Sixteenth Century French Verse* – Sixteenth Century French verse contains the rule that "the encounter of two unelided and awkward vowel sounds is to be avoided". I rest my case.

Corneille *Le Cid* – Famously stroppy writer who would sulk for months if anyone criticised his work.

Beckett *En Attendant Godot* – Much parodied title (*Waiting for Godot*). Two men wait and nothing happens. Sounds like Sutton.

Molière *Dom Juan* – Part of his slightly sarky Hypocrisy triology with Ecole and Tartuffe.

Racine *Bérénice* – The third of the 'Big 3' along with Molière and Corneille, this tale is another Greek love tragedy.

Madame de Lafayette *La Princesse de Clèves* – France's first historical novel. Unlikely to be the best, then.

Montesquieu *Lettres Persanes* – Heavy tale of two Persian noblemen who write a lot down.

Prévost *Manon Lescaut* – Short. And it was banned. Promising.

Voltaire *Candide* – Epic story about optimism. The epic bit worries me.

D. Parker *The Making of French Absolutism* – I really can't.

Marguerite Duras *Hiroshima Mon Amour* – Written in the 20th century! And there's a film!

Guy de Maupassant *Boule de Suif* – A short story, and it inspired a Western. Top of the list.

Bruno Bettelheim *The Uses Of Enchantment* – Mental Austrian child psychologist who wrote loads about the dark side of fairy tales before committing suicide with a plastic bag over his head. No 2 on list.

Jean-Paul Sartre *Le Mur* – Short, and about a firing squad. No 3.

Balzac *Eugénie Grandet* – Another 'classic'.

Etcherelli *Elise ou la Vraie Vie* – French feminist novel about an assembly line and Algeria. You couldn't make it up.

Nathalie Sarraute *L'Enfance* – She challenges her own capacity to accurately recall her past throughout her work. Oh yes.

Cannes 90210

October 18

Oh Happy Day.

Went to see Monsieur Guy Rufin and he looked worried by my appearance. I explained that I could not afford to buy razor blades so he delved deeper. I didn't tell him about the stealing but he has brilliantly lent me 1000 francs. I am going to see my friend from school, Wolfy, in Montpellier who is similarly on a year out but rather than teaching he is studying there.

My lack of integration is beginning to bother me and is certainly not helped by spending almost every weekend drinking with all my fellow British language assistants. I do not want to be one of those people who goes abroad for a year then comes home with the French language skills of an American. I am also aware that I am currently operating at somewhere around the 'A-Level'. I am doing a degree for fuck's sake. I'm finding the French somewhat hard to get to know. My fellow teachers have been friendly but slightly cool when it comes to the invites. It is also logical that I hang around with the new friends I have made and not choose to sit alone in bars waiting for the youth (girls) of France to come and talk to me. Sport is normally the default move but even that is proving tricky. There is not the vast Saturday and Sunday league system for joining a football team here and although there are teams around there do not appear to be any openings at my level (Upper Pub Level, Sunday League London South). Tennis is even more of a no-go as the clubs in Cannes make the British tennis system look inclusive. And I am too in awe of Monsieur Guy Rufin to want to see him in shorts.

October 19

Today I taught my best ever lesson. It may be because it was on The Beatles and I set it to music (second side of 'Abbey Road'). But it also happened to coincide with a classroom visit/inspection from the Central Bureau's Chief of Police. Or similar.

1962 / 1970

THE BEATLES

THE EARLY DAYS

1. WHERE DID JOHN LENNON AND PAUL MCCARTNEY MEET?

2. WHAT WERE THEY CALLED BEFORE "THE BEATLES"?

3. WHERE DID THEY GO IN 1960 WHEN STUART AND PETE WERE IN THE BAND?

4. THEY GAVE 300 PERFORMANCES AT THE CAVERN CLUB IN LIVERPOOL IN 1961 AND 1962. WHO JOINED THE BAND THEN?

5. NAME THE FOUR **BEATLES**...

6. "LOVE ME DO" IN 1962 REACHED WHAT NUMBER?

And in the end, the love you take, is equal to the love you make..

"BEATLEMANIA!"

7. WHICH NEWSPAPER FIRST USED THE PHRASE, "BEATLEMANIA"?

8. WHEN THE BEATLES ARRIVED IN AMERICA, HOW MANY PEOPLE WATCHED THEM ON TV, AND WHAT HAPPENED?

9. HOW MANY SINGLES DID THEY HAVE IN THE US TOP 5 IN 1964?

10. WHAT DID PEOPLE CALL THE BEATLES BECAUSE OF THEIR HAIR?

11. IN 1964/65 THEY MOVED FROM LIVERSOOL TO ....?

12. IN 1965 THEY GOT MBEs, WHO SAID, "I THOUGHT YOU HAD TO DRIVE TANKS AND WIN WARS TO GET THE MBE'?

"BIGGER THAN JESUS"

13. JULY 1966, LONDON EVENING STANDARD, JOHN LENNON, "CHRISTIANITY WILL GO... WE'RE MORE POPULAR THAN JESUS NOW." WHERE WERE PEOPLE VERY ANGRY?

14. IN THE "BIBLE BELT" WHAT DID GROUPS LIKE THE KU KLUX KLAN DO?

15. IN 1965 AND 1966 DID THEY START TO DO MORE POP MUSIC OR MORE EXPERIMENTAL MUSIC?

16. WHY IS THEIR CONCERT IN 1966 AT CANDLESTICK PARK, SAN FRANCISCO VERY FAMOUS?

SERGEANT PEPPER

17. WHO WASN'T ON THE COVER?

18. IN WHICH STUDIO DID THEY MAKE THE ALBUM?

19. WHAT DID PEOPLE SAY ABOUT IT?

20. WHO WAS THE SONG "HEY JUDE" WRITTEN FOR?

21. WHAT SORT OF FILM WAS "YELLOW SUBMARINE"?

THE END

22. JOHN AND PAUL'S GIRLFRIENDS WERE OFTEN BLAMED FOR THE END OF THE BEATLES. WHAT ARE THEIR NAMES?

23. WHICH SONG BY THE BEATLES WAS ABOUT THE GROUP AND THE END?

24. WHICH MOVEMENT DID JOHN SUPPORT AND WRITE MUSIC FOR?

25. WHO ANNOUNCED THE END OF THE BEATLES?

26. WHAT DID JOHN LENNON DO IN SEPTEMBER 1969 AND WHY?

AFTER "THE BEATLES"

27. WHICH TWO BEATLES ARGUED ALL THE TIME?

28. WHAT DID GEORGE HARRISON DO?

29. WHAT DID RINGO STARR DO?

30. WHAT DID PAUL MCCARTNEY DO?

31. WHAT WAS JOHN LENNON BETWEEN 1975-80?

32. WHAT DID JOHN LENNON'S MURDER ON DECEMBER 8TH 1980 MEAN?

NAME 3 BEATLES ALBUMS...

33.

34.

35.

35

All You Need Is Love

4 pm SNCF Train 6179 Cannes-Marseille-Montpellier
St Raphaël, Toulon, Marseille and now about an hour from Montpellier.
I was sitting alone in a cabin just outside Cannes when in walked the
actor Jason Priestley from the hit TV show 'Beverly Hills 90210' and
a pal of his. He smiled a Hollywood smile and asked if I would like an
apple. I said yes, actually fearing some kind of 'Snow White' situation
(Perrault's version, not Disney).[49] And so all three of us bit into apples.
The two guys couldn't look at each other and were giggling
uncontrollably. Brilliant, I thought, I have either been poisoned or they
are taking the piss out of me. It turns out that neither of these were true.
They were both just incredibly *cassé*.[50] The one who looked like Jason
Priestly was called Yvan and his buddy was called Laurent. I think it
may have been a turning point.

Jason Priestley and Laurent were heading to Marseille and after a few
minutes of chatting Jason Priestley pulled out what looked like one of
those giant Christmas Toblerones and asked me if I wanted to *rouler*.
What, here? On the train? With Toblerone? In broad daylight? *"Bien
sûr"*, I said. It was more hashish than I have ever seen. It looked like all
of the hashish. We all had a right laugh. I understood about 20% of it.
But laughed anyway. The blurry journey to Marseille has now cemented

49 In the seventeenth century Charles Perrault put together written verions of the
   popular fairytales, which had an oral tradition. He added in a bit of his own style,
   made up some bits and called them the *Histoires ou Contes du temps passé (Stories or
   tales of Times Passed)*. The big-hitters in there included such tales as *Little Red Riding
   Hood, Bluebeard, Snow White* and *Sleeping Beauty*. The tales were superficially just
   a bit of a laugh but often had deep, and dark underbellies. *Little Red Riding Hood*,
   on the surface a nice little ditty about steering clear of talking wolves was a massive
   allegory about sexual maturity and girls' menstrual cycles. Whiney *Cinderella*'s story
   was not always one of the slighted stepsister. In a pre-Perrault version she murders
   her first stepmother when she doesn't get her bratty way. The nasty stepsisters then
   actually hack off bits of their feet to try and get them into the shoes. Not in the
   Disney version, that bit. Sleep sex looms large over some versions of *Sleeping Beauty*
   as the star of the tale is impregnated as she dozes and is only woken when she is
   about to give birth nine months later. The married man who raped her turns up,
   triumphantly, admits he is married and then gets hitched to the Jerry Springer-esque
   Cinderella. In some versions (including the Brothers Grimm one) the wicked queen
   has to parade around in a pair of red-hot iron shoes until she dies. Not so many
   fairies in there!
50 Stoned.

Jason Priestley, the dude and doppelganger, as my first, proper, all-new French friend. And terrible influence, I reckon, as regards getting anything done.

October 21

Montpellier was brilliant. Wolfy, my friend from home, has established himself in a pad full of hedonistic Europeans from his course and is therefore living in a kind of 'The Real World' house, but with Swedish girls. Unlike me he doesn't appear too concerned about integration. He is studying for some kind of European business diploma which no-one has failed in its history.

The old city is packed with students and fun and seems to be entirely pedestrianised. The absence of cars gives it a kind of holiday feel. The coastline is like a giant swimming pool with a gentle wave machine with white sand, crystal clear water and a gently sloping sea floor. I sound like Judith Chalmers again. It is much younger and considerably more vibrant than Cannes. It has fewer obviously iconic buildings, less history and worldwide fame, but it is hipper and more modern. And a hell of a lot cheaper.

On the Saturday night I did something pretty stupid. We went out *en masse* for the birthday of a Swedish guy living in the house. We had started off by sampling *glög*, a kind of clove-flavoured syrup wine (*miam-miam* – mmmm in French), which is a speciality in Sweden. Needless to say it is rocket fuel and we poured out of the flat at 11 already well on our way. By the time we had visited a few bars and negotiated *les videurs*[51] at the door of the nightclub I could barely see. I stumbled to the toilet to find a giant queue, and one in which I was in no state to wait. I had a solution. I wrestled my way to the front door where I explained in perfect not-at-all-slurry French, standing perfectly still on the spot and holding up my front door keys, that I needed to fetch something from my car, which was parked just over the road. The *videurs* laughed at my feeble excuse for wanting to piss in an alley and told me that there was strictly no re-admission. So I laughed at them laughing at me, people in the queue laughed at me, the *videurs*

---

51 The bouncers, or more literally and appropriately translated as 'the emptiers'.

laughed with them. So everybody was laughing at me. As with most scenarios like this the laughter soon stopped and unfortunately I was very much still there when this happened. As I insisted, they resisted and they became irritated by my presence. I made one plea too far to go to my fictional car with my fictional keys and the most aggressive of the three very aggressive *videurs* told me that I could go back in or leave for good but one more word and I was out.[52] I called the doorman something between a racist and paedophile. I was picked up by my shirt and deposited on the other side of the club's entrance.

Paralytic and needing to get home, with no idea where I was. I decided to go up to the *videur* and tell him what I thought of him. I said, "*Va te faire enculer*"[53] which is less articulate than that. I remember me hitting the wall, only two metres behind me, then the warm and weirdly comforting taste of my own blood running from my nose into my mouth. I was then picked up by one of the other *videurs* and dragged out of the way to a cosy doorway round the corner.

About ten minutes later, and no doubt sobered up by the straight punch to the face from an amateur boxing champion, I headed back to the door. Just like Paul Newman in *Cool Hand Luke*.[54] I think they almost took pity on my generally pitiful existence. They demonstrated this by gently getting hold of me by the shoulders and depositing me in the same doorway round the corner.

I slept soundly until Wolfy found me at 4.30 am when he left the club with a fully-integrated French girl on his arm.

But hey, I'm alive. And I have a French friend who looks like a TV star.

> "Wait a minute, it stopped hailing,
> Guys are swimming, guys are sailing,
> Playing baseball, gee that's better,
> Muddah Fadduh please disregard this letter."

52 An inability to control my mouth would come back to haunt me in France.
53 Go fuck yourself.
54 I like to compare myself to cinema's greats. In this one the bloodied, beaten Luke repeatedly picks himself up only to be knocked back down again.

NE PRENEZ PAS INFRACTION: DES ACTIONS ET DES GESTES DES GENS DU MIDI

- Putting your change not in your hand but on the counter
- Kissing you (men)
- Being offensive (men, women, children, dogs, *videurs*)
- Queue-jumping (weirdly women the most)
- Treating dogs better than humans
- Appearing arrogant
- Ignoring you (waiters, attractive girls, attractive women... all females)
- Slating British cuisine (yes, even children, who know nothing, do this)
- Slating British weather (zzzzz)
- Asking you to give them a cigarette as if asking you for the time
- Being brusque and inappropriately supercilious (waiters, people who work in bakeries)
- Treating you as if you are dog pooh in shops
- Smoking all over you (men, women, some children)
- Raising their voices (it's the Mediterranean, they externalise their feelings)

Charlotte's Web

October 23

Today I taught some basic conversation to the youngest class. It involved getting them all in pairs and them learning the basic phrases to say to each other. It was a mess but there was lots of laughing.

Monsieur Guy Rufin has forced me into playing him at tennis next week. I am so out of shape it is untrue. I had no choice.

Start with the basics.

October 24

Today I taught colours and numbers to two classes of 12-year-olds. It was actually quite rewarding.

It is coming up to my Dad's birthday. I am wondering whether to send a card. I only have 4 francs (40p) in the world. I think the postage may cost more than that. I hope he calls me. Though that isn't really the protocol on one's own birthday.

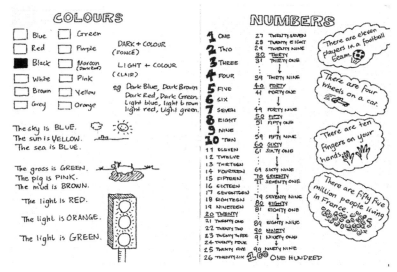

I learnt it all from Tricolore.

October 25

Everyone is coming to my flat today. Charlotte is coming early. I am quite excited by that.

Cannes, octobre 28 1994

Sod,

This is the one.

I have met her. The Charing Cross Girl.[55]

Not a mention of a shark, I promise.

And I cannot stop listening to 'Let it Loose'. I think it is about me and HER.

The maddest stuff has happened/is happening. On Friday I held my first apartment party. Obviously of my

---

55 As teens we would walk past the Charing Cross Hotel, thinking it splendid, and I always said that one day I was going to stay there with 'the' girl for me.

whole life. Everyone came; Pollyanna Peters, Andreas
and some mates, Alistair, Rhiain and, of course,
Charlotte Love. Due to teaching schedules it turned out
that Charlotte would be coming to Cannes earlier than
everyone else as we both had Friday afternoon off. This
was in no way going unnoticed and I was wrenching at
the leash as I waited for her train to come in. She seemed
a bit pissed when she got in at 2 pm (turned out that she
had already started on the red wine on the train. I think
she had done at least a bottle on the hour-long journey
from Hyères). It was incredibly hot for October, even by
Cannes' standards. Naturally, like a young Cary Grant, I
suggested we pick up some spaghetti bolognese crisps and a
bottle of red from INTERMARCHE, from where you could
nick plastic cups from the drinks machine, and head
down to the beach. What a dreamboat.

Sitting on the secluded rocky end of the beach eating
and drinking the finest Provençal produce, the heat-
sandy rocks combo became vaguely unbearable, along with
my head-groin apex situation, having racked up 4 weeks
without the slightest hint of action. A seriously long
time. My desperate attempt to remain quixotic was being
tested to the extreme. So when Charlotte suggested going for
a swim I almost choked on my crisps as she quite clearly
didn't have a swimming costume. Being the shy and
retiring type she told me that her knickers were lace at the
front and see-through so could we go further along where
the rocks would protect her modesty. At this point I was
practically sobbing. The clear implication here (I had to
spell this out to myself, the rosé was taking hold) was that
it was OK for me to see the knickers going see-through but
not for other people. Was this because she had the hots for
me? Or (cue horrifying dawning of terror music) because I
am no threat?

We headed over to the rocks and I carefully positioned
the remnants of the wine and crisps in a crevice. When I
looked up Charlotte was crouching on the rock in a white
lace thong the size of an espresso spoon, a white cotton
bra which was already completely see-through and a smile

that was lighting up my trousers. So much so that I didn't yet want to take them off. In fact, I couldn't take them off. I stayed there in the crevice (literally stuck between a rock and a hard place!) until Charlotte had disappeared in the water and then braved the strip off, hoping for the best. The cool Mediterranean Sea did the job, almost too well. It did it until we both climbed out of the sea and back on the rocks and Charlotte spread herself, like a mermaid, across a giant flat sloping rock, to dry off. Her lace underwear was now not just see-through, but seemingly highlighting the glories underneath. There was nothing else for it, I had to lay face down and endure the pain of rock-on-horn.

Man. This was the most ridiculous day. I couldn't believe it was actually happening to me here and now. But there's more.

An hour or so later we got dressed and wandered back to the train station to meet the others. We were having the most brilliant conversation about kids' books we used to read. Aside from being pants-wettingly hot she is also really cute and a bit like a child. Either I was in love or the London rock fraternity (I have begun to think she actually is going out with Michael Hutchence) did this kind of thing all the time and I am a bit wet behind the ears. She is probably just one of those Marianne Faithfull — naked under a fur coat with a Mars bar[56] — kind of girls who enjoyed a bit of attention but only really puts out for the 35-year-old rock stars of this world. I had no chance, I agreed with myself. Read on.

We met Pollyanna, Alistair, Andreas and his mate at the station, bought wine and fags and headed up to my flat. Seven of us in total piled into my studio and I unfolded the table from the wall (reducing the floorspace by a half instantly) and getting the mood lighting on. I only have one light so I half-covered it with some curtains I found lying around, giving the whole flat a kind of Penthouse misty soft-focus quality, which matched

56 A made-up story, apparently.

my addled eyesight/libido. I played a killer set of acid jazz classics on my portable CD player which hardly jumped and looked over constantly for approval. The cheap red wine flowed, the crisps just kept coming and I increasingly began to think that Charlotte was mine for the drunken flailing.

At around ten we headed down into Cannes where we stumbled upon a bar strangely called Le Chelsea. Fortunately there appear to be no links with your disagreeable club of the same name but a general fondness for all things British. Apart from us. A proper drinker's bar and they had no truck with our Erasmus-scheme bonhomie. But they did have a machine in the corner called a 'VideoJuke' which, aside from making me feel once again like I was in 1950s Milwaukee and playing '7 Seconds' every "7 minutes" breathed life into our drunken foray. My repeated playing of the 'Love Spreads' video by The Stone Roses was not going unnoticed by my flirty friend and when it came to doing a cigarette run to the tabac a few blocks away there was only one companion for me. (Her, in case I am being too rambling here.)

As she slipped her hand in mine I actually found myself wondering again if this was normal behaviour for an IT-girl. When she put her tongue in my mouth on the corner of the Rue d'Antibes I was pretty sure I was on to something. My heady night (I could barely see) was getting headier.

Mi casa, su casa! Sometime after 1 am we all headed back to my apartment armed with more booze. As there were already seven of us and a distinct shortage of beds I thought it would be a good idea to phone Jason Priestley and invite him round to meet my friends for the first time.

He cheerily agreed and at 2 am three French guys arrived to the Dionysian carnage of my flat/friends. Jason Priestley did his best to style out his surprise at the level of debauchery and I remember (it would have been one of the last things I remembered seeing and so therefore quite memorable) seeing Alistair walk past him drinking wine from an ashtray. How his friends must have marvelled at our controlled and classy English way of letting our hair down. Then the flat caught fire. My makeshift moodlighting went up like it had been soaked in petrol and this in turn swept into one of the sheets, which was also surrounded by candles. Literally sparked into life by the need to be with it as danger engulfed my new home and uncontrollable with worry about the safety of the people and possessions I fell fast asleep on the bathroom floor.

At 11 am I woke up, effortlessly spooning a very undressed Charlotte (her arse has replaced her tits as my favourite part of her anatomy...what's next???!!!!) We had progressed to the hallway, which is in a sense still the bathroom. My immediate joy turned to a red wine-coloured numbness as I saw two people I had never met before asleep on the table and Andreas asleep, behind the television. There were six people asleep on my double sofabed. The sofabed, rather worryingly, had purple stains all over it. "It's the red wine," said Alistair, helpfully. I later found out that the cheaper the red wine, the purpler the stain. Andreas found it all hilarious and sat up screaming the chorus to his revised version of the Prince classic, Purple Stain.

Brilliantly, at that moment, the doorbell rang. Even more dream-scenario, it was my all-time dream woman, Madame Cocheteux. As I held the door as closed as I possibly could without looking like I was concealing a dead corpse I could feel her glance peering over my shoulder. Because I am in love with her I did not want her to see me in this juvenile and immature setting. Because she is my landlady and holds the keys to me not being homeless I did not want her to be cross with me. But it was really the first one. She was as charming as she always was and, frustratingly for me, she had genuinely popped round to see how I was getting on.[57] She had also

---

57 I would use this Madame Cocheteux 'just-popping-round' scenario extensively over the coming year as a tool for easing sexual frustration.

brought me a bottle of red wine as a little welcome present, which was a thoughtful, if untimely, gift.

But she departed swiftly and, as the headache eased, I began to enjoy the fruits of the previous day's labours. Especially when the labours were drinking heavily, eating crisps and removing clothes from Charlotte. She looked great in the morning. I am totally smitten.

This letter is quite long.

She is EVERYTHING.

'7 Seconds' is still number one.

LE PETIT GUIDE CANNOIS (PARTIE 3)

In 1946 the first Cannes film festival finally took place. The new venue wasn't built yet (you could see how the French had been somewhat (pre)occupied in the intervening years, boom boom) but the old winter casino was used and ageing cinema big hitter (as in 'he and his brother invented it') Louis Lumière was the first ever President of the Jury. The next year they built the Palais but the roof blew off, leaving literal and financial holes that would lead to no festival for the next two years. By 1951 the smarmy Italians were out on their own with Venice so Cannes went in for another go, also moving the festival to spring. Over the next ten years they got their act together, invented the golden palm leaf, the *Palme d'Or*, making the whole event a competition, and encouraging filmmakers to market and make deals on their sandy shores.

In 1963 Marcel Pagnol, author of *Jean de Florette*, controversially exclaimed whilst visiting the Cannes Film Festival, "Cinema is dead; long live television." He would prove eerily wrong. The film festival just kept on growing. In the same year an as-yet unknown young model decided to give acting a go. It would prove incredibly influential and a career path, which would be followed by literally every model ever. She was called Brigitte Bardot and when she whipped her skirt off to reveal a bikini she was embraced by France as the epitome of woman (more on her later). In 1968 the angry French students did manage to replicate a Word War when they ground the whole event to a halt. After days of sit-ins, and withdrawals from Godard, Truffaut, Louis Malle, Polanski and Lelouch, the festival was officially pulled.[58] But it would prove a minor blip as it saw

58 The student revolution was an uprising against the modern consumer society and was a largely left-wing phenomenon, culminating in the students coming very close to overthrowing the de Gaulle regime. These Situationists were formed in 1957 and based in France. They were believers in a libertarian Marxism which became popular after the mass strikes of 1968. Lasting only fifteen years, some people think the movement's ideas were deeply influential, and have formed a major part of Western society. When the police shut down the Sorbonne University, these previously-considered apathetic young thinkers were having

off all comers to become the world's leading festival of glitz. And sometimes cinema. This was certainly the case in 1976 when the jury president Tennessee Williams awarded the *Palme d'Or* to Martin Scorcese for *Taxi Driver*, as Cannes cemented its love for the auteur cinema storyteller.

Booing films off stage became as much part of the fun as the cheering with Depardieu one of the first to suffer. Not for the first time in her film career Madonna took her clothes off in public. Her 1991 classic *In Bed With Madonna* required almost no introduction but she whipped off the silk sheet she was wearing and displayed her Jean-Paul Gaultier conical bra to an adoring world in case they missed the subtlety of the title.

And so Cannes' history has very much become the history of its film festival. But with other festivals too Cannes has become something of a stopover, like a giant market stall. With events all year round Cannes now also celebrates the worlds of boating, shopping, advertising, premium property, the game of bridge, fireworks and luxury travel. You can see why they hated the fishing village period.

none of it. It led to a general strike involving ten million workers, at the time the biggest general strike in history. This Marxist uprising of the workers, it was claimed, proved how dependent on them society was, paralysing the country. Managers were locked in their offices by workers who forced, them to ask for toilet visits. More than that it was one of the best-looking Revolutions ever. These cats were writing poetry like they were on a creative writing course in Provence and coming up with slogans like they were interns at advertising school. All the while wearing black rollnecks and mohair. It was the first ever Situationist Revolution. Even when they trashed stuff they came up with an elegiac chant. As bits of concrete from the pathways rained down on the police they would chant, "Under the paving stones – the beach!" The police were bemused. They were being attacked with words.

Waiting for Enzo

October 29

Pollyanna Peters has started to tell us about her boyfriend back at university in Nottingham. Having had such a successful loan spell there myself she has also quizzed me as to whether I know who he is. Spending a year watching from the wings whilst everyone else experienced university life, it is with some regret that I can say that I very much do know who Vincenzo Cilenti is. He was the swarthy-looking guy who had been sat amongst a flock of the finest beauties at the university, as I quietly imploded in humiliation in the lecture hall. Strangely he doesn't seem to remember me though. I would say that too if I was going out with Pollyanna Peters. But nice to hear, anyway.

'Enzo' has managed his life to perfection. Being both Northern now that that's back 'in' and also being Italian, which has never been 'out'. He has his panini extra virgin olive-oiled on both sides. His innate coolness means, like some kind of Kenickie-figure, that he failed his second year and so could not get on the assistant programme. Instead he is driving down (probably in a vintage Alpha Spider) any time soon when he will get a job (probably restoring old hot rods in a garage full of chrome) and cool his way through the rest of the year. Pollyanna reckons that we will really "hit it off". I kind of know full-well that we won't. It tends to be the case.

Spoke to Charlotte on the phone for three hours. I have never had a phone call this long before.

October 30

Last night, like a proper professional, I prepared like a professional for the single most important sporting event I have been involved in in years. Jason Priestley picked me up and we went round to a friend's where they just happened to be melting hash into chocolate yoghurts.

I'm pretty sure that's Boris' ritual the night before a Slam final. Three hours later, at one in the morning, we were inexplicably hurtling along the A8 autoroute towards Monte Carlo. Jason Priestley, driving, said, "*C'est tellement bizarre, ça…. le chauffage.*"[59]

Monsieur Guy Rufin picked me up at 11 am. I felt like a complete pikey. I had had two hours' sleep and I was still stoned. Humiliatingly I had to borrow a racket and some shorts more appropriate for tennis than my Umbro England football ones. I was also wearing white shell-toe adidas with jumbo laces. In short I looked like a *gitane*.[60] Monsieur Guy Rufin was immaculate in pale blue Lacoste polo, white Lacoste shorts and socks, a pro tour bag containing about eight rackets and a set of spare shoes. He even had a Lacoste water bottle.

The gulf in class was embarrassing. When he came in for smashes at the net I couldn't lift the ball anywhere near him and he had to go back. After 20 more minutes of me grinding in the clay and him gliding across the ground he saw a get out.

One of my pupils at Collège le Big Fun is a tiny lad called Luca who plays a bit, judging by the oversized racket bag he lugs around most days, like a double-bass. We often chat about matches we have seen, but he is 14 and the idea of actually playing together hadn't really crossed my mind. Monsieur Guy Rufin jumped on this opportunity in a second and when my third consecutive backhand hit the fence behind the court called him over.

So me and the future of French tennis went back to the court. Monsieur Guy Rufin sat down, absolutely not sweating at all in the small stand backdropped by the most spectacular view over the bay of Cannes. It quickly became apparent that he was incredibly good and I was getting worse. I was also shattered. Normally when you play tennis with someone new you have a bit of a hit, feel each other's levels out a bit, nothing too serious. Today was different. Luca came to the net and asked me to call for the right to serve or receive. We actually started playing a proper match!

His parents watched impassively from the stand as their young

59 "It's so weird, this…driving."
60 Gypsy.

protégé tore me to shreds 6-1, 6-2. But it was more the manner of the defeat. Slaughtered. Eviscerated. By a child. The fact that I got really cross with myself too didn't help, with a few foul-mouthed self-rebuttals particularly frowned upon by the watching members. Like McEnroe, but without the talent.

So embarrassing.

Charlotte rang me at 2 am and wanted to see if we could "break our talking record". She fell asleep on the phone. The last thing I remember was the '7 Seconds' video on M6. Still No. 1.

October 31

Seismic and ground-shaking meeting of minds with Enzo took place last night in the streets of Vieux Nice. The Principe Ereditario of Nottingham University has just arrived after a lengthy drive down. I did my upmost to look underwhelmed and he just hated the whole idea of me. As a general rule of thumb blokes don't massively like blokes who befriend their girlfriends when they are not there. Especially if that guy is only vaguely memorable to you as someone with no friends and who wore his clothes backwards. We shook hands and barely looked at each other, giving nothing away. When Pollyanna left us to go to the bar we had only ourselves to talk to and it was largely silent.

November 1

Today I taught 15-year-olds about Halloween. To almost complete indifference.

Y ←Bats

The Pumpkin

Witches are supposed to ride broomsticks across the sky on Halloween night. **Bats** are often seen in the sky and near the witches.

The **Pumpkin** is a vegetable which people eat in pumpkin pie, especially in America. On Halloween night people cut out the inside, make an evil face in the pumpkin and put a candle inside.

HALLOWEEN is celebrated on the 31st October. It is a very important night in America but a lot of people also celebrate it in England. It is traditionally a night when ghosts, witches and ghouls come out to scare people. Halloween occurs just after All Saints Day, to remind us of the powers of evil. Evil spirits are supposed to come back from the dead to show us that there is a hell as well as a heaven.

In England and America children play a game called "TRICK OR TREAT". In this game, children dress up as ghosts or monsters and go and knock on peoples doors. When they open the door the children say "Trick or Treat?", if the person says "Treat" the children get a small present; some chocolate, sweets or fruit. But if they say "Trick" or just close the door then the children can play a trick on them or try and frighten them. Sometimes people get very angry with children who play this game.

Also on Halloween night people often have "Halloween parties", adults as well as children. For these parties people dress up as ghosts or monsters, or Dracula or Frankenstein. They drink red "punch" (a mixture of lots of drinks) because it looks like blood and they play scary games and tell ghost stories.

HALLOWEEN est une nuit très spéciale et importante, surtout aux États-Unis mais en Angleterre aussi. Halloween est célébré le 31 octobre et c'est une nuit très traditionelle. On dit que les phantômes et les monstres sortent pour effrayer des gens. Halloween vient juste après le Jour de Toussaint pour nous montrer qu'il existe des mauvaises puissances du Diable et aussi les puissance de Dieu.

En Angleterre et aux États-Unis les enfants ont un jouet qui s'appelle "TRICK OR TREAT?" Les enfants s'habillent comme des phantômes ou des monstres et pis ils vont chez leurs voisins ou les gens de leur ville. Quand quelqu'un vient à la porte les enfants disent "Trick or Treat?". Si la personne dit "Treat", les enfants recevrant un petit cadeau comme un peu de chocolat, des bonbons ou du fruit. Mais s'il dit "Trick" ou ferme la porte les enfants peuvent faire quelque chose un peu méchante contre cette personne, mais pas trop serieuse. Des gens ennuyeux sont souvent très fâchés contre les enfants qui font cet jouet.

En plus, on a souvent des "Halloween Parties" sur cette nuit, les enfants et les adults aussi. Des gens s'habillent comme les phantômes ou comme Dracula, Frankenstein ou "The Addams Family" et ils racontent des histoires effrayantes et ils pratiquent les jouets effrayants.

Getting quite confident now.

COMPRENDRE POURQUOI SERGE EST SI IMPORTANT POUR LES FRANCAIS

"When he died in his bedroom on 2 March 1991, a month short of his 63rd birthday, France went into mourning. Brigitte Bardot, who'd slept with him, gave a eulogy; President Mitterrand, who hadn't, gave one too. He was 'our Baudelaire, our Apollinaire', said the head of state. 'He elevated the song to the level of art.' Flags were flown at half-mast – a less fitting symbol for the priapic pop genius than the bottles of whisky and *pastis* and packets of *Gitanes* cigarettes left as tributes by the crowds who descended on the police barricades erected around the *Rue de Vernueil.*"

So said Sylvie Simmons in her definitive biography of Serge, *A Fistful of Gitanes.*

Serge is the great contradiction in French history. The establishment-baiting *enfant terrible* who got worse as he got older who was also so accepted by the mainstream that he was practically afforded a state funeral, his death creating shockwaves in France on a par with JFK's assassination. He was misunderstood pretty much everywhere outside of France. In the UK he is a sex-mad old lech. In France the illegitimate son of Baudelaire and Marie Antoinette. He is internationally known for two things. Primarily THAT song. *Je t'aime (moi non plus)* was his only international hit (English speakers don't like songs in other languages, apart from *Una paloma blanca*) and afforded the ultimate accolade when our favourite guardians of moral righteousness, the Vatican, declared the tune "obscene". His Gallic word play was pretty much lost on everyone, including a lot of French, but when he spoke in groans it worked, and gave him the taste for notoriety which he dug, almost a bit too much.

His song titles are brilliant:

- *'N'écoute pas les idoles'* (Don't listen to your idols)
- 'Lemon incest'
- *'Les sucettes'* ("lollipops", innuendo-heavy song about girls sucking things)

- '*L'homme à tête de chou*' (The man with the cabbage head)
- Sea, sex and sun
- '*Je suis venu te dire que je m'en vais*' (I just came by to say that I'm off)
- 'Baby alone en Babylone'

The other thing he is known for is his 'Whitney Houston moment'. Repeatedly shown on French television's 'Best Of' shows, a grey, greasy, drunk Serge leans over to Michel Drucker, the host of an early evening chat show, and, with millions watching, gestures to a very prim and proper (pre-Bobby) Whitney and says, "I want to fuck her". Drucker, forgetting that Serge has said it in English, translates it as, "He says you are great". Shocked, she can do nothing but laugh and playfully cuff the old dog.

Death in 1991 floored France. When people tried to compare him in tributes they came unstuck, France's Bob Dylan? Serge was more playful and silly. The French Jim Morrison? Serge wouldn't call himself a 'poet'. Even though he was. The French Lounge Elvis? Oh please, Elvis didn't even write his own songs. Serge is just 'Serge'. Shy yet lewd, rude, selfish yet generous, sleezy but harmless, sexual, yet child-like. He is most often viewed as being ahead of his time. I wonder what was the point in being so far ahead of your time? What a waste. Most of all he is referred to as a national treasure. He is a mass of contradictions and, aged twenty, I relate to that.

The Paving Stone Roses

November 5 – Wasted on 33 Export

I feel that it is important to record this. I feel inspired. I have met someone who has INSPIRED ME. Pollyanna and Enzo came to Cannes tonight. We started at the flat. He was friendlier. I behaved in kind. We got chatting about music. We covered the obvious reference points:

- *Screamadelica*
- The second half of *Abbey Road*
- *Paul's Boutique*
- *Off The Wall*
- *Pet Sounds*
- All Stevie Wonder pre-1980 – up to and including *Hotter Than July*
- The Spencer Davis Group
- The Charlatans
- The La's
- New Order
- Etcetera, etcetera.

Then we started talking about The Stone Roses.....

We started off chatting about how The Roses' debut album has a strong French leaning.[61] When I said my favourite lines were "Soak me to my skin, Will you drown me in your sea, Submission ends and I begin", Enzo came back with "Choke me smoke the air, In this citrus sucking sunshine, I don't care you're not all there."

The Roses are everything to me and all at exactly the right time. Enzo

---

61 It uses the tricolore of the French flag on the cover and has a whole song dedicated to the May 1968 student riots – 'Bye Bye Badman'. The album also features three slices of lemon on the cover which, legend has it, had come from a story told to lead singer Ian Brown while he hitched round Europe. An old French guy had told Ian how the rioters used lemons as an antidote to tear gas (it took the effect away). So The Roses had sliced some up for their debut album cover.

says he is EXACTLY the same. This is seismic. I HAVE LITERALLY JUST PUT THE FIRST ALBUM ON. I love the childish Beatles-y sound of their music, I love their clothes, I love Ian Brown's hair, I love their northern swagger, I love John Squire's guitar sound and the fact that he designs all the artwork for album and single covers, I love the fact that they sound a bit like my Mum's old Simon and Garfunkel records. I love their stance, what they are all about and what they stand for. I also love how important they are. And we agreed that the people who don't think their decision to call their second album *Second Coming* is anything other than entirely appropriate are IDIOTS. His best mate is taping it and sending it over the day it is released at home. COUNTING THE DAYS.

I showed Enzo the *MOJO* I just got sent from home with the front cover of Oasis and the headline 'You've Got the Band You Always Wanted'. We bonded over Noel saying stuff like; "Lennon would be shite if he were alive today", and especially, "Phenomenal band, the Bees Gees."

Right now they seem like the most urgent, exciting group we have produced since The Roses. Even if they are named after a leisure centre in Swindon. After Ian Brown, Liam has the life I want, he well looks like he is enjoying it. And 'Columbia' makes me feel like I can conquer the world, or at least shows me how to.[62]

---

62 We had heard rumblings of a band from Manchester when a demo of a song called 'Shakermaker' was given away free as part of an *NME* tape cassette in early 1994. Even the title sounded right. The album was released in August 1994 and was to provide the perfect soundtrack to what was to become the most hedonistic year of my young life. And just as my own ego began to take its fully-fledged form. More significantly we had not had a great British band since the Stone Roses, and they had disappeared into a Welsh hole for the previous five years with no real sign of coming out. We had had good British rock bands, like the Charlatans (whose better second coming had not really yet come) and The Happy Mondays and crossover bands like Primal Scream or New Order and we had had one great British soul band in Jamiroquai. But more than anything we had had years of trauma injected into our brains via successive angst-ridden American bands currently culminating in Nirvana, Soundgarden and, my preferred genre of musical disquiet, Pearl Jam. But the lead singers, unlike this new sound emanating from the North, certainly didn't look like they were enjoying it. And surely that was the point? The American groups reminded me of being lectured to by someone's annoyingly self-aggrandising older

I admitted an early craving to be Andrew Ridgeley. Enzo countered with Tony Hadley.

Everything has changed.

November 7

I don't know if it's the hangover, the life-changing music chat with Enzo or the fact that I am on my own, but today I feel chronically homesick for some reason.

'7 Seconds' is still number one.

brother, when all I wanted to do was to go and play air guitar at ZZ Top's house. A year or so later my Dad sermonised me on the subject of why Oasis were boozy, derivative and leaden, before showing me a copy of 'Slade In Flame' (brilliant, by the way) on VHS to observe the similarities. It may have been old music to him, but it was new to us. And boozy, derivative and leaden was probably a good summation of where we were at in our lives.

L'Hiver

The staff room

November 9

I am really getting into the teaching. It's quite 'give a little, get a lot back'. Being quite geeky about the lessons but if you are even a tiny bit prepared it is the least onerous job in the world. It is a joy! The age range from 12 to 17 makes the lessons pretty varied. My favourite class are at Le Slab and comprise around twenty 12-year-olds. They are all absolutely brilliant. They should film them and put it out as an advert for the job of teaching. They are charismatic and charming in bucketloads. Today was them at their absolute best. I taught them the children's song 'I went to the animal fair', the lyrics of which are:

> "I went to the animal fair,
> The birds and the bees were there,
> The giant baboon,
> By the light of the moon,
> Was stroking his golden hair. (Pretend to brush hair, they love this)
> The monkey fell out of his bunk, (make falling sound)
> And slid down the elephants trunk, (whizzing sound)
> The elephant sneezed (sneeze sound),
> And fell on his knees, (all do this)
> And what became of the monkey (Monkey, monkey, monkey…repeated continuously)."

I had the whole class chanting 'Monkey, Monkey, Monkey…' joyously and then started the second half off singing from the start again. They are infectious. In that moment today I would have given everything up to take a job teaching them for the rest of my life.

November 10
Can't write. Hellish hangover. Not all schnapps is peachy.

November 11
Charlotte got the train down last night. She met me at lunchtime and we went to eat in Collège le Big Fun. She thought it was amazing. It was going so well until she started the "let's just be friends" crap chat. Apparently her situation at home is not great (really???!!!) and Michael Hutchence has kicked off about everything. Makes me feel sick just thinking about him. She said "It seems like it is probably for the best" as though I am not involved in the decision-making process. It is probably for the best FOR HIM.

So I acted like I completely think we should just be friends, but in a slightly offish way which I think confused Charlotte. Which was exactly my plan. Acting all Harry to her Sally in the bit when they go to galleries and stuff I did something I have always wanted to do – take a girl to a football match. Ha, how platonic! We went to see AS Cannes beat Montpellier 3-0 and she was all cute and wrapped up and being inquisitive about the game. Pissed me right off. I showed her Le Slab and we decided to walk all the way back, stopping to buy wine in a two-litre plastic bottle which we drank in the two-hour walk.

We slept in my bed together and she tried to get all cuddly but I said, "Hey Charlotte, friends don't fondle."

November 12
I just re-read yesterday's entry and in hindsight that probably sounded really gay.

I now have almost 50 photocopies and lesson ideas! This is because it seems for the most part that I am not so much assisting as actually taking classes on my own while the teachers sit there wading through marking. Or shopping lists. Or staring into mid-space. It is also because I have such a ridiculous amount of spare time in which to create them, and absolutely no money to spend on anything distracting. It's like being a child, but with a more restless mind. The lengths I am going to on my drawings and colouring-in is actually making me regress to childhood. Note to self!

I am also supplying my master sheets to all the other assistants like a Mediterranean worksheet dealer. This means I am pretty much the only person doing any work. I say 'work'. 'You are my Sunshine', 'Imagine' and pretty much anything by The Beatles have turned out to be absolute winners when it comes to lyrics lessons.

Charlotte and I also had sex last night as she decided to stay one more day. This is not something I normally do with my friends and will not happen again.

November 12
Some observations:
The differences between the two schools are becoming narrower. Every class has its characters and its menaces. Often the cute ones at the front are really the evil orchestra conductors running a campaign of terror coming at you from just a few rows behind. Without getting all Dead Poets Society some of the harder classes, particularly at Le Slab, are definitely the most rewarding and relationships forged with some of these kids make going to work something I have literally started to look forward to! It is an incredible feeling, the like of which I couldn't have imagined until I did this. Even if this is teaching with a giant safety net. I am getting a real rush out of it though.

Cannes (I never tire of writing that)
November 13

Word.
Right, I am going to try not to write too much about Charlotte (I am not in the mood and we are going through something of a trying phase) and this is more in response to your "what else are you doing?" question and what my other teachers are like and all that.
This little story will help shed some light.
Two weeks ago one of the teachers from Le Slab (the shit school, the clue is in the name) first invited me to a get together and from there on in it has become an almost weekly event. The teacher is called Françoise (Fran) Collins and she is a kind of mumsy take on Kate Bush, quite fit in

a kind of Radio 2 way. I actually quite fancy her (this is a recurrent theme). She is no Cocheteux, but still. She lives in this classic Provencal village of flagstone streets and watercoloured houses near Mougins, a rich enclave about 10k from Cannes. It is the kind of place where people buy tablecloths and old (fake) tin Perrier and Orangina signs and annoying English people wang on about it to their friends.

They have this massive house they called 'La Villa de Collins' as that is their surname. Literally on a sign. Egged out yet? You will be. This place has a big pool and about five bedrooms. She is married to a Welsh guy, called John Collins. He is unaffectionately known as 'Jonno', a parody of a name he seems to have appropriated for himself. He is uxorious towards his wife to the point of obsession, it's weird. I instantly disliked him for no reason at all when I set eyes on him. Like that Dr Fell[63] that Pop always recites. He is porcine and sneering and weird and as different from his wife as it is possible to be. Amongst the female teachers who know him at the school he divides opinion. Some appear to openly dislike him, others just hate him. If it is possible, he gets worse when you get to know him. There is even less to him than meets the eye. Also I think that he really quite hates me and spots me looking down his wife's top when she ladles out soup.

As a couple they have the world's most annoying habit of calling each other, in a faux-flirty way, "Mr and Mrs Collins". As in "Would you pass the baguette, Mr Collins?", "Yes I will, Mrs. Collins." This phonic foreplay can go on for hours. And he looks round the table to check that we

---

63 Dr Fell is a nursery rhyme from the 17th century, written by the satirist, Tom Brown. Whilst studying at Oxford he misbehaved and was sent before the Dean, a Dr John Fell. Dr Fell was an English vicar and the Dean of the college, later going on to become the Bishop of Oxford. Dr Fell let Tom Brown have both barrels but before expelling him he set him a translation test, the challenge being that if Tom passed the test he would get off scot-free. The passage to translate from the Latin was: "*Non amo te, Sabidi, nec possum dicere quare; Hoc tantum posso dicere, non amo te.*" Brown's successful translation was: "I don't like you, Sabidius, and I can't say why; all I can say is I don't like you."

are all finding this as riotously good fun as he is. (Clue: we aren't.)

On my third visit there this week Fran suggested I go and help Jonno with the barbecue he was meticulously preparing. Jonno didn't look like he wanted much help with the barbecue. I felt a little bit like being told to go and play with the pet bull shark in the pool. It was apparent that Jonno doesn't just dislike me, he dislikes everyone. Unlike Sartre and his classy dislike of other people I have just read, L'enfer, c'est les autres.[64] A statement so well constructed and understated it makes being disliked seem preferable to being liked. No, Jonno is a snarling Welsh, rugby-loving/all other sport-hating little Jack Russell with sharp teeth that'll nip you when no-one is watching.

I ambled over to the barbecue, all long hair and an earring (what's not to like, I ask you?) and he watched me all the way, ready to pounce on my first indiscretion. I have already had about ten indiscretions with him at various other meetings. All of these had been genially laughed off by lovely Fran when he has pounced in company. These have included liking football (it is for girls), being from London (teeming with homosexuals), asking me if know how a jet engine works (Yes. No. Don't care.) and not showing any interest in going to a paintball event with him (seriously, you wouldn't).

He is one of those irritating casual male chefs who make big, showy statements like having 'trademark recipes' which he wheels out when people come over. The fact that his wife is a better cook to the factor of about a hundred and also probably cooks around 99% of the food in the house is disregarded when a gathering is treated to his 'special sauce' at barbecues or 'secret ingredients' coq au vin. Displaying all the patronising gastro-tourism of the foreigner he often talks about "keeping the old French recipes alive". What with the French being so lame at preserving their culinary history.

---

64 Hell is other people.

I had recently read about the origins of the word barbecue somewhere. Knowing that he would hate that he did not know this I led with it. I told him that barabicu is a word, which came from the Taoino people in the Caribbean roasting goats in a charcoal-laden hole they would cover, and they also used the terms barbicoa or barabicoa. This went down brilliantly. My mistrust of him increased even further just after when he refused my offer of the moutarde jar and opted for slathering his meat with mayonnaise! Heavy and constant self-analysis have forced me to train my palate to enjoy stronger mustards and a preference for horseradish over mint sauce. It is most definitely time to be a man. Mayonnaise is quite clearly My First Dressing and primarily for kids.[65]

Sophie, aged five. This is a child so hideous that we have to gather round at family parties as she 'performs' 'We Will Rock You', culminating in her literally screaming the refrain face-to-face with all the guests, but primarily it seems, me. As she sits strumming on her plastic toy guitar in the wild hills of their garden in Provence, all stormy hair and food smeared over her face she reminds me of a cross between the banjo-playing kid in Deliverance and Regan from The Exorcist.

Peace. And out.

PS Charlotte and I had sex again last week and we are now making Christmas plans. How gay does that sound?

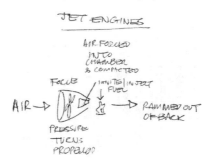

---

65 I have continued to apply this food:personality link, making similar observations about negative traits in adult males and enjoyment of any pizza with prawns on, Ragu-style Italian Bolognese sauces, overly enjoying baths and spaghetti carbonara.

PPS *Not that gay really, considering her enormous breasts.*

PPPS *I just learnt the word uxorious. Look it up.*

The Last PS. *Perturbed by my lack of knowledge I asked my dad to explain how jet engines work and wrote it down while on the phone.*

November 16

Fran's best friend Muriel invited a few of us over for dinner last night. Even better as Jonno is never invited. They all want to speak English, but still. Muriel is single and 40 – rare in France – and should have been a chef. I said this at the table and when I left she gave me a cardboard box full of food including leftover quiches, flans and homemade jam. Looked like I said it on purpose. Last night we ate *gratin dauphinois* and drank *Mirabelle*, a kind of plum brandy and she smoked prolifically. I have discovered that I am quite adept at smoking other people's cigarettes myself.

Also, in terms of cultural insight, Muriel bought cinema tickets on a little machine half of French people have in their houses. It's called a Minitel and it's like teletext but you can talk to other people and buy stuff. Mental.[66]

The less I worry about Charlotte the more she seems to act like our relationship is an inevitable force neither of us can control.

November 17

Got a letter from Nan and Pop today. They sent it on the old blue paper as an 'aerogramme' and signed off with "Take care over there, it can be dangerous abroad." From a man who served for nine years in the Royal Navy and was on the HMS Sheffield when it got torpedoed.

---

66 *Minitel* is a French phenomenon (weird, they are considered a bit technophobic) which has many of its own books written about it. Way before the internet, in the early 80s era of Pacman, France Telecom gave away millions of little boxes which were hooked up to a phone line. The terminals in homes and offices are typically accessed to buy train or cinema tickets, check business figures, publish small ads, search, use chat rooms or send messages to other Minitel users. They were charged on their phone bill. Amazingly figures show that Minitel still has over 10 million regular users in France!

November 18

I think my life has begun to settle down and everything is beginning to fall into place as I think it should. I love the work, I have a gargantuan balcony, I am getting to know France and its people pretty well. I am also having friend-sex with a proper, bona fide rock chick.

Corsica starts on England, France steps in

November 20

My cooking skills are going mental. On their way back from the *hypermarché* Muriel and her on-off boyfriend Daniel brought me all the ingredients for something called *daube provençal*. Daniel told me that the French have the lowest obesity rate in Europe, but they also have the best film about overeating. Are there any other films about overeating? Does *Stand By Me* count? France has a film all about overeating. It is called *La Grand Bouffe*, and him and Muriel are going to invite me over one night to watch it.

November 21

Cooked *daube provençal*. Was a revelation.

Daube Provençal

Cinnamon, loads of carrots in slices, cubes of beef (3lb), lean bacon, one (or two) bottles of wine, loads of garlic, (a bit of Cognac?), loads of chopped onions in a bowl & leave for 24 hours.

Take beef out, toss in flour & brown it in oil. Chuck it back in a dish & put in oven for 2-3 hours.
Cook tagliatelle and pour it over the lot.

November 23
Cooked more *daube provençal*. I am a creature of habit.

November 24
Watching M6 music channel and eating *daube provençal*. '7 Seconds' came on the '*Boulevard de Hits*'. Still number one. Neneh Cherry, Youssou N'Dour and *daube provençal* are the dominant forces in my life.

November 25
I am over *daube provençal*.

November 26
Just heard. Elton John's 'Can you feel the love tonight?' knocked '7 Seconds' off the number one spot after 16 weeks.

November 27
Strange thing happened today. Monsieur Guy Rufin asked me if I would like free flights home to London in exchange for being the language assistant for the four-day trip to London to see the lights and all the Christmassy stuff. I think I actually welled up. Am I subconsciously homesick and I just don't know it?

LA CORSE

I have been to Corsica, it is beautiful. Like a cross between Newquay and the Maldives. It is between France and Italy in the middle of the ultra cool bit of the Mediterranean known as the Ligurian Sea. West of Italy and southeast of France, just north of the Italian version of it, Sardinia. It is one of France's twenty-six régions [67] although it is kind of seen as a separate place (despite them having a team in French football's first division, called 'Sochaux').

Napoleon Bonaparte was born in Corsica in 1769. He was a rich kid from a family of Italian nobility. He was a military genius, became the French equivalent of Prime Minister and then chucked in the title of 'Emperor of the French' for good luck. Just made it up. He staged a *coup d'état* in order to be proclaimed as this Emperor and then became even more of a firebrand. Suffering from extreme small man syndrome, he started on anyone who looked at him funny. The conflicts he kicked off were somewhat arrogantly named (by him presumably) 'The Napoleonic Wars' and essentially involved him kicking off with pretty much everyone else on the mainland. Thanks to this yappy streak France became the prominent force in continental Europe. This was in no small part helped by Napoleon's habit of putting friends and family in control of whole other countries. He started up his own code (called, you guessed it, 'The Napoleonic Code' – this guy made Louis XIV look modest), which was used across Western Europe as a kind of template.

Even Napoleon couldn't get out of his 1812 attack on Russia. He had picked a fight with a much bigger dog. The crushing defeat of his *Grande Armée* there led to a series of other defeats. A year later he was forced to abdicate and was exiled to the island of Elba (Elba, by the way, is beautiful, there's exiled and there's exiled). He got bored and managed to return to power, wasting no time in starting on us Brits at the celebrated Battle of Waterloo. We locked him up on the island of St Helena in the Atlantic and he died, probably poisoned, in 1821.

---

67 France is divided up into 26 régions: 22 on the mainland, plus four overseas regions, called régions d'outre mer (ROM).

They also have the world's best flag, which looks like it was designed by a five-year-old, but I imagine Napoleon had something to do with it.

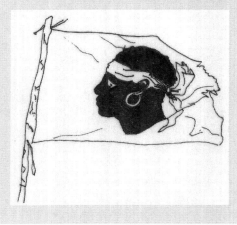

November 28

Today was not a good day.

Corsicans are notoriously feisty and aggressive. My first experience of this has come at the hands of a woman I barely know, a gnomic history teacher called Madame Muglioni. The fact that she is really attractive adds nothing much to the story, other than clarifying the fact that I am on heat as a permanent state.

One of my small classes of cool 12-year-olds were waiting patiently outside our classroom when I arrived. Our allotted room was occupied and rather than make a fuss I thought the sensible thing to do was to take the empty room next door. Seems obvious.

Ten minutes in Madame Muglioni storms into the room like a Corsican separatist, doing away with the traditional civilities, like knocking, saying hello or smiling. Instead she aggressively placed herself between me and the students and proceeded to let rip. I couldn't understand most of what she was yelling about but the gist was that she had been looking to use the room for some prep for a class, had pre-booked it with Monsieur Guy Rufin and I was a potato with the face of a guinea pig.[68]

At this point Monsieur Guy Rufin magically appears and starts trying to calm the harridan down. All of a sudden...*BADABOUM!*[69] I think she said something disparaging about him, in her Corsican French. He went at her in his controlled, yet terrifying way. The particularly well-behaved children watched on with a mixture of horror and boundless joy, it was like an episode of Eastenders, with suntans and better hair. The final twist involved Muglioni gesticulating wildly at two particular students, which led to two of said students bursting into tears. In Africa they say, "when elephants fight it is the grass that suffers".

This seemed to pour water on the Corsican fire and, like an injured panther, she retreated to her cave. Monsieur Rufin, of course, took it all in his sizeable stride.

The *mistral*[70] had passed through and my class looked shocked. In my first moment of any real Frenchness I smiled reassuringly, placed a look of amused faux-puzzlement and said, "*N'importe-quoi.*"[71] My students

---

68 "*Vous etes une pomme de terre avec le visage d'un cochon d'inde*" is a very real Corsican insult.
69 French Boom!
70 Big Mediterranean storm, see chapter 33.
71 Whatever.

all laughed. Didn't exactly bring the house down but a connection.

November 29
I am reading Sartre's *Le Mur.* Quite good actually.

November 30
Cooking *moules* is much easier than you would imagine. Muriel gave me a recipe.

December 2
Weekend with Charlotte in Hyères. We drank, smoked and had sex for two days.[72] The hedonistic living was only interrupted by either a) calls from her rich Daddy about how she was managing to spend so much money on her phone bill or b) Michael Hutchence himself wailing down the phone.

Brilliantly Charlotte, after essentially one full weekend together, has told Michael Hutchence all about me and how serious it is. She said she was confused as to where this left their two-year relationship. He did not take it well. I thought it was a shade premature of her but I am smitten and nothing in my life at this point really makes any sense.

I reckon Hutch phoned three or four times a day and once Charlotte cruelly placed the phone on the bed so that I could hear his rebel yell, his primal screams, his devil inside. I didn't really like this and it doesn't bode well for any future differences of opinion we may be about to have.

This weekend was also notable for the fact that Charlotte broke pretty much everything in her apartment. Wine glasses, a coffee table, the telephone, a couple of dinner plates and the glass shelf in the fridge which broke when she slammed a bottle of rosé down on it. Can you be addicted to breaking things? Like a fetish thing? There was so much broken glass that the place resembled a crack den. We spent the weekend walking around in flip flops. It wasn't particularly relaxing. And I really hate flip flops.

December 3
Beef tomatoes on French bread covered with olive oil and salt is a new one. Like summer on a plate.

---

72 Artistic licence.

December 4

Really long phone chat tonight with Charlotte and I feel on edge again.
I know that most of the time she's a real laugh and happy and great
company. And seems to be on a one-person mission to have fun all
the time. This is what I love about her. But deep down I'm starting to
think that maybe, deep down, underneath it all, she's not totally happy.
Maybe I should encourage her to be herself more?

P R I N C E

OH YEAH!
In France a skinny man died of a big disease with a
little name . By chance his girlfriend came across a
needle and soon she did the same .
At home there are seventeen year old boys and their idea of
fun is being in a gang called the Disciples high on crack
and totin' a machine gun .
TIME ... TIME ...
Hurricane Annie ripped the ceiling off a church
and killed everyone inside .
U turn on the telly and every other story is telling U
somebody died .
Sister killed her baby 'cause she couldn't afford to
feed it and we're sending people to the moon .
In September my cousin tried reefer for the very
first time , now he's doing horse , it's June .
TIMES ... TIMES ...
It's silly , no ? When a rocket ship explodes and everybody
still wants to fly . Some say a man ain't happy unless
a man truly dies .
OH WHY ? TIME ... TIME ...
Baby makes a speech , star wars fly , neighbours just shine
it on . But if a night falls and a bomb falls , will
anybody see the dawn ? Time ... Time ...
Is it silly , no ? When a rocket blows and everybody still wants
to fly . Some say a man ain't happy truly 'til a man truly
dies' . Oh why , oh why , sign OF the times . Time ... Time ...
Sign OF the times ... mess with your mind , hurry before it 's
too late .
Let's fall in love .. get married .. have a baby .. we'll call him
Nate (if it's a boy .)
TIME ... TIME ... TIME ...

T I M E

Seminal

114

December 5

A breakthrough day with the older kids. We listened to, then learnt the lyrics for, Prince's 'Sign ☮' The Times'. I was pretty much welling up when they realised the significance of the "big disease with a little name". What a wrist.

December 6

Cooking calamari, on the other hand, is much harder than you would think. Alistair came over and I offered to cook some for him. I bought a whole squid from the fishmongers and attempted to chop it into rings using my Swiss Army knife. I then deep-fried torn squid torso in an old sticky frying pan. We ate fishfingers instead. In France they are called *bâtonnets de poisson*, which sounds much better.

December 7

I went to Madame Cocheteux's today. She was watering plants in her garden wearing a long brown linen dress and a little shawl. If I stood slightly to the left the sun made her dress completely see-through. Her hair was tied up like Sophia Loren. On the way back I felt like 'Good Vibrations' by The Beach Boys was playing on loop in my head. "I don't know where but she takes me there", swirling around really loud.

December 8

I have started writing lots of letters to people from my past. If I am honest I like telling them that I now live in Cannes. Today I wrote to Joanne Bannister.[73] I told her a lot about Cannes and how I live here. That was about it really.

December 9

Last night Enzo and I went to a Jamiroquai concert in an incredible open-air theatre in Nice. He did a twenty-minute version of 'Blow Your Mind', which totally blew mine. After that he did a really long scat-jam, the lyrics being "Legalise, don't decriminalise" while he waved a massive spliff in the air. Enzo thought it was shit. I felt proud to be English. In fact, maybe I felt European.

---

73 I went out with Joanne Bannister from Bromley when I was 14. Our relationship was based on tonguing and listening over and over to 'Man in the Mirror'.

December 10

Reading back from my diary yesterday I think I should make it clear that it was Jay Kay, the lead singer of Jamiroquai, and not Enzo who did the twenty-minute version of 'Blow Your Mind'. I did my first Christmas lesson today using John and Yoko's 'Happy Christmas (War Is Over)' to great effect. Absolute winner! They loved it and I actually think I'm starting to get through to these kids. No surprises that it's John Lennon breaking down the barriers. We played it a bit loud but a nice moment occurred when Madame Muglioni walked past, shook her head…smiling…and then peered in and told me that she wouldn't complain today because she liked this one!

Still no rent rebate. I'm really skint.

War Wasn't Over.

JEAN-PAUL SARTRE (DANS LE CAS OÙ VOUS L'AURIEZ MANQUÉ)

Novelist, playwright, existentialist philosopher, friend of Jean Genet, Nobel Prize winner (which he refused), literary critic, occasional firebrand, lifelong partner of Simone de Beauvoir and bumper-sticker quote merchant.

> *Les mots sont des pistolets chargés.*
> Words are loaded pistols.

Jean-Paul Sartre was born in Paris to a naval officer, who died when little Jean-Paul was just fifteen months old. Sartre never wrote much about his biological father. Sartre lived with his mother, with whom he was incredibly close, and his grandfather, before she remarried and the family moved to La Rochelle. At school, he was brilliant (theme), but also cocky and badly behaved. He graduated in 1929 and from 1931 to 1945 he worked as a Professor of Philosophy at Le Havre as well as travelling in Egypt, Greece, and Italy before studying in Berlin in 1933–34.

Sartre published his first novel, *La Nausée* in 1938, in which he gloomily argued that human life has no purpose. In the same year he published his collection of short stories, *Le Mur* (The Wall), which dealt with the small matter of existence.

He was imprisoned in Germany during World War II a year later and got away in 1941. The experience of loss of freedom scarred him, and inspired the torrent of expression which was to follow. In Paris he joined the Resistance movement and founded a monthly literary and political review, *Les Temps modernes* (named after a Charlie Chaplin film). He was a big fan of the cinema.

> *"Une victoire racontée en détail on ne sait plus ce qui la distingue d'une défaite."*
> Once you hear the details of victory, it is hard to distinguish it from a defeat.

L'Etre et le néant (Being and Nothingness), in 1943, was the one that really made him as he started to popularise philosophical thinking like the whole world was one big dinner party round at his. He took on the unenviable task of attempting to reconcile existentialism and Marxism and flirted with the French Communist Party. Had a close friendship with Albert Camus, although Camus's novel The Rebel in 1951 caused a break between the two clever chums.

> *"L'homme n'est point la somme de ce qu'il a, mais la totalité*
> *de ce qu'il n'a pas encore, de ce qu'il pourrait avoir."*
> Man is not the sum of what he has but the totality of
> what he does not yet have, of what he might have.

He was fascinated by the Soviet Union, but they weren't always quite so enamoured with him. The O.A.S. (*Organisation de l'Armée Secrète*), exploded bombs (twice!) in 1961 in Sartre's apartment in Paris. The world's finest pub chatter, he made the distinction between things that exist in themselves and human beings who exist for themselves. Conscious of the limits of knowledge and of mortality, human beings live with existential dread, and one we would do well to shake.

Sartre was unsurprisingly right behind the student revolutions and was opposed (vocally) to the Vietnam War. In 1967 he found himself heading up the International War Crimes Tribunal, judging American military conduct in Indochina.

In the early 1960s the Cuban economic and social revolution fascinated Sartre more. He also met Fidel Castro, but became disillusioned with all that later. In the late 70s he lost his eyesight and controversially bequeathed the rights to his literary heritage to his mistress since1965, and not Simone de Beauvoir. He died in 1980.

> *"La vie est une panique dans un théâtre en feu."*
> Life is a panic in a theatre on fire.

Play the way you're facing

December 11

Last night I attended my second AS Cannes home game at the Stade Pierre de Coubertin. I was going to go on my own but it randomly came up in conversation with Monsieur Guy Rufin and he was going anyway so suggested a lift. I immediately bumped into teachers from the other school and most of the male student body who go *en masse*. It is very much a Mediterranean take on the watching of a football match. The game is no more than incidental. There is a proper bar, which serves anything you might want. We arrived, said hello to a few people (Monsieur Guy Rufin knows EVERYONE), had a *pastis*, had a couple of beers, ate some olives, drank some wine, ate a sandwich, had an espresso. Most fans appeared to have their backs to the game for most of the time, turning round every now and then to check in. There were probably only about 5,000 of us there.

It was nothing like English football. This was more like an evening at the theatre, only with less concentration and more booze. At the hub of the team is a young French-Senegalese player called Patrick Vieira[74] who is about 19. He is head and shoulders above the rest.

---

74 The future France (Arsenal, Inter Milan) captain would brilliantly be someone I would later go on to become mates with. I say 'mates'. He probably won't put me in his book. But I did hit it off with him. This was largely because, in a later career in advertising, we had booked him for a shoot. The celebrated photographer Nadav Kander was poncing around so much that I said something to that effect in French to the vaguely irascible Patrick. He couldn't believe that there was another French speaker, less that I had watched him play twenty-odd times when he was 19. We both said amusing asides about the photographer all evening, exchanged numbers after the shoot and I had the good fortune to see him a few times after that when he would introduce me to players like Thierry Henry by saying, "*C'est un pôte Cannois!*" Which all made me particularly vainglorious.

December 12

Went round to Muriel's with Daniel. He amazed me by offering me a spliff when we were driving there from mine. Seeing as I say yes to EVERYTHING I said yes. Then pulled the most enormous whitey. Forgot who we were going to see, thought I was going to fall down when we went to get bread, laughed hysterically BEFORE the punchline in his joke. Then had the most unbelievable munchies. Watching a film called *La Grand Bouffe* (The Big Eat) in this state, and before we ate, was not ideal.

The story is simple; four suicidal wealthy middle-aged men head out to a chateau in the country with the express purpose of eating themselves to death. (Why?) They get some prostitutes to join them and add sex in to the mix. I think it then becomes an increasingly scatological and satirical take on Western society's deranged consumption. But I was asleep.

December 13

Charlotte didn't call. I live in perpetual fear of being dumped. And I'm not even going out with her.

Cannes, December 13

Dear Sod,
"Pretty Maids All in a Row".
These are the top 10 Rolling Stones songs of all time.
And yes, I did consider 'Satisfaction'.
  * 'Let it loose'
  * 'Sympathy for the devil'
  * 'Sway'
  * 'Moonlight mile'
  * 'Shine a light'
  * 'She's a rainbow'
  * 'You can't always get what you want'
  * 'Start me up'
  * 'Street fighting man'
  * 'Undercover Of the Night'

All good here. Just had Pollyanna Peters and Alistair over for a few days. Whilst she sounds like it Pollyanna

Peters is not your typical rosy-cheeked flicky-haired, Surrey-born public school girl. Her Guildford upbringing has not created a spoilt or snotty monster. She is also not classist and has apparently never ridden a horse. She does not appear to be pro-fox-hunting either. Although she does have that whole slightly flushed I-just-got-in-from-having-a-snowball fight thing going on. Which I am quite envious of. She is also the most optimistic and upbeat girl I have ever met. Without managing to be the kind of 'wacky person' who openly bangs on about how the glass is half-full, she just kind of does. She manages to find the nice things in everything. If this means that sometimes she sees the world through rose-coloured spectacles then it just makes me want to buy some of those. Possibly to replace my rosé-coloured ones which I seemed to be wearing on a daily basis, especially when I am with Charlotte.

Pollyanna Peters' relationship with the extremely well-dressed Enzo must have helped in the sartorial stakes but she is already pretty cool on her own. She is sincere and considerate and a great laugh to hang around with. We make her tell us stories about elocution lessons and playing lacrosse. She humours us well. She does also make the odd faux-pas, like the night she told us that she once went to a party in Camden where she witnessed first hand, I kid you not, a bloke skinning up a spliff on a Bible. We fell about. She has regretted forever telling us that one.

We had had the brilliant idea on Friday of getting Pollyanna Peters (she has the poshest voice, even in French), to phone up some of the clubs in Cannes and tell them that she was the PR for the group OASIS and that the group would be visiting the club later. This was all done in the vague hope that we would get VIP treatment. Only one of the five we phoned showed any interest. We got our outfits ready, our normal clothes, rocked up and looked properly the part (we were wearing sunglasses at night). We went to 'Le Loft' in Cannes, Pollyanna Peters did her bit and we went in. To admittedly slightly questioning looks from the emptiers.

Le Loft is an awful Eurotrash paean to bad taste.
Its cheap décor and completely unironic use of cheap
glitterballs give it a kind of Costa Brava feel. But without
the cheap drinks. The French get a well good deal when
it comes to their reputation for being classy and tasteful.
They have their moments, but so does everyone. They also
have a lot of horrific moments...and this is an installation
of that.

There was no bottle on the table but there was a big
menu with big numbers next to the drinks. We decided
on beers (they had the smallest numbers next to them but
I can now see how this may have been an error – go big)
and settled back to enjoy our faux stardom. Before the
beers even arrived a serious-looking monsieur walked
swiftly over and asked us to leave the table as it had
been reserved. Pollyanna Peters admirably mentioned
something about our management but we were on
Cannes streets in no time. Not before I had caught site
of a number of girls from the top class at La Bocca (I am
beginning to see why we had that lecture, I am only 20
to their 18 and some of them are ridiculously fit), who
I desperately hoped hadn't noticed me as I was forcibly
ejected from the club. So that's why rock stars wear shades
at night!

Mea Culpa. Society really does frown on petty crime.

B

PS Charlotte is doing my head in and writing about her
will result in an almighty outpouring of emotion which I
really don't fancy doing today.

PPS "Where there's muck, there's brass." Do you get
that???

December 14

French society was rocked in a mild way this week by a magazine publishing a photo of President François Mitterrand's daughter, Mazarine. It wouldn't have been newsworthy if not for the fact that no-one knew he had one. It turns out that the President has had a mistress for most of his married life, a museum curator called Anne Pingeot.

He has been spending half his time, and no small amount of taxpayers' money, with this second family, keeping them in a highly-policed and guarded apartment in Paris. Like a dark fairytale the little daughter, who was named after the bookshop her parents loved in the capital, was never allowed to tell anyone who her father was. The strangest thing, especially coming from England, is that no-one in France really seems that bothered!!!!

December 15
The run-up to Christmas and the London trip is getting really good; the kids are incredibly excited about seeing my foreign land. I am excited by their excitement and lessons have became one long Christmas Eve. I feel like my fingers smell of satsumas. I feel like the Pied Piper of festive fun.

In my lessons I have embraced the world of television. We have been watching 'The Snowman' and 'A Charlie Brown Christmas', even a few episodes of 'The Box Of Delights'[75]. Through their eyes it's like seeing them for the first time. The world seems magical and unaffected. With the younger ones we read a Rupert the Bear story and I played them the 'Frog Chorus' video. They had a hard time reconciling that with the intense Beatles education they are getting. No wonder.

December 16
Charlotte's awful habit of breaking things[76] is becoming a bit of a drag. After her visit yesterday my apartment resembles the inside of a bottle bank. My last visit to see her in Hyères was just as bad and Jason Priestley (who accompanied me), possibly understanding more of the subtext around her new life, appears filled with dread for my future. Charlotte is having no problems making friends in the town's bars, particularly amongst the blokes. She appears to have got in with the entire wrong crowd of Hyères in the space of about a week and it is beginning to grate.

Her cute habit of calling at all hours is cute when it is kind of sexy and loved up, less so when she rings with an apartment full of strangers,

---

75 BBC Christmas classic from 1984 based on the equally classic John Masefield book.
76 Hearts especially. I had mentally adopted the brace position.

who all seem to be called Didier and Karim. Being woken up at 3 am on a Tuesday night is wearing a bit thin. I must have a word. Off to Nice to see Enzo and Pollyanna Peters.

Well pissed now. Bit worried about how little French I am speaking. Not helped by the fact that we keep drinking in a bar called *Chez Wayne*. *Chez Wayne* does a roaring trade in the heart of Vieux Nice. Tonight was Elvis night. I read somewhere that there are 85,000 Elvis impersonators in America, compared to just 150 in 1977 when he died. If we carry on at that rate, I read that one third of the world will be at it by 2019.

December 17

Charlotte and I were invited to Enzo's flat in Nice for dinner with him and Pollyanna Peters last night. It was an incredible evening for one reason and one big fuck off reason alone. 'Second Coming' has arrived in the post. We played it in its entirety recurrently for about five hours. In a word? GENIUS.

Charlotte got more and more pissed and more and more contrary and outspoken. Like a long-tailed cat in a room full of rocking chairs (haha, I read that somewhere) I was constantly on edge. Her peak (her view) and nadir (everyone else's) came when she told us all that she didn't think the first Stone Roses album had any good songs on it. WHAT? And that it was "music for wankers". Enzo vehemently disagreed and a semi-heated argument took place, which only ended when Charlotte suddenly screamed with laughter and said, "I was thinking of The Simple Minds this whole time, not the Stone Roses!" Almost a whole minute later she placed her wine glass on the very rounded edge of the table and we all watched in silence as it gently slipped off and shattered into a thousand little pieces all over the tiled floor.

"Not The Simple Minds," Enzo corrected. "Just Simple Minds."

Enzo and Charlotte don't get on at all. In fact there is a simmering revulsion that crackles every time they share air. They despise each other and, as we tucked into Enzo's carrot risotto, I had the first inkling that this Charlotte thing might not be right. Her knack of picking fights is a bizarre side to her otherwise kind personality and the frisson it creates never a welcome one. We left before she broke anything else i.e. as quickly as we could and Pollyanna Peters smiled sweetly at me as we left. I totally know what that smile meant.

londres

December 18

Volte face.

Charlotte and I spent an amazing night together last night at the flat. She was like a completely different person. Is that a good thing? I think we're going to be OK. She told me she needs me to help her. I think I am up for it. I feel kind of like a man.

December 19

School trip leaves tomorrow. Can't wait.

Heard today that we will be staying in a small *banlieue* called 'Sutton' and all the kids will be housed in families round there. Sutton!!! This has cheered me up immensely. Not that I was 'down'. Just a bit flat. And poor. It doesn't take much to swing from happy to sad.

One of the youngest students today asked why they called London '*londres*' in France, not even with a capital L, yet Manchester stays as 'Manchester'. And Edinburgh is 'Edimbourg'. Why? I am flummoxed. It is true. Who makes the rules? Why do we call Barcelona exactly that and the French call it Barcelone? Who gave the rest of the world the right to say Rome when the people who came up with it call it 'Roma'? It makes no sense.[77] Los Angeles is called that everywhere, *non*? I feel like a stumped father must who has just been asked by a child why the sky is blue, why the moon comes out at night or how they get those tiny boats with big sails inside tiny bottles.

Tonight there's a kind of Christmas pageant and one of my classes is

---

77 I also wonder about languages where they used their words in the midst of another. So the Scottish say 'loch' instead of 'lake'. Do they therefore go and watch a ballet called 'Swan Loch', or their prog-rock fans stay in and listen to 'Emerson, Loch and Palmer'?

singing 'Silent Night' in French then in English. Quite chuffed about that.

> "*Douce nuit, sainte nuit!*
> *Dans les cieux ! L'astre luit.*
> *Le mystère annoncé s'accomplit.*
> *Cet enfant sur la paille endormit,*
> *C'est l'amour infini,*
> *C'est l'amour infini!*"

Sapphic Christmas

Christmas Eve

"I do not believe in God, his existence is belied by science."

Sartre said that. Unsurprisingly. I am pretty sure I am with him. But come Christmas we all believe. Loving seeing the students I know from my newly-alternate world in Provence here in south London where I grew up. It seems strange, like when you see two friends of yours from entirely different groups chatting at your birthday party. Feeling proud of my hulking great home megalopolis, it seems vast and sprawling and dominant and vital.

Christmas Eve, 6 pm

Oh this is a good entry. Real Christmassy, this one. Charlotte (who I have not seen since my return, she lives in very west London), phoned me to tell me that her best friend, the 40-year-old rock hag, called Saffron, has been having a lesbian affair. Intriguing. Clearly drunk, and having been out with Michael Hutchence ("amongst others" she said, lying) her yo-yo-ing tale was waning when she invented the game of guessing with whom Saffron might be having an affair. As I rattled off the names of friends of hers I exasperatedly said, "I dunno...you?" "Bingo," I remember her saying.[78]

My initial thoughts of "Let's have a threesome" quickly disappeared (I don't know how you organise it) and I find myself listening to the story of how my newly Sapphic girlfriend has been unfaithful to me, soundtracked by giggling and glasses being downed. I ended our Christmas Eve call by putting the phone down. Unsurprisingly she called back a few times and I had to ask Dad to not answer.

---

78 Funny how some things stay with you.

December 26

k.d. lang aside I have managed to settle down to a relatively enjoyable and traditional Christmas. I always feel that all is right in the world as soon as I see the sign saying 'You are now in Bedford Falls' and safe in the knowledge that George Bailey's journey to the brink will only involve teetering and that in just under two hours I will be reassured that it really is a Wonderful Life.[79] Gutted about the Saffron thing though. It makes me feel sick to the bottom of my stomach.

Later...

French anti-terrorist police stormed a hijacked jet at Marseille airport and killed four Islamist terrorists. Watching the footage made me miss France. Which was weird, considering.

December 27

The Collins Family Newsletter was sent directly to my parents' address despite the fact that my parents have only met one of the Collins' once, and they had yet to meet the charmingly arid 'Mr. Collins'. The newsletter tells the story of how the Mediterranean Partridge Family have all been busy learning ancient Asian languages, developing everlasting fuel reserves and re-inventing the wheel. It even has a cartoon drawing of them as something of a logo, which appeared at the bottom of the page. It was drawn by the multi-talented rock singer herself. I feel a bit bad writing this as Fran has been so nice. But he's such a dick.

I have heard k.d. lang's 'Constant Craving' twice on the radio today. It's the new '7 Seconds'.

December 28

A load of us went to the Wag club for a club night called 'Leave My Wife Alone' which we always go to. London is decidedly cooler than Cannes. I can't stop thinking about Charlotte tonguing Saffron. And not in a good way. Like tonguing an ashtray.

---

79 *It's A Wonderful Life* was originally planned as a vehicle for Cary Grant, and not James Stewart, movie fans. Would have made a pretty good fist of it.

London December 29

Sod,

It's weird a) you not being back here at Christmas and b) being back here myself. I feel like a tourist. It's 7 in the morning on Saturday Dec 29th and I just got in to bed. I have to write this down before I forget it. French girls are pretty amazing and all that. But tonight changed everything. In good and bad ways. I have never felt so sexual in all my life, never seen a more sexual, more attractive chick. A Billion Dollar Babe sucked my ice pole. And no. That is not allegorical. Unfortunately. Oh, and Charlotte's a lesbian.

We went to Peach, at Café de Paris. Since I left London apparently every girl in the city wears an A-line skirt. The girls at Peach are a work of art. One girl was really tanned and she was wearing knee-high boots and a short flowing black skirt and as she danced she hitched her skirt around her waist and showed her white knickers to everyone. Every time she did it everyone cheered. There was another girl, not lifting her skirt up who was wearing a t-shirt saying 'Dress code: No Knickers'. Loads of the girls had their fags in their knickers and would just casually lift their skirts up to get them out. Like it was normal!!!!

But there was this one...'Billion Dollar Babe'. Long dark hair parted, a funk chick, a tank girl, Bardot but a Latina version, dark brown boots and white over the knee socks, with long, perfect brown legs. She was the biggest ten I have ever seen. The shortest panty-teasing white tennis skirt so short that you could see the curves of her butt. An exposed midriff and a dark brown flat tummy before the tiniest, flimsiest pale blue t-shirt. She wasn't wearing a bra and her boobs were absolutely perfect. Small, but perfect, with a hint of bounce. She was the most sexually attractive girl I have ever seen. Every single bloke was looking at her, people were actually laughing. She was that fit. When she gently pushed her butt out to the Italina piano house you could see her knickers and then she would spin round and you could see everything, so much so that you could see the skin above the top of her knickers and below the waistline of her skirt!!!! Pretty sure I had eye contact, it was like we were having sex, I had sex with her on the dancefloor...in my head! Rick bought me an ice pole, she strolls over, her big dark brown baby seal eyes all starey, doesn't say jack, just gives me a kind of cosmic control look that makes me just hand her the ice pole which she takes and spins away, turns back and just sucks it!!!! I thought I was gonna shoot my load, I honestly did. I had to turn away. She brings it back and I ask her (I can barely see) what it says on her t-shirt. Without saying anything she just presses her breast out so her nipples are straining against the material and she mouths the words BILLION...DOLLAR...BABE. I almost fell over. I am on the verge of a nervous breakdown. Best sex I never had.

I was pretty shocked. Thought about trying to ask her if she wanted a drink but seemed pretty pathetic in the face of her life-changing hotness.

How's Munich?

B

PS I know what you are thinking. 'What the fuck are you talking about and where is Charlotte?' She has completely betrayed me. With a woman. That old dog she is friends with. She's 40. I live in CANNES.

PPS I am in bits.

PPPS Enzo told me that 'where there's muck, there's brass' means 'where there are dirty jobs to be done there is money to be made'. I listened to Jimmy Ruffin's 'What becomes of the Broken Hearted' I reckon 40 times today. It has the best lyrics for a man in my state.

"As I walk this land of broken dreams,
I have visions of many things.
Love's happiness is just an illusion,
Filled with sadness and confusion.
What becomes of the broken hearted
Who had love that's now departed?
I know I've got to find
Some kind of peace of mind
Maybe.
The fruits of love grow all around

But for me they come a tumblin' down.
Every day heartaches grow a little stronger,
I can't stand this pain much longer!
I walk in shadows,
Searching for light.
Cold and alone,
No comfort in sight.
Hoping and praying for someone to care,
Always moving and goin' nowhere.
What becomes of the broken hearted
Who had love that's now departed?
I know I've got to find,
Some kind of peace of mind."
Help me...

December 30

I have completely avoided getting sucked into the Bacchanalian world near Ealing that is Charlotte's life.

December 31

The rest of Christmas when not lying on my bed listening to Jimmy Ruffin I have been dining out on my Mediterranean existence. This is becoming very boring for some of my friends and they have started a system of initially putting their hands over my mouth and then bundling me if I mention anything French or in any way linked to France. This has become ridiculous as I cannot discuss any football teams with French players in, quite a lot of food-related subjects or order Kronenbourg. They also chucked in the ordering of Stella which, when I pointed out that it was in fact Belgian, was rejected on the basis that, "It thinks it's French". But it is great to be home, especially with a tinge of excitement that I will soon be escaping the biting cold and getting back to the relatively clement Mediterranean climate.

And Charlotte has not called me for five days now. I think we both know it's over.

I am flying tomorrow afternoon. I hope she is not on the same flight again.

Going to Heavenly Social for NYE.

January 1
Did a really stupid thing today. Even by my standards. Darryl Woodbridge is working in Safeways full-time now. I went in to get razor blades and he showed me the Hawaiian Tropic stand as it had topless girls from Honolulu or somewhere in the pamphlets. He dared me to try some 'tanning cream'. By the time I got home everyone was staring at me on the bus. My mum was horrified when she saw me and thought I had vitiligo. My hands are as dark as a Nigerian's and that's only on the underneath. I have scrubbed my face about eight times but I am so brown on one side of it I look as if I am permanently in shadow. Told my Mum's friend Fiona that it was creosote from a fence I am working on but she blatantly didn't believe me.

Flight BA124 London Heathrow – Nice
NEW YEAR'S RESOLUTIONS
- Speak about ten times more French than I am now.
- Get a supplementary job.
- Forget about Charlotte and learn from it.
- Get a French girlfriend.
- Find a new cool drink to have which is not beer or wine or gin & tonic.
- Make more of an effort to go to Nice to see Enzo.
- Explore the unknown Cannes more.
- Save up to buy a scooter.
- If I can't get a French girlfriend, sleep with more French girls.
- Get the other side of my face brown.

VINGT

What do you do for money, honey?

3 janvier

To quote Mick Hucknall, money really is too tight to mention. But this morning in Collège le Big Fun's staff room one of the profs mentioned how my predecessor as an assistant (they talk about her so much I am beginning to feel like I am in *The Magus*)[80] had supplemented her wages with a couple of private lessons for some of the more challenged students. I have loads of challenged students.

Spent ages doing a new music-based lesson plan for the Boomtown Rats' 'I Don't Like Mondays'. I will explain all about how 16-year-old Brenda Ann Spencer opened fire from her window on a school in San Diego in 1979, killing two people and injuring nine others. I will also tell them how when she was asked why she committed the attack she replied, "I just did it for the fun of it. I don't like Mondays. This livens up the day." They'll love this.

4 janvier

I am reading Molière's *Dom Juan*.

Charlotte called. She is still in London. She said she missed me and I said "Why? I don't have a vagina." And she put the phone down.

5 janvier

My private teaching empire is open for business. I am calling it '*Allons! Londres*'. This means 'Let's Go...London!' Arnaud and Etienne are 12-year-old twins and they are also like something out of a French film

---

80 Spooky tale about teacher who arrives on a Greek island only to discover strange goings-on and a predecessor who may know a whole lot more.

I DON'T 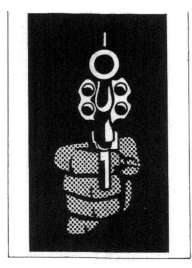 LIKE MONDAYS

BOB GELDOF & BOOMTOWN RATS

THE SILICON CHIP INSIDE HER HEAD
GETS SWITCHED TO OVERLOAD
AND NOBODY'S GONNA ___ __ _____
SHE'S GOING TO MAKE THEM _____ __
AND _____ __ _ _____
HE ALWAYS SAID SHE WAS AS ____ __ ___
AND HE CAN SEE NO REASON
COS THERE ARE __ _____
WHAT REASON DO YOU NEED TO BE SHOWN

TELL ME WHY
I DON'T LIKE MONDAYS (x3)
I WANT TO SHOOT
___ __ _____ ___

THE TELEX MACHINE IS KEPT __ _____
AS IT TYPES TO A WAITING WORLD
AND _____ __ ____ _____
FATHER'S WORLD IS ROCKED
AND THEIR THOUGHTS TURN TO
_____ __ ____

SWEET 16 AIN'T THAT PEACHY KEEN
NO, IT AIN'T SO NEAT TO ADMIT DEFEAT
THEY ____ __ ___ ____
COS THERE ARE NO REASONS
WHAT REASON __ __ ___ (TO BE SHOWN)

CHORUS

ALL THE PLAYING'S _____ __ ___ PLAYGROUND
SHE WANTS TO PLAY WITH HER TOYS AWHILE NOW
AND ____ __ _____ AND SOON WE'LL BE LEARNIN
AND ____ _____ IS HOW TO DIE
AND THEN THE BULLHORN CRACKLES
AND THE CAPTAIN TACKLES
WITH THE PROBLEMS AND THE HOW'S AND WHY'S
AND HE CAN SEE NO REASONS
COS THERE ARE NO REASONS
WHAT _____ __ ____ ____ _ ___

CHORUS.

She really didn't like them.

by Jean-Pierre Jeunet. Like *La Cité des Enfants Perdus*.[81] I noticed them
in class as two of the very few kids who take packed lunches to school.
There is something very endearing about a packed lunch. These two

81 Two lost twins living in the dystopian dreamland in which they were being chased
by a mad scientist who wants to steal their dreams to retain his childhood.

carry their lunchboxes with pride and I liked them before I met them. They are such space dudes that the other kids just kind of leave them to it. I have agreed to teach them for an hour once a week.

6 janvier

The hour with Arnaud and Etienne is the hour by which I will measure all hours. Within seconds my ambrosial French chums can drift off into a land that would do Jeunnet's imagination proud.

Road tested my new 'I Don't Like Mondays' with an older class today. They were subdued, but I think it made them think.

Charlotte called again, back in France now. She wants to come down at the weekend to have a chat about "us". I told her that "there is no us".

I am devastated.

8 janvier

The lessons with Arnaud and Etienne have quickly begun to show up one thing in particular. They can't count. I sit them opposite me, both grinning the most adorable, peaceful grins imaginable and we set off counting, them alternating the numbers. "One, two, three, nine, twenty…" Woah! One of them smiles impishly and I explain how we missed out 4, 5, 6, 7 and 8. They both nod in agreement and off we go again.

Sometimes I think that they are two super smart kids who are taking the piss out of me in this kind of smart-kid way. Perhaps they are clandestinely working on something akin to 'Foster's Theory of Maximum Likelihood'.[82]

9 janvier

Got called in to see Monsieur Guy Rufin. He was not happy. Apparently my 'I Don't Like Mondays' lesson plan featuring a hand pointing a gun at the reader has really upset two 15-year-olds in one of my classes. Some of the other parents thought it was too sensitive a subject for me to be dealing with at my age.

---

82 The foundations of which are impossible to explain to mortals and considered impossible to grasp, such is the complexity and the size of the giant leaps in the thought process.

10 janvier
My private teaching empire is growing. I now have four different students lined up and this could seriously sort out the bank balance. It is also proving a real insight into France – going into people's homes means I am seeing the real France, what goes on at tea-times, how the families tick. I think this is what I signed up for!

12 janvier
I am thinking of teaching as something I might want to do for the rest of my life. I find it intensely rewarding and, for all that I am still effectively playing at it, with none of the real pressures of delivering results and dealing with proper discipline issues, I really do love doing it. A bit like doing a best man's speech the crowd are really on your side from the start. I am the fun in their day. My newly discovered charm is carrying me along on the crest of a Mediterranean breaker.

13 janvier
My life might be about to become a 1970s sex fantasy film called 'Confessions of a French Language Assistant'. I bumped into Madame Cocheteux at the local shop during one of the 15-minute slots when it is actually open. This was actually the second time I have seen her since I fell in love with her (the first time was when she popped round the day after the debauched first night in the flat) and I possibly greeted it with an enthusiasm it did not merit. I actually tried to explain serendipity to her.

Madame Cocheteux listened in her sultry way (even silent, she is sexual, all wet lips and dreamy eyes) to my boring tales of teaching kids she doesn't know or care about and just when I was scared I was going to lose the high priestess of my own fantasy Madrague she touched my forearm lightly and asked if I would consider taking her on as a new English student? I had to stand outside of myself to check I was actually here as this is exactly the kind of thing I spend idle hours daydreaming[83] about happening. She said she would look at her "plannings" and pop by and let me know when would be best. *Oh. Mon. Dieu.*

---

83 A choice word.

I really missed Charlotte today. Maybe it is a breast thing.

Still no rent rebate.

15 janvier

Next week's "plannings" now include around seven hours of private tutoring. As all of my students are kids I know from the schools this makes it easier as we can pick up on where I know they are at in their lessons.

Charlotte called again and we agreed that we need to talk. She sounded really different on the phone. She is coming tomorrow.

Absinthe makes the heart grow fonder

Dear Sod,

Pretty full on few days, will try and rattle through as fast as I can.

Charlotte came by yesterday for our big summit chat. Whatever I said about her before doesn't really matter. I think she has changed and may be taking this as seriously as I am.

Wolfy came over from Montpellier a few hours after our chat and we all drove to Nice.

All slept in the same room, Charlotte and I shared a bunk bed.

Wolfy and I went to Monte-Carlo, went to the crappy Italian Riviera, had a pizza in Ventimiglia which was a bit cold, slept outside the San Siro, got roughed up by a load of gipsys who tried to nick our football. With two massive clubs you would think there would have been a game. Nope. The only weekend in the year when not. Italian international. Started to drive to Venice. Not going to make it. Picked Charlotte up in Nice. I booked a hotel under the name of Mr & Mrs Liam Gallagher as I thought it was rock n roll. It was less rock n roll when they asked for my passport for the ten quid room and my name was obviously not Liam Gallagher.

She didn't even find it that funny.

Then she told me that she doubted my feelings for her and that's why she acted up. Gave her a lay-it-on-the-line speech telling her how much I care for her, pretty emotional, told her I hated Michael Hutchence and was jealous of him. I got really cut up, I mean I was crying my eyes out. What a dick. She may well give up a perfectly good relationship for what we have. I feel terrible about it too. Told her I got off with a couple of other girls at Christmas and she did her fruit. We were naked in bed, sobbing, Wolfy was lying on the floor somewhere, wherever he fell over last. We went for a walk dressed only in towels. We ran naked round the pool (her lils are sooo perfect and massive) and all round the trees for ages. When we got back Charlotte told me that she is in love with me and I said I loved her. And I meant it.

We're completely in love. We speak 4 times a day when we are not together. But it scares the shit out of me. I told her about the Charing Cross Hotel and told her I am going to take her there. She said she was 'touched'???? What?!!!

I think this is long-term. She just knows me so well. I love the physical and mental attraction combined with the volatile nature of our relationship. A French bloke in a bar said we were like Harry and Sally. Shit shit shit shit. I have bitten off more than I can chew, I know it.

...I'm gonna live forever.

19 janvier

Excellent news. Enzo has got a job working at a hotel near Cannes and has four nights off a week! Crisp and booze consumption to sky rocket. The Arc Hotel, Mougins is the place. It's a 3-star 40-room hotel about 5km inland from Cannes. It has a pool and a bar, and that is about it. When festivals are on, it's buzzing, when they aren't apparently it just exists.[84] He has made a mixtape to celebrate the fact.

84 Inspiration Jean-Paul Sartre

maxell UR POSITION
IEC TYPE I • NORMAL

UR *Les Veilleurs de Nuit* maxell

A DATE / N.R. ○YES ○NO   **B** DATE / N.R. ○YES ○NO

A	B
Everything's Gonna be Alright - NBN	When You Gonna Learn? - Jamiroquai
Rhythm of the Night - Delarge	Lost + Found - DJ Shadow
In the Night - Pet Shop Boys	The Bomb - The Bucketheads
The Crown - Gary Byrd Experience	Jailbird (Toxic Trio Free Mix) - Primal Scream
Fight the Power - Public Enemy	High + Dry - Radiohead
Protection - Massive Attack	Nathan - The Dave Pike Set
Columbia - Oasis	The Sounds of Science - Beastie Boys
She's a Rainbow - The Rolling Stones	Nothing Can Stop Us - Saint Etienne
Obsolete - Mc Solaar	I am the Resurrection - The Stone Roses

'7 Seconds' not featured.

20 janvier

Enzo and I went down in to Cannes and discovered the ultimate sandwich. In a price to effectiveness ratio we designed. A meal for a whole day, like the Cornish pasty was to the miners. As we hack away at the harsh coalface of the French education system and hotel industry respectively we have come to see ourselves as workers too. The food torpedo comes served in a baguette and is called the *sandwich américain*. They are sold everywhere in the region. Like Pinks hot dogs in LA, Berthillon ice creams in Paris, Manze's pie and mash in London, there is only one place in the world to go in our minds. *Jonathan's*, next to Cannes' bus depot. *Jonathan's* is run by Jonathan and his seductive wife, who we think is called Joanne and doesn't speak a word. She does a lot of the graft and Jonathan, who looks like a Lego character, does the front-of-house bit. Clearly the wrong way round and we renamed it '*Joannathanne's*', in tribute to her.

Joannathanne's seats eight inside and six outside. This only adds to its appeal. It's exclusive. The hero product is half a baguette stuffed with a griddled *steak haché*,[85] French-dressed salad, french fries and smothered in Dijon mustard, tomato ketchup and mayonnaise and wrapped up in tin foil like a giant truncheon. It also represents, in gastronomic form, the love–hate relationship between the French and their American lovers/enemies, taking its influence from '*le hamburger*' but with the Gallic twist which deems it acceptable. It is the world's first triumph of style, substance and sustenance. If it was a Marvin Gaye and Diana Ross duet it would be 'You Are Everything'.

23 janvier
The last three evenings Enzo and I have spent eating Intermarché's own-label spaghetti bolognese-flavoured crisps and drinking red wine at about 80p for a plastic litre bottle.

24 janvier
Orange tea gin has been invented by Enzo and I as a relaxant and a stimulant, if that is possible. The oranges we used were dried up and juice-free and the gin was stale and foul. The boiling water was the best thing about it. We are developing an egg and lemon soup now.

Charlotte phoned and had the arse to say that I have not been proactive in wanting to see her. Probably true. I feel weird.

25 janvier
Walked along the *Rue d'Antibes* and saw an amazing coat in the Lacoste shop. It is a golf mac and costs 3000 francs!!! That is about 300 quid! It is also dead thin. It shines out from the other merchandise like Excalibur's sword.

Fourth day on the trot in *Joannathanne's*. Polite yet indifferent service, and a complete lack of acknowledgement that we have ever been in there before. We have a theory that Madame Joannathanne is secretly in love with one of us and we are about to embark on a *Jules et Jim*[86] style adventure.

In the corner of *Joannathanne's* is a small television set permanently

---

85 Higher quality minced beef burger often served to children who reject burgers.
86 *Jules et Jim* is a mental 60s film about a ménage-a-trois and two best friends, Jules and Jim, who are led a merry dance by the unhinged Catherine.

to a channel called 'M6'. It is fantastic.

Les Filles d'à côté[87] makes 'Home and Away' look like 'Twin Peaks' and follows the general format for an M6 show. This is to build a horribly bland apartment scene and then populate it with girls and women aged 15 to 25 in unbelievably inappropriate clothing who speak in nothing but platitudes and innuendo. This regularly involves swimming costumes and underwear and constant references to breasts and bottoms. The guys all look like the ones you get in older barber shops modelling hairstyles and wearing polo shirts and ironed jeans with no belts. Despite the amount of Class A female attention they are getting they all manage to seem vaguely homosexual.

In France The Smurfs are called *Les Schtroumpfs*.

26 janvier

Hit a new M6 peak last night when we discovered re-runs of a quite incredible keep fit show. I had to ask Monsieur Guy Rufin about it this morning. 'Gym Tonic' was a French institution during the 1980s and was credited with launching the aerobics phenomenon in France, way before Jane Fonda. It had originally been on in the afternoon and was an incredibly kitsch studio-based show presented by Veronique and Davina. They were in their thirties and they would prance around in lycra, smiling at everyone and teaching a class of skimpily attired models – who halfway through TOOK THEIR TOPS OFF – how to open and shut their legs. In the amazing Best Of Show we watched as they created an interesting new take on what to run as a backdrop to the end credits. Quite incredibly, they both took all their clothes off on camera and had a shower together. I am so into France right now.

27 janvier

I have dumbed too far down. Tonight I will start *Gargantua*, or, *La Vie très horrifique du grand Gargantua, père de Pantagruel* (The Very Horrific Life of the giant Gargantua, father of Pantagruel), from which the word gargantuan derives. It is one of five in a series by Rabelais (Gargantua's aforementioned son, Panatgruel, gets another one). Charlotte studied it

---

87 'The Girls Next Door'.

last year and told me that it is a story so grotesque that it makes Porkys seem like Pinter.

28 janvier

Last night, Eric Cantona launched himself over an advertising hoarding and feet-first into the crowd with a kung-fu kick to attack a Crystal Palace supporter. The fact that he was dressed all in black gives the moment even more drama and serves him well in his role as the Jim Morrison of world football.

Spoke to my Mum and Dad tonight. They are pretty great about everything. At Warwick there are all these kids from wealthy families with huge pressure on them to do well. I thanked my parents for being supportive and not pushing me into doing anything. Even though I know how much they want me to do well.

I need to start doing well.

LE GUIDE EXISTENTIEL DU FOOT FRANÇAIS

The existential heart of the game in France goes a long way back. Albert Camus, the French Algerian philosopher and author, and one of the fathers of existentialism once said, "All that I know most surely about morality and obligations I owe to football." Camus had been a goalkeeper of decent standing in Algeria whilst also, after Rudyard Kipling, being the youngest winner of the Nobel Prize for literature. Asked by a friend whether he preferred football or theatre he responded, "Football, without hesitation."

> *"La vie est toujours trop cruelle. Tout ce que nous pouvons faire, c'est essayer de passer le ballon et laisser le soleil briller."*[88]

But it really found its anti-hero with one Eric Cantona.

Cantona arrived in the French game at Auxerre in 1983 where he began his one-man CV of bad behaviour. Setting his stall out early he punched a team-mate in the face at Auxerre, hastening his departure. Then when he was honoured by selection for the national team he called the then French coach *"un sac à merde"*.[89] At Olympique Marseille he threw his shirt to the ground when substituted (in a friendly), then twatted the ball into the crowd and was subsequently sacked by the club. He had a fight with a team mate at Montpellier culminating in him throwing his boots in the other guy's face, and was promptly sacked. Then he did the logical thing and quit football altogether. Had a rethink. Learnt nothing.

Threw a ball at the referee while playing for Nimes, and was banned for two months before he turned up on British shores at Leeds United in 1992. He then almost single-handedly won them the league title. Nine months later, in one of the most surprising, and consequential, phone calls of English football history the Manchester United manager Alex Ferguson had chatted to the manager of his club's arch-rivals Leeds and enquired as to the availability of their talismanic, championship-

---

88 Life is always too cruel. All we can do is try to pass the ball and let the sun shine.
89 A bag of shit.

winning cult hero, fully expecting a polite *enculé*. It turned out that Cantona and the Leeds manager had had a blistering row two days earlier and he wanted shot of the red hot *pomme de terre*. He signed for Manchester United two days later and in his first season catapulted them to their first league championship in twenty-five years.

"Quand les gens parlent de toi, c'est que tu existes."[90]

Incredibly popular with fans and the team-mates he didn't physically assault, his anti-authority streak did not extend to his playing style. Whilst single-handedly winning games with bucket loads of goals he was one of the more selfless stars in the history of the starry game. But at Manchester United he played out his role in one of football's great love affairs. The refrain of "Ooh-aah, Cantona" would ring out over Salford as 75,000 turned out every other week to worship.

"Je ne joue pas contre une équipe en particulier. Je joue pour me battre contre l'idée de perdre."[91]

In the press conference following the kung-fu attack Cantona didn't say much. Already established as a Rimbaud-loving (the press had a field day with misunderstanding Rimbaud as Rambo) literati he sipped from his water and said:

> "When the seagulls follow the trawler it is because they think sardines will be thrown into the sea. Thank you very much."

And he got up and left.

The journos loved his gallic loopiness and went into overdrive.[92] In France they seemed less bothered by the sentiment, slightly embarrassed even by their awkward bastard son making random and,

---

90 Only when people speak about you do you truly exist.
91 I don't play against a particlar team. I play against the idea of losing.
92 I found it amusing that they referred to this in various terms but most often as a "cryptic", "existential" analogy of his relationship with the media. It's clearly not that cryptic. It's hardly as if he actually was talking about sardines and seagulls.

to them, slightly pretentious sardine-shaped statements. L'Équipe even predicted the beginning of the end of his English playing career:

> "*Ce geste, plus terrifiant que tous ceux dont il s'est déjà rendu coupable, signifie probablement la fin de sa lune de miel avec le football anglais.*"[93]

Trevor Brooking called the incident, "the most horrendous incident involving a player I have ever witnessed at an English football ground." The press in France went loco but a few dissenting voices started aiming the shame at the feet of the fan and his racist bile. Banned for nine months and stripped of the France captaincy, he disappeared from the public's view like a big hairy Greta Garbo. He has rarely spoken of the incident since, saying only, "The most important thing for me is that I was who I was."

A few years later he would be voted the Greatest Manchester United player of all time. By the fans.

---

93 "This gesture, more terrifying than he has already been found guilty of, most likely signifies the end of his honeymoon period with English football."

29 janvier

Watching TV for vast swathes of the day means my flat has become a dump. A thin layer of dust covers the whole place. If it is true that 90% of dust is human skin then the other 10% must be soot from the fire at my first *soirée*. My alcohol intake is becoming ridiculous. Tomorrow's absinthe party is not going to positively affect that. Charlotte phoned to say she can't come as she is going back to London to "sort her fucking life out". My distance from the problem seems to be making me more attractive to her. I can't even remember what I feel. Crying in the hotel in Nice seems a lifetime ago already.

31 janvier

It has taken me two days to write anything. The absinthe party was the nadir. Of my all-time drinking. Weirdly, Pollyanna got hold of some from an oddball guy in the village she lives in and brought two bottles of the green with her on Thursday night. Her, Enzo, Alistair and me. We all had Friday off. Having already drunk at least five beers and a bottle of red wine this was probably not my finest hour to try "the aphrodisiac of the self", as Dracula calls it in the movie. In no time I was all over me.

All of the ceremony around the burning and the spoon made me feel like a crack addict and when my second shot kicked in I developed a weird tunnel vision in my own flat whereby I could only see the door. Apparently we all decided to go out but I had chronic vertigo standing up, I thought I was hanging off the side of the Eiffel Tower.[94] My devotion to the green faerae knew no bounds and they call this moment '*L'Heure Verte*'. I embraced it fully. When we left the flat I was ricocheting off toilet walls in bars in Cannes, believing myself to be sharing a table with my other absinthe-necking friends, Ernest Hemingway, Oscar Wilde, Edgar Allen Poe, and Pablo Picasso.

Somewhat fittingly for something named '*Notre-Dame de l'oubli*' Enzo told me that I kept forgetting halfway through the conversation what we were talking about and would then break out into hysterical

---

94 Much has been written on the *Belle Epoque*, Montmartre and the role '*la fée verte*' played in the downfall of the epileptic and vaguely psychotic Vincent Van Gogh.

laughter. I was finally sent home when I pinched a massive bloke's bum and ran into the toilets in a restaurant. Pollyanna found me sobbing outside telling a waitress about my heavy heart and the fact that I knew that I really loved Charlotte and I wouldn't let her go this time. '*L'atroce sorcière verte*' had me under her spell. This has to stop.

1 février

I read in a magazine that at any given moment 0.7% of the world's population is drunk. This makes me feel better. The French drink less than us in the sense that they don't go out with the express desire to get wasted. But it is much easier to be an alcoholic in France. Here in the south they start drinking as soon as they get up. They give cute names to small versions of proper drinks. From around 8 am the men of Cannes can be found drinking any one of these:

- *Une bok/un galopin*: a quarter of a pint, often necked in two gulps
- *Une demi/une pression*: a half-pint, a few gulps, but still not taken seriously
- *Une tango*: a beer with some grenadine[95] in it
- *Une Monaco*: a beer with grenadine and lemonade
- *Une sérieuse*: a pint (much rarer, this signifies intent)

For hard booze they have also come up with an inventive way of allowing people to drink early in the day with no fear or guilt, again it involves cute names:

- *Un foetus*: a 1cl serving of alcohol, with a shot of mixer
- *Un bébé*: a 'baby' was a 2cl serving with a little mixer
- *Un normal*: a 4cl serving

I am becoming entrenched in the French way of life. I will not even consider starting to drink beer without first having a couple of *pastis*. I even have a preferred type, which I actually ask for by name. 'Pastis 51'. *Le vrai*,[96] all the way from '*Planète Marseille*'.

---

95 Syrup, originally made of pomegranate, which is '*grenade*' in French.
96 The real thing.

3 février

Gargantua is a gargantuan yawn. Like how Shakespeare's comedies are the least funny thing ever. I'm going to start *Candide*.

4 février

Candide is good.

5 février

Last night AS Cannes played the mighty Paris St Germain. David Ginola is the much maligned but incredibly glamorous poster boy of French football, playing for PSG.[97] The stadium was packed and AS Cannes, riding high at an incredible third in the French first division, beat PSG 3–2. One of the few games that everybody actually watched and the tiny stadium was rocking. After the match we all went out to celebrate in local bars I was previously too intimidated to go in. Riding high in the Azurean sky.

> "And I was 'round when Jesus Christ
> Had his moment of doubt and pain
> Made damn sure that Pilate
> Washed his hands and sealed his fate."

6 février

Tomorrow is my first lesson with Madame Cocheteux at her house. Fail to prepare. Prepare to fail.

7 février

Oh. Mon. Dieu. Madame Cocheteux is without doubt the most attractive woman in the world. She may be more attractive than Sophie Marceau. We had the most wonderful hour, I didn't want it to end. We laughed and we kind of flirted and I made up stuff about speaking English to impress her. I loved every second of it. And she tipped me. Quite a high-necked top on though. Can't do another lesson for two

---

97 He ballsed up royally playing for the national team a few months before which led to them not qualifying for the World Cup. He also has long hair and gives interviews which start with him saying, "Before every match I listen to 'Sympathy for the Devil'."

weeks. Out of desperation I said I could take a sicky from school. Dick. Looked so desperate.

8 février

I can see what all the fuss about *Candide* is about. It's a rollicking good story about the illegitimate young Candide, his brilliantly upbeat tutor, Pangloss (this world we live in is "the best of all possible worlds") and a madcap travel tale zig-zagging the globe. Takes in an earthquake, the Inquisition, raping and pillaging, cross-dressing, cannibalism, Eldorado, hookers, syphilis and lots of discussions about 'what comes around goes around'. At the end they realise that working on a simple farm really is the root of all happiness and, with all their time devoted to the project, and no time for vice, quarrelling or excessive navel-gazing they really will all live happily ever after. I really think I know what they mean.

9 février

Even by his own high standards Monsieur Guy Rufin looked like a dude today. A skinny suit like they wore in the 60s. Most people would think it was too small. But they would be wrong. He is so cool. He is the kind of guy who would put an arm around a misbehaving student, smile his oaky smile and say, "Hey kid, don't misbehave," and they would say, "*Oui, vous avez raison mon Monsieur, mon héros.*" He is, in a nutshell, a class act. Every time I see him I hear Cat Stevens singing, "Look at me, I am old, but I'm happy…"

10 février

There is a new kid on the block. Estéban, an assistant like me, is the guy who never made it out to the pre-teaching course in Nice a few months ago. I quite envy his anti-establishment self-confidence, and he sounds like a drug dealer. He has contacted me through the school and invited me out for a drink tonight. Enzo and Jason Priestley too.

11 février

Estéban is a lugubrious Andalucian North Londoner, who can do the world's best Robert de Niro impression and looks like he is in a Spanish version of the Inspiral Carpets. He has exactly the same taste in music as me and was wearing a vintage Vasco da Gama shirt.[98] We all liked him immediately. On the way home we discussed the creation of the Mediterranean Monkees, the plan to form some kind of pop/rock group.

13 février

Valentines Day tomorrow and I haven't seen Charlotte properly in weeks.

Jason Priestley drove us round to Estéban's apartment in an area humbly-named 'Super Cannes'. It is spectacular. Spiral staircase, mezzanine bedroom, JACUZZI!!! It looks like something from Hugh Hefner's grotto. Or a Côte d'Azur take on *The Shining* as there is literally no-one else there in the whole place. It looks out on to the bay of Cannes and the two looming Cannois islands of Ste Marguerite and St Honorat.

---

98 Brazilian first division team who wear a shirt with a black diagonal sash and the Coca-Cola sponsorship.

LES ÎLES CANNOISES

Not many people who go to the festivals in Cannes know that it has two beautifully serene islands just off the coast. They are a fifteen-minute ferry ride away and an incredible distraction from the superficiality of Cannes itself. Saint Honorat is the smaller, and further away, of the two (the other is Sainte Marguerite) but by far the most interesting. The story goes that the island was known to the Romans as 'Lerina' and was uninhabited until Saint Honoratus (you see what they did there?) built a monastery on it in 410. He lived as a hermit but his disciples followed him there and by 427 there was a fully-blown monastery in situ. Legend even has it that Saint Patrick, of foam Guinness hat fame, studied there in the late 5th century. But there are no photos to prove it.

The Saracens were a grabby bunch and would regularly raid the island. In 732 there was an almighty massacre there. Another legend has it that many of the monks had already escaped as an angel had warned them of the imminent attack. This sounds made up but stay with it. In medieval times St Honorat was a famed place of pilgrimage. In 1635 the Spanish captured it, and two years later the French captured it back. The attacks became tiresome and by 1787 there were only four monks left, which technically just made it a very religious house, and the monastery was disestablished. It became property of the State during the Revolution and was then sold to an actress called Mademoiselle de Sainval. In 1870 a Cistercian religious order was established there, and it remains there to this day. They make a clementine liqueur, which you can still buy. But at 50% proof, you should go easy.

Je m'appelle Paul Newman

14 février

Heading to see Charlotte on the train.

Estéban, or Taba, as he is known to friends, is teaching at the *lycée*,[99] which means that he knows more French youth closer to our age and therefore has more access to the hidden world of Cannes fun. As well as a hell of a lot more French speaking. His students all hang out in the cafés and bars of the less flashy, but more functional, boulevard in Cannes, *Boulevard de la République*.[100] Went there with him this afternoon. French youth seem, if it wasn't for their awful dress sense, to have the whole journey into life thing down a bit more than us Brits. Sitting in cafés sipping espressos and Orangina between lectures seems incredibly grown up compared to what we used to get up to at home. But what they wear to sip their espressos in leaves a lot to be desired. At the moment they all wear Chipie and Chevignon. Conservative EuroBland, the sweatshirts normally have something non-sensical in English written on them, like ALL STAR CLUB OF FEDERAL TEAM or CHEVIGNON COMPANY ESTABLISHED FOR COLLEGIATE. The clothes also come in an endless selection of shades of green, brown and beige. I miss the energy and cool of life back home.

15 février

It was al-reeeet.

We went for a meal, I didn't want to spend the earth in case she did something mental. She talked a lot about how much it had all upset

---

99 Grammar school. There were about five in Cannes and they provided a three-year course of further secondary education for students between the ages of 15 and 18, after they left collège. The pupils study for their baccalauréat there (they call it le *bac*) which is like A-Levels and leads on to either higher education or a job.

100 The other being the grand old *Boulevard Carnot*, which runs right up the middle.

THE PERFECT PARTNER

MARILYN MONROE • BRIGITTE BARDOT •
MEG RYAN • VANESSA PARAD
MADONNA • PRINCESS DIAN
CLAUDIA SCHIFFER • ANNA N
CINDY CRAWFORD • ELLE
JAMIE LEE CURTIS • TABAT
SHARON STONE • PAMELA A
MICHELLE PFEIFFER • ERIKA

DAVID CHARVET • BRAD PITT • MICHAEL J
CHRISTIAN SLATER • TOM CRUISE •
RIVER PHOENIX • TAKE THAT • A
EAST 17 • JOHNNY DEPP • KEVIN
BRUCE WILLIS • KEANU REEVES • AR
JACK NICHOLSON • SYLVESTER STALL
PRINCE • EDDIE MURPHY • JOHN
KURT COBAIN • JIM MORRISON

EVERYONE HAS A DIFFERENT IDEA OF THE IDEAL BOYFRIEND OR GIRLFRIEND. PUT THESE
QUALITIES IN ORDER OF IMPORTANCE. (1 - MOST IMPORTANT   9 - LEAST IMPORTANT)

Ⓐ Good looks.... ☐   Ⓕ Let's you decide things.... ☐

Ⓑ Patience.... ☐   Ⓖ Sexiness .... ☐

Ⓒ Plenty of money. ... ☐   Ⓗ popular with your family... ☐

Ⓓ Interests you both share.... ☐   Ⓘ Popular with your friends.. ☐

Ⓔ A sense of humour.... ☐

YOUR QUALITIES...
PUT THESE QUALITIES YOU HAVE IN ORDER.
(1 - YOUR BEST QUALITY   8 - YOUR WORST)

Ⓐ Good looks . . . . . ☐

Ⓑ Patience . . . . . ☐

Ⓒ Plenty of money . . . . . ☐

Ⓓ Sensible attitude . . . . . ☐

Ⓔ Sense of humour . . . . . ☐

Ⓕ Sexiness . . . . . ☐

Ⓖ Friendly . . . . ☐

Ⓗ Intelligent . . . . . ☐

your WORST QUALITIES...
PUT THESE BAD QUALITIES IN ORDER.
(1 - YOUR WORST QUALITY   8 - NOT REALLY YOU)

Ⓐ Stubborn ☐

Ⓑ Lazy ☐

Ⓒ Talk too much ☐

Ⓓ Selfish ☐

Ⓔ Mean ☐

Ⓕ Thoughtless ☐

Ⓖ Untidy ☐

Ⓗ Drink too much ☐

It was the street art heading that made it.

Hutchence and he was really down. I said I didn't care. We agreed to
"take it step by step" which sounds really grown up but I don't know
what it means. Charlotte didn't break anything in the flat. I kind of
missed it. No sex. Missed that more.

16 février

Taba is the funniest person I have ever met. He is like a cross between a hippie Spanish waiter and Eric Morecambe. He knows so many jokes that he can literally recite them all evening. He can tell you anything and make it funny, mainly because it seems to be cracking him up so much whilst telling it. Peter Cook and Tommy Cooper are his preferred reference points. He has tried to translate his favourite joke into French a few times unsuccessfully. The Tommy Cooper one about the fact that one in five people in the world are Chinese. Taba, as Tommy, goes on to say how there are five people in his family, so it must be one of them. It is either his mum or his dad. Or his older brother Colin. Or his younger brother HoChaChu. But he thinks it's Colin. 'Colin' in French is a kind of fish used to make fishfingers. Which doesn't help.

Later

So if 'Colin' means fish what Christian name do the French have to replace Colin?

17 février

My 'The Perfect Partner' lesson, a kind of dating game with my own graffiti headline, went down a treat today with the 16-year-olds.

Cannes, février 19

Dear Sod

We have a new mate called Taba. You will love him. He is Spanish–North London. He is introducing me to a post-Charlotte (although officially we are still together) world of reunions. The first of these symbolic meetings came in the café opposite Taba's lycée. It is brilliantly called Le Johnny Milk and the closest thing I have ever known to Arnold's diner of Happy Days fame.

Fabressa is a sultry, smouldering Latina-looking woman with a tousled mane of cappuccino hair. She looked bored by the boys talking to her and was possibly older than them. Her breasts strained petulantly at her red and white-striped pullover and her vintage Levis (this sartorial detail is crucial to an understanding of her) could barely contain her pear-shaped derriere.

She is everything I dream of and quickly I scoured her for imperfections like a lazy eye, undercut hair, a Bob Marley t-shirt or a nose ring. Nothing. Taba introduced me to her (he is Spanish so still in the same relationship he has been in since he was 6) and was happy to play the Sancho Panza role to my Don Quixote, littering sanchismos everywhere, all Spanish irony and witty asides. Fabressa is the girl who takes Italian conversation classes with the students at the school. I wasn't even able to do the pretending-to-not-be-interested-so-that-she-is-marginally-interested-hopefully thing. As I gulped for oxygen Taba politely left us alone.

"I like the way you look," I thought, like a young Paul Newman. "Do you work at the school over there?" I said, like Captain Dullard, a middle-aged tax inspector, having already just been told that she did. "Is someone taking up a lot of your time these days?" I thought, like a 20-year-old Cary Grant. "I never know whether a Monaco has grenadine in it or not." I said, like the winner of the Most Vapid Human In France competition.

In a vain attempt to quash the silence I attempted a technique I have recently been developing after watching On The Waterfront. This involves me mumbling like Marlon Brando does, hoping to create intimacy and pull her in physically closer so she could hear. Unfortunately it just meant that she couldn't understand me and thought I might be ill. Added to that I think when she actually understood me my observation that, "This bar is a real classic in design" just finished her off. After fully 40 seconds she could take no more. She didn't even say goodbye, she just smiled in a vaguely sympathetic way, cocking her head and mane to one side so that she looked like the embodiement of unattainable gorgeousness. As she walked off I became aware of a few people being aware of my snub. "Hakuna matata,"[101] I said, to her disappearing back, trying to save a tiny amount of face. In no way did I look pretentious or pathetic at this point. I am in a shit

---

101 "No worries", I probably saw it in a film.

place with women.

B

PS If I was an ABBA lyric I would be "Seeing me so tense, no self confi-dence."

PPS Charlotte's London clan are coming out to Nice on Friday and she actually wants me to go and meet them. Unbelievably Hutchence might actually be there? What the fuck does she want me to go there for? So we can break up LIVE????

20 février

Last night I dreamt that I wore the Lacoste rainsheeter to a nightclub with white shorts and cowboy boots. It is the gayest dream I have ever had.

21 février

Taba came round and taught us how to cook paella. It is much easier than it looks. I would have had it high up on my list of complicated things to cook along with meringues, risottos and Scotch eggs. But it is actually up there with beans on toast.

Paella

Fry onion, garlic, parsley & chicken until golden brown.
Add tomato + (tin of) + salami
(prawns, muss, calm)
seafood & saffron & salt & pepper
Add rice & water (1 cup rice = 2 water)
taking into a/c the water from the tomatoes. Let it simmer. Water should boil away. Not too hot. Shr ev. so often. lovely
justly

22 février
Still no rent rebate.

23 février
Tried *Gargantua* again. In this bit he pisses all over Paris, between the towers of Notre Dame, his first words are "Drink, Drink, Drink!" and together they piss and fart their way round France. Promising.

24 février
Bought a scooter today. In principal. The family of Laure, a girl I am doing private lessons with from Le Slab, have a big garage and sell them. This is a cool red Honda and he will sell it to me for about 400 quid. Just need that rent rebate.

26 février
Taught Madame Cocheteux again today. Big improvements, much better attire. Her top was scooped out so that you could see pretty much everything and when she was concentrating and leant forward her breast rested on the table, gently moving up as if inflating. I am forgetting about Charlotte in direct correlation to how much time I spend with HER.

28 février
I started another new lesson today with the older kids called 'Are you SEXIST?' Pollyanna and Alistair were reading it and thought it was hilarious. One of the questions cracked them up:
   You have a little brother. For his birthday he says he wants a pink t-shirt. Do you:
   A. Buy him the exact t-shirt he wants.
   B. Tell him boys don't wear pink and buy him a football instead.
   C. Buy him a blue t-shirt.
I think the bigger question here might revolve around the little brother and not whether you are sexist or not.

1 mars
In Cannes the bus tickets now all have the images of the posters of old

Are you SEXIST?

1

YOUR BATH HAS A HOLE* SO YOU CALL A PLUMBER.* THE PLUMBER WHO COMES IS FEMALE. DO YOU...

(A) SAY IT'S OK NOW BUT WHEN SHE'S GONE CALL ANOTHER PLUMBER.

(B) GIVE HER A CHANCE BUT OFFER TO HELP.

(C) INVITE HER IN TO SOLVE* THE PROBLEM.

2

A FEMALE FRIEND OF YOURS SAYS SHE HATES IT WHEN MEN OPEN DOORS FOR HER. YOU THINK...

(A) SHE SHOULD LET MEN OPEN DOORS AND THANK THEM.

(B) SHE IS RIGHT.

(C) SHE IS WORRIED ABOUT NOTHING.

3

YOU SEE A LADY IN A FUR* COAT IN AN EXPENSIVE FERRARI. YOU THINK...

(A) SHE MUST HAVE A RICH HUSBAND OR BOYFRIEND.

(B) SHE MUST HAVE A HIGHLY PAID JOB.

(C) A POOR INNOCENT ANIMAL DIED FOR HER COAT.

4

YOU VISIT A FEMALE FRIEND. AT HER HOUSE HER BROTHER IS REPAIRING HIS TROUSERS. YOU...

(A) TELL HER SHE SHOULD DO IT FOR HIM.

(B) LAUGH AND ASK HIM WHERE HE LEARNED TO DO IT.

(C) ASK HIM IF HE COULD MEND* YOUR TROUSERS.

5

YOU ARE IN A CAR. THE CAR IN FRONT GOES THROUGH A RED LIGHT YOU SAY...

(A) "THAT DRIVER MUST BE COLOUR BLIND.*

(B) I'M SURE THAT WAS A FEMALE DRIVER.

(C) "THAT DRIVER IS VERY IRRESPONSIBLE.

6

A GIRL IN YOUR CLASS HAS SEXY PICTURES OF MALE POP STARS OVER HER BOOKS. YOU THINK...

(A) IT IS BAD THE WAY SHE TREATS MEN LIKE SEX* OBJECTS.

(B) SHE HAS TERRIBLE TASTE IN MEN.

(C) IT'S OK FOR MEN TO HAVE PICTURES OF WOMEN BUT NOT FOR WOMEN TO HAVE PICTURES OF MEN.

7

YOU ARE EATING AN EXCELLENT MEAL IN AN EXPENSIVE RESTAURANT AND WOULD LIKE TO TELL THE CHEF. NEAR THE KITCHEN, IN A UNIFORM, YOU SEE A LADY. YOU ASK HER...

(A) "COULD YOU TELL ME WHERE THE CHEF IS PLEASE?"

(B) "ARE YOU THE CHEF?"

(C) "DO YOU WORK HERE?"

8

YOU ARE WORKING IN A RESTAURANT. A MAN AND A WOMAN FINISH THEIR MEAL AND ASK FOR THE BILL* DO YOU...

(A) PRESENT THE BILL TO THE MAN.

(B) PRESENT THE BILL TO THE WOMAN.

(C) PLACE THE BILL ON THE TABLE BETWEEN THEM.

9

YOU ARE ABOUT TO BUY A BOOK ABOUT HISTORY AND POLITICS. YOU SEE THE AUTHOR'S PHOTO. SHE HAS LONG, CURLY* BLONDE HAIR AND A LOT OF MAKE UP. SHE IS WEARING A TIGHT BLOUSE AND A MINI SKIRT. DO YOU...

(A) DECIDE YOU WANT A BOOK WHICH LOOKS BETTER AND MORE SERIOUS.

(B) LOOK INSIDE TO SEE WHAT ELSE THE AUTHOR HAS WRITTEN.

(C) BUY THE BOOK.

10

YOU HAVE A LITTLE BROTHER. FOR HIS BIRTHDAY HE SAYS HE WANTS A PINK T-SHIRT. DO YOU...

(A) BUY HIM THE EXACT T-SHIRT HE WANTS.

(B) TELL HIM BOYS DON'T WEAR PINK AND BUY HIM A FOOTBALL INSTEAD.

(C) BUY HIM A BLUE T-SHIRT.

125-150 POINTS : OUCH! YOU NEED TO LOOK AT MALE AND FEMALE STEREOTYPES. YOU ARE DEFINITELY SEXIST.

75-120 POINTS : YOU ARE CONFUSED! SO IS EVERYONE! YOU HAVE GOOD INSTINCTS BUT NEED TO THINK THINGS THROUGH MORE CAREFULLY.

50-70 POINTS : NO WORRIES! YOU ARE NOT SEXIST AT ALL. YOU ARE SENSITIVE TO BOTH MALE AND FEMALE POINTS OF VIEW. DO YOU HAVE A LOT OF BROTHERS AND SISTERS?

VOCAB

Male

Female

* hole

plumber

to solve (a problem)

Fur coat

to mend (trousers)

colour blind

sex object

the bill

curly

B.P.C 1994

What could possibly go wrong?

film festivals on the back so you can collect them. Amazing, in south London our tickets get you a pound off a McChicken Sandwich if you buy two.

159

Le hard stuff

2 mars

Went for a meeting with Taba and his mate from school, called Lucas. He was wearing a t-shirt emblazoned with the line 'IF YOU'RE NOT WASTED THE DAY IS'.

3 mars

Enzo and I discussed our idea of a band at length with Taba. He is very much 'in'.

4 mars

The dude in the WASTED t-shirt is one of Taba's best French student friends, and a massive exception to the sartorial generalisation, as a hard-rockin' 19-year-old, called Lucas. He is the spit of James Hetfield from Metallica and he makes lunar landscapes out of molten candle wax. His friends are all exactly the same and together form an intimidating gang of hardline horse-frighteners. When he arrived at my flat today he faux-bust in through the door and slid onto his knees in my corridor/kitchen/bathroom screaming, "We will melt your face!"

Taba, Enzo and I have decided to launch the band, based largely on drinking lots of gin & tonic and talking about forming a band. This is easier if any of you actually plays an instrument, but it is not a complete preventative.

Sensibly we warmed up for the session with some military-grade marijuana. After half an hour we were all lying around my apartment, listening repeatedly to 'Lost & Found' by DJ Shadow in which an unknown raconteur abruptly calls time on the song to say…

"Get high…
Get above yourself

Look down upon yourself
Until you're inside o' yourself
Look to the front or the back o' yourself
To the back or front of yourself
It's inside yourself
And then you see your own head
And know yourself is yourself

'cause when you find yourself
You're gonna find that yourself is only yourself
And the self that can only be yourself
So when you're in front of the back of yourself
You're gonna find that your mind is in the centre of yourself
And God is nothing but yourself

And when you reach for yourself
You'll know that yourself
Is the only thing
That can happen to yourself
So that nothing can put you down"

The dulcet tones of the man's voice were stoner manna from heaven. We all lay there in silence, staring at my smoke-stained ceiling, wondering whether God was indeed an extension of the self. And whether there were any Haribo left.

5 mars
Taba told us a story of two Spaniards looking at a sculpture. One says to the other, "Do you like it?" And he replies, "I love it." The second one says, "I like it, but, well, I don't understand it." The first one replies, "Do you like lobster?" "Yes, of course, I love it!" the second one replies... "But do you understand it?"

6 mars
We have had another idea to form a girl band and manage them like pop svengalis. A kind of French Martha Reeves and The Vandellas, provisionally called 'The Monkey Sluts'.

We have decided to call our band 'Tardelli', based entirely on the life of the Italian midfielder, Marco Tardelli.[102]

This is the basis of our band: an Italian footballer's celebration. Our first song will be a cover version (no covering, just miming) of The Charlatans' 'I never want an easy life if she and me were ever to get there'. The exercise will involve the band being filmed making a music video in Cannes all chopped in with the repeatedly sampled image of Tardelli's goal celebration.

The video started with a darkened room. As the light fades gradually up Taba's oddly-shaped face appears with Enzo and I in the background. Taba had said that he would introduce the film and he started to speak, in a kind of Spanish drawl, long, drawn-out sentences...

> A man walks in to the bedroom with a sheep under his arm, his wife is lying in bed reading a book about the Communist impact on the Catholic church during the 19th century.
>
> The man says, "This is the pig I have sex with when you've got a headache."
>
> The wife replies, "I think you'll find, that is a sheep."
>
> The man replies, "I think you'll find I was talking to the sheep."

We all pissed ourselves – we didn't know he was going to tell a joke – and the music kicked in.

7 mars

The Head of English told me to stop teaching the 'Are you sexist?' lesson as one of the 15-year-old kids has told his Mum and she has complained, thinking I am teaching a lesson called 'Are you SEXY?'

---

102 Marco Tardelli scored one of world football's most memorable goals when, in the World Cup Final of 1982, he cemented Italy's win over Germany with the third goal, putting them in to an unassailable 3–1 lead. The goal was good, but the celebration was incredible. His utter disbelief as to what is happening to him, right here, right now transforms his face as he runs off, shaking his head and roaring at the same time. Tears appear to flow down his cheeks. It is everything you dream of.

8 mars

Got a letter back from Joanne in Bromley. She said that it "sounds like you are having a cool time in France". That's it. Then she told me that she had bought a Nova and split up with her boyfriend called Tony. She told me that the highlight of her year had been going to Manhattan and that the view from the top of the Empire State Building was "spectacular". Really??? I haven't even been to America but I knew that already. She told me she was "smitten" with a guy called Carl. He sounds like a tosser. "Carl." She told me that she has "never felt like this before". I assume she knows that I used to go out with her. Implication being that I never made her feel, "like this", like "Carl does". I live in fucking Cannes!

I'm going to buy that Lacoste rainsheeter and wear it with a massive tan to her engagement party in some shit pub in Bexleyheath.

Cannes.

9 mars

Alistair is gutted that his geographical location further down the coast in the scarily named 'Draguignan' prevents him being in the band. As the only musician he might have been a bit out of place. He said that he feels like one of those blokes who left bands just before fame.[103] He might not need to worry.

10 mars

'*Lucas et Le Gang*' came over to the flat for the premiere of our first music video. Loved it. I am now drunk on our imminent success, as well as the five litres of *Vin du Pays* which *les rockers* brought round.

11 mars

4 am this morning the phone rang. "They're smoking heroin in my apartment." Then crying and giggles. She was ringing to tell me that she

---

103 Andy Couzens who left the Stone Roses, Chad Channing who left Nirvana just before *Nevermind*, Dave Mustain left Metallica before they became monsters (although he did form the not-unsuccessful Megadeth), Pete Best who left a band called the Beatles before 'Love Me Do' (not entirely his choice) and even Stephen Duffy, the original Duran Duran lead singer.

was scared. My interest is at an all-time low. The conversation dragged on. Her friends are coming over on Friday. She asked if I was looking forward to meeting them.

14 mars
Interesting few days. Enzo, Pollyanna, Alistair and I all went to Nice for a weekender. Charlotte called Pollyanna to say that she was meeting her friends from London, including Saffron and Hutchence, in *Chez Wayne* at 10. Enzo and I went for a few early drinks then I went to meet Jason Priestley and a couple of his friends in another bar. By the time I got to *Wayne's* there was a queue around the corner and Charlotte (even more drunk than her normal Olympic gold standard) came out and attempted to drag me in past the obviously resistant bouncers. After an hour or so of waiting, a dick friend of Andreas' came out to slurrily inform me that Charlotte was sitting on the bar snogging "some old bird". We left the queue and went to another bar, me desperately trying to not look bothered. Somehow a bleary-eyed Charlotte found me and dragged me outside for her explanation. It was all of course an "enormous mistake". As she sat sobbing in the street next to the kebab shop, she told me that Hutchence had just told her that he had been having an affair with Saffron the whole time she had been away.

I do not quite know what to do with all of this. Except for maybe flush it down the bog.

15 mars
Tonight a phone call confirmed the finality. She actually seemed surprised.

Here we go, a brave new year… Cannes, what have you got? I am a young Cary Grant, newly single, armed with a rifle ready to shoot and peering into the barrel teeming with Mediterranean Cannoise mermaids.

16 mars
It really is darkest just before dawn.

I am going to quote verbatim from the lesson.

Me: "When you go to the beach you take a swimming costume and a towel."

Madame Cocheteux: "When we go in the beach we take only a towel! Not costume."

"Then you take a bikini."

"No! We never have clothes in the beach. We are *naturiste!*"

My hands are shaking.

17 mars

There is a special offer on trains to Paris for 200 francs (20 quid) return. I am going to go tomorrow.

Madame Cocheteux is a naturist.

Paris, mars 19

Fuck Charlotte. The End.

Madame Cocheteux is a naturist. Not a naturalist. A naturist.

I am in Paris. A proper fuck off city with big buildings and history and an underground and all that.

I have decided that I believe in a long, prolonged, derangement of the senses in order to obtain the unknown.

I am reading 'No One Here Gets Out Alive'. Jim Morrison in Paris. Springtime in Paris. Other clichés.

Haven't got with a lady for ages. I am like a striker just signed for a new club, waiting for that first goal to get the pressure off, then loads will come. But I am a bit concerned.

Went to Père Lachaise, about 50 people round Jim's grave. James Douglas Morrison. Police as well....loved it, think the cemetery will feature in my dreams, it was like a huge gothic city with streets and everything.

Now in huge lecture hall at the Sorbonne, daydreaming about playing strip poker with all the girls here in their little French knickers, white cashmere jumpers and knee socks, rolling around in their white beds that smell of lavender.

Went to see the 25-year-old waitress I pulled in France last year. So much older than me, she is a bit of a shocker in real life — soooo old! All her really gay mates really hate me. She works in a clothes shop called 'Marlboro Classics', as in clothes inspired by Marlboro fags!

We really didn't get on and she was argumentative and difficult. Went to a club called Bataclan and she was really drunk and went mental. Started screaming 'fuck you I won't do what you tell me...' in tune with the Rage Against Machine song right in my face!!!!

There were men in thongs all dancing and putting hands in each others' pouches. It was quite scary.

I was shit with girls tonight. If Ian Brown was watching he would stand behind me and just say "amateur... amateur".

mars 20

I fuckin' hate Paris. It's always cold and wet when I am here, it's totally exclusive and I spend my days in Crapelet (Chatelet) eating cheap kebabs and reading Milo Manara's erotic books or pervy photographer tomes in FNAC. It's pathetic. It's only still pretty cos they collaborated with the Nazis and none of it got bombed.

Me. Reduced.

I feel like a has-been. But I am only 20. But better a has-been than a never was eh?

PS Think of us as erotic politicians. Jim also said that.

PPS I don't even mean that.

23 mars

Chatted to Arnaud and Etienne's Mum and agreed that they aren't progressing exactly according to plan. We have agreed to give it some more time but is more out of goodwill[104] than anything. I discussed the situation with one of my other teachers and I have come to the conclusion (what with all my experience of child development behind me) that they could well be dyslexic. They are having some pretty sizeable problems in their own language, too.

---

104 When I said goodwill I probably meant 'my bank balance'.

A la recherche du temps gâché[105]

24 mars
Nothing happened.

25 mars
Even nothing didn't happen.

27 mars
I am living in a fog. And fogs sooner or later lift. I read that somewhere.

29 mars
Last night I pulled a girl called Fannie. That is her real name. She is blonde and looks like a puppet from a space show. She is super-tanned and as mad as a box of frogs. She carries a massive bottle of water everywhere she goes.

30 mars
Fannie flipped out when she didn't have her bottle of water in the *Rue d'Antibes* today. She acted like we were in the desert and not a civilised city with shops and stuff.

31 mars
Fannie is a complete mental case who, like many French girls I am beginning to understand, loves a row. She also likes the bit just before the row, and really likes the bit after a row, when we make up. And I have known her for precisely three days.

---

105 In Search of Wasted Time. This is a very clever pun on the book *A la recherche du temps perdu*. No. Haven't read it.

Le Printemps

CLAUDE MC ET LA MONTÉE DE HIP HOP FRANÇAIS

Initially sniffed at in the UK, French hip hop actually worked perfectly with the beautiful sounds in the French language. A lot of the energy in and around hip hop in France in the late eighties and early nineties was emanating from the multi-ethnic banlieues, suddenly realising that they were at the forefront of a phenomenon: the rebirth of French music. A *Newsweek* feature in 1994 called it "a blunt, assertive new cultural energy", attributing it to the stagnation of the country's high arts and academies and a burgeoning "global ghetto culture".

Verlan, a slang originating from the inversion of the syllables, aims to confuse the untrained ear and creates a kind of colloquial language of its own.[106] This explosion of French hip hop also coincided perfectly with a national debate over the amount of French language music being played on the French radio. Famously protective of their rich language there were quotas applied to stem the flow of what was seen as the infiltration of French culture due to an excessive swing towards American and English language music.

Claude M'Barali, AKA Claude MC, AKA MC Solaar was the French hip hop star who made French hip hop work, and opened the floodgates for a host of other artists. He described himself as "negropolitan" and listed Sartre and Lacan as his biggest influences. Born in Senegal but raised in the northern Parisian estates, Solaar started writing poetry and verses when the invasion of France by American rap left him feeling alienated. He trashed the clichéd American hip hop culture in pithy interviews, "Yeah, I was from Brooklyn. It was a jungle. I had to sell crack. Victim of Society." Blending poetry and music he began performing on the streets, moulding his own style of philosophy, humour and lyrical word play. The complexity of his language and the sheer joy he found

---

106 *Mère* (mother): *reum, Femme* (woman): *meuf, Flic* (cop): *keuf, Arabe* (Arab): *beur, Juif* (Jew): *feuj,* Français (French): *céfran*

in the sound of French made him an icon. His post-grad degree in philosophy and intelligent musings also made him something of a rarity. And his teaming up with Gang Starr in New York and recording on our favourite London labels, Acid Jazz and Talkin' Loud, made him very, very cool in our minds.

He released the album *Prose Combat* in June 1994 and it exploded. The Serge-sampling 'Nouveau Western' had been a massive hit and you couldn't turn on the radio without hearing Claude's smart riff on life, love, gorillas and Gary Cooper. The standout track was called 'Obsolète'[107] and it was a stinging indictment of all things American and trash-cultured. If gangster rap, to a non-gangster, was a bit of a stretch, (they might as well have been rapping about their gas bills as far as the French were concerned) then this guy was like André Gide. For many rap fans French hip hop's crafted, almost poetic phrasing and vocabulary starkly contrasted the aggression and thug culture of American gangster rap. Seizing his opportunity to grab the middle ground between the two – a kind of Marvin Gaye meets Charles Baudelaire of hip hop, sensitive and superbly sampled, but with a killer edge – was MC Solaar.

---

107 I would go on to study this song as part of my final year oral exam, actually writing a 2000-word thesis on its influence.

Another one bites the dust

1 avril

Watched a film tonight called *37°2 le matin* with Fannie. AKA *Betty Blue*. I said to Fannie that she is a bit like Betty. She went home. But at least she didn't scratch her own eyes out.

2 avril

I have started the 'Emile Roux Music Club'. This will be a once-a-week lunchtime session in which 30 or so of the older kids can propose and vote on which song they want to study the next week.[108] I designed a logo too. Even assigned myself the copyright in case it gets big. Like Nike.[109] Bought tickets to see MC Solaar in Nice. Can't wait.

Later

Went out in Cannes with Fannie. It transpires she is a kind of she-wolf. We walked into a bar and she became a pneumatic nympho-hussy with an addiction to men and free drinks/cigarettes/flirty innuendo. I could only watch. Slightly drunk, slightly embarrassed, semi-turned-on.

3 avril

Le Cannet library has Milo Manara books![110] Libraries at home never stock him and you can only purchase most of his work in selected 'bookshops' in and around Soho. They must have eight or nine of the bad boys. They also have the complete *Pirelli Calendar Annual*, tons of

---

108 I say study, it will largely mean me writing up the words on a white board and being able to explain to them what they mean.

109 The Nike swoosh was thought up by a student at the University of Oregon in 1964 and Phil Knight paid her $35 for it.

110 Milo Manara is a particular favourite of mine, largely as the Italian is renowned for his ability at drawing erotically charged dream Cocheteux women.

old copies of acceptable-because-it's-art jazz mag '*PHOTO*' and pretty much everything which ever left Helmut Newton's dark room. Happy day.

4 avril

The weather is ropey. As a result I am becoming increasingly glued to the OJ Simpson trial. I have never been to America but I could now drive you from Brentwood to Rockingham in a blindfold without missing a turn. I could tell you Ron Goldman's shift hours and the size of OJ's Bruno Maglis, I am so versed. No magazines here are covering it, which I just don't get. I am getting a hearsay fix almost every day at Emile Roux OJ Club where three of the other teachers have satellite TV and fill me in daily. We are obsessed. Two days ago I found myself asking a class of bemused 12-year-olds what they thought of the crime scene photos and was genuinely considering a new lesson plan based on piecing together the exact timetable OJ followed from his daughter's recital to his flight leaving LAX. Fell down on a lack of vocab-learning opportunities, with glove, blood and blade not high up on the curriculum.[111]

5 avril

Still no rent rebate. And to make matters worse the most irritating song ever recorded, 'Zombie' by The Cranberries, is now number one. I almost miss '7 Seconds'.

MC Solaar live in Nice tonight.

Much later

The majority of hip hop gigs I have been to have been absolute baba so this one had nothing to live up to. Enzo, Taba and I went to a beautiful Roman amphitheatre in Nice, le Théâtre de Verdure. Got tickets from a mate of Jason Priestley's. Solaar strutted on in vintage British checked suit and played for almost three hours. It was the cat's Burberry pyjamas and within about two minutes the best hip hop concert I have been to. This is because most rappers have the onstage presence of a mic stand,

111 In 1995 almost no-one had the internet.

and Claude MC has the onstage presence of Elvis' '68[112] comeback tour mixed with Jackson[113] performing 'Man in the Mirror' at Wembley in 1988.

Today was also the first anniversary of the death of Kurt Cobain.

A tumultuous day for all of us at the Emile Roux Music Club.[114] Nirvana are without a doubt the most popular band amongst the angsty older kids who attend the music club and today it all came out. I had, somewhat presciently, decided to focus on the REM song 'Everybody Hurts'.

Most of the class came in wearing all black, and many with Nirvana t-shirts on. There were teenage tears and tantrums and lots of sitting on the floor shaking heads. Felt like a slightly weird Seattle Sunday School teacher as I launched into my soul savin' sermon. Talked at length to my captive audience about a subject I know absolutely nothing about. Suicide. Veering dangerously close to a kind of Jim Jones[115] rhetoric. I implored them to reject the idea that Cobain had in any way committed a heroic act. Quite enjoyed the sound of my own voice, opining that

---

112 Pre-fat/gun-toting era.

113 Pre-REALLY weird.

114 The year before the Seattle-born rock legend Kurt Cobain of Nirvana had blown his brains out with a shotgun.

115 Jim Jones was the ordained founder and leader of a Christian doomsday cult called The Peoples Temple, which by the 1950s had over 900 members in Indianapolis. Preaching a pretty standard gospel of freedom, equality, and love at first it started to get more vitriolic against other Christians and took on elements of communism. On the plus side it was very inter-racial. When the group moved west to California Jones began to go loopy and preach the imminent end of the world. By the mid 1970s the media had started to take notice and suspicions were raised as regards illegal activities and human rights violations in the Temple. So Jones moved it to the jungle of Guyana and built a community called, you guessed it, Jonestown. They created a kind of communist agricultural society, raising animals and farming. While this was going on Jim was busy writing a document called *Translation*, which advocated mass suicide in order to reach their destination, another planet for a life of peace and serenity. Leo Ryan, a Congressman, visited Jonestown in 1978 to check out the set-up. Satisfied, he left but some Temple Security guards took offence at some Temple members wanting to leave with the party and opened fire. Congressman Ryan and four others were killed. The Temple leaders decided now was the time to commit group suicide which they did by ingesting a grape drink laced with cyanide and sedatives, leaving 914 dead.

J'accuse Ben.

it was probably a kind of anti-suicide song that REM wrote with their friend in mind. Fielded questions on whether he had actually faked his own death to escape from the media. Pooh-poohed them.

It is very rewarding, being a cross between a prophet, a music journalist and a young, slightly trendy religious cult leader.

6 avril

This morning the school received five different complaints from parents. I was called before my idol for the first time in ages. The image from a newspaper at the top of the page for the Cobain Memorial Music Club had the caption, "The picture that shocked the world".[116] Can't believe the furore. Next week when we do 'Sweet Child O'Mine' o' mine' I am definitely not going to tell them now that 'Axl Rose' is an anagram of 'Oral Sex'.

Alistair came up today He has CANNES written in chalk on one side of his saxophone box, DRAGUIGNAN, where he lives, on the other. I was telling him about my classes. He is working in a *lycée technique* where most of them spend all day working on lathes.

7 avril

Sartre (who else?) said that 3 o'clock is always too late or too early for anything you want to do. Even when this consists of getting stoned or drunk. Maybe even especially so. Alistair has just came back in. His busking hat split on the Croisette and spilt all his francs down a handily-placed drain. Incredibly he then used Hollywood strawberry chewing gum on the end of a palm tree branch to painstakingly retrieve all but three or four of the coins.

---

116 The image was of Cobain lying prone on the floor, his blown off head not visible but remnants of his suicide all around him.

LE SUPERMARCHE FRANÇAIS: TOUT CE QUE VOUS DEVEZ SAVOIR

There are a number of French supermarkets. The big ones are Auchan, Carrefour, Champion, Shopi, Casino Géant Casino, Franprix, G20, Leader Price, Groupe Casino Spar, Intermarché, Netto, Super U, Système U, Aldi, E.Leclerc. To name a few. There are many in Cannes but there is one which rises like a giant plastic phoenix above the rest, the finest name, the finest produce, four different types of lettuce, a bar…Casino.

Casino is not a French concept in gambling with food, even if it does kind of sound like a French idea. Casino is the leading French supermarket chain and they have a colossal outlet just near the centre of Cannes. When you have time to burn you could burn it here. The allure of the trashy side of their culture hits the spot.

Nutella is obviously one of the best brand names ever but they also have *Bigard* frozen meats, *Créaline* soups, *Mamie Nova* yoghurts and *Lustucru* pasta. Crap stuff looks great with much better names. Baked beans become *haricots blancs en sauce tomate*, lager is sexy and when referred to as *la bière blonde* it sounds like a promise. Although bacon is often sold as *le lard*, which takes the edge off a sandwich a bit.

Another thing that will take the edge of a sandwich is bread from a supermarket. Don't do it. No-one who knows anything does. But this may be their only flaw. Apart from maybe milk, and *Candia* is the only milk brand which isn't foul. But then they don't drink tea all day, they use it to mix with chocolate powder and make a lovely drink (there is so much sugar in that that you could mix it with bog juice and you'd be ok). Butter is also never salty which will take some getting used to, but you'll live longer. So swings and roundabouts.

Overall the French love to make out that they all buy their meat from the boucherie, the bread from the boulangerie (they do do that one), their vegetables from the local farmer and their dried fruit from the old blind lady who sits in the market square. Nonsense. They love a big mega supermarket and in France, the bigger, the better.

The best ones are like coliseums, even the trolleys are called *chariots*.

8 avril

It's boiling today. But I am feeling homesick. The things I miss most are:

- HMV
- Football Focus
- The talking clock
- Top of the Pops
- Birds Eye fishfingers
- Sarcasm
- Horse racing on the TV on a Saturday afternoon
- Stuffing with a roast dinner
- Twiglets
- Heinz beans with cheddar cheese melted in

Although I never enjoy horse racing or the talking clock when at home. I just miss the idea that they are there if I want them.

Sometimes I worry no-one really knows me here. They only get to know a Ben who is defined by a very finite vocabulary and grammatical limitations. Everyone seems to think I am really 'sweet'. They don't know my bad boy side.

C'est qui, Ben? I don't really know at the moment. Is that a problem?

9 avril

Alistair told me that he heard from another assistant that Charlotte had a party at her flat and then they all went to the beach and she sunbathed topless in front of everyone. Nothing like not being invited to a party you didn't want to go to. I would have gone to the beach bit though.

Those breasts. Like a young Madame Cocheteux.

10 avril

I should never have put Madame Cocheteux in the same class as anyone.

The 'Emile Roux Music Club' has been decommissioned by Monsieur Guy Rufin after several more complaints from parents over the handout image. I hope there is a Student Revolution.

11 avril

Note to self: Remember your audience. Especially when teaching people who are 12 years old and in a language of which their knowledge is rudimentary. The greatest ever Englishman, Shakespeare, was an obvious choice for a lesson. But it would have been worth remembering that I am not teaching at Charterhouse in the 1920s. Lesson today at Le Slab consisted of putting ten Shakespearean phrases up on big bits of paper and then asking the students to match them to a list of all Shakespeare's plays. I don't know what I was thinking. I chose phrases Shakespeare had coined that were still used in this day and age, highlighting his incredible prescience and longevity as a creative force...

- mum's the word
- short shrift
- wild goose chase
- green-eyed monster
- love is blind
- the world is my oyster
- makes your hair stand on end
- good riddance
- wearing your heart on your sleeve
- all corners of the world

Not one single student out of the 30 knew any Shakespeare plays. They didn't understand the phrases. They are almost impossible to translate in to French – "mum's the word"!!!! With minutes to go I was stood on a chair singing 'London Bridge is Falling Down', accompanied in my head by the sound of barrels being scraped.

12 avril
I think its over with Fannie. I think she quite dislikes me.

13 avril
Brilliant night.
So here in Cannes it is currently the Cannes Porn Festival. I didn't even know such a thing existed but apparently it does.
Enzo has been working like a dog as they have loads of the porn people staying there. He has been going on about all the birds and how they come in wearing big coats and when he serves them drinks in the

evening he can see all their rubber suits and stuff underneath.

Last night Taba came over with his friend Kathrin from the *lycée* and we were whingeing a bit about not seeing Enzo for ages and so we rang him up. Or rather, as a joke, we got Kathrin to ring up and act all like she was one of the porno stars staying at the hotel. She rang up and says in a porno-y Germanic French accent, "*Hallo, J'appelle de chambre soixante-neuf*" and he didn't even clock that it was an outside line! So we were pissing ourselves and then she asks for a bottle of champagne "*avec 2 coupes*" and he is being all straight and stuff so then she says, "*Une coupe pour toi*" and he laughs all nervously and says, "*Je ne peux pas quitter la réception*" and then she says, in ENGLISH!!!... "Vood you like to join viss me here?" After this huge long silence, he manages to stammer "*AVEC GRAND PLAISIR*". We were all laughing so much she had to say she was going to call back and then she did and just said "*Tu t'appelles Enzo?*" And he is all surprised and she says, "*Vincenzo Cilenti? Du supergroupe Tardelli?*" and then we were all lying on the floor and I honestly don't think I have ever laughed so much in my life.

35 MOTS FRANÇAIS QUE VOUS AVEZ OUBLIE QU'ON UTILISE EN ANGLAIS

apéritif   Cocktail, coming from the Latin word for 'open'.

art deco   Decorative art, which is what this is short for.

au fait   Up to speed, meaning 'conversant'.

avant-garde   Before guard, which again translates badly, but means innovative, often in the arts.

blond, blonde   Fair-haired, brilliantly this is the only adjective in English which agrees in gender with the person it modifies. That means that a man is blond and a woman is blonde.

brunette   Small, dark-haired female, using the word 'brun' for 'brown' and –ette means little and female.

cerise   Cherry, which is a colour often used for make-up.

critique   Critical, normally a noun in English for an overall review.

cuisine   Kitchen, a type of cooking, like 'Spanish cuisine'.

cul-de-sac   Bottom or butt of the bag, but we know it as a dead-end street.

débutante   Beginner, but both French and English use it for posh girls making their formal entry into 'society'.

encore   Again, as in another performance, particularly used in the theatre.

en masse   In mass, as in a group, all together.

fait accompli   Done deed, or something you set out to do, done.

faux   False, used across everything in English.

fiancé, fiancée   Engaged person, and that's all.

gauche   Left, but normally clumsy, tactless and lacking social grace.

genre   Type, used in the arts, especially film.

hors d'œuvre   Outside of work, is the misleading translation of what we all know as an appetiser.

mardi gras   Fat Tuesday, the celebration before Lent.

née   Born, used here for a woman's maiden name.

nouveau riche	New rich, used in the most arriviste negative way.
oh là là	Oh dear, and misspelled as 'ooh la la' in English.
passé	Past, meaning old-fashioned.
petite	Small, normally in an attractive, positive way.
pied-à-terre	Foot on ground, or a temporary habitat.
pince-nez	Pinch-nose, those little nose-balanced glasses.
protégé	Protected, but normally someone is being trained by someone as they are a bit special.
risqué	Risked, suggestive, slightly provocative.
rouge	Red, like cerise a cosmetic powder/colour.
sans	Without, particularly in typefaces like the sans serif types.
savoir-faire	Knowing how to do, meaning tact or social grace, savvy.
soirée	Evening, which we would use for a more elegant party.
souvenir	Memory, but for us a keepsake or novelty.
vol-au-vent	Flight of the wind, but more a light pastry shell filled with meat or fish in sauce.

VINGT-SIX

Nu

14 avril

Dear Me,

This is a good one.

Voici, the French equivalent of *Hello*, carried a front-cover picture today of Vanessa Paradis and Lenny Kravitz at a nudist beach in the Bahamas. Photos of her fanny are discreetly kept to page 4. I really like that. I really like the French attitude towards nudity. Madame Cocheteux's especially.

The financial situation is fractious and there is no clear sign of when/ if I will ever be seeing any of my rent rebate. Two weeks ago I saw an advert on the notice board at my local supermarket for an art class at a college up the road. The supermarket is called the 'Ed Leclerc'. Brilliant name for a supermarket. Sounds more like a rock star. Headed down as thought it might help with designing flyers. The class was good. It ended strangely as everybody followed the tradition of showing their work to the classmates. I unveiled my etching of a kind of Chinese flower in black ink. Looked like something Charles Manson would draw in his cell using his own blood and toilet paper. It just came out. People looked visibly disturbed, me especially.

As everyone packed away we were told about next week's lesson on life-drawing. The tutor also told us she had been let down by the model and asked if any of us knew anyone who wanted to pose, she said it paid well. Cue much guffawing. And my brain whirring into action. I am so skint that I would volunteer to test experimental parachutes. A sizeable 200 francs for the session (about £20 for standing there for two hours). I asked her if I could do it and she cheerily agreed. With the blood flower thing the class probably think I am a right nutter. We have arranged to meet 15 minutes before the start of the class the next week.

15 avril

I am reading Chris Waddle's autobiography. I am supposed to be reading *En attendant Godot* by Samuel Beckett. I am at the bit where he is working in a sausage factory on Tyneside.

Enzo phoned today. He made me promise that under no circumstances would I mention the German porno affair to Pollyanna or ever say the words "*AVEC GRAND PLAISIR*" in his presence ever again.

16 avril

Last night I met a girl called Amelle for the second time through a friend of Enzo's at the hotel. Significant because we ended up getting it on atop a stack of sun loungers by the pool. The first time we met she seemed pretty normal. Last night she added that she is a 'Scientologist'. I think it is not actually a religion but a kind of evening class.

She's not really hot in the most obvious way but her whole cosmic thing is pretty cool. And she listens really intensely when I talk to her.

17 avril

Forgotten what apathy feels like? I am compiling this list of animal adjectives…
- aquiline – eagle
- assinine – donkey
- bovine – cattle
- cancrine – crab
- canine – dog
- cervine – deer
- corvine – crow
- equine – horse
- elapine – snake
- elaphine – deer
- feline – cat
- hircine – goat
- leonine – lion
- leporine – rabbit, hare
- lupine – wolf
- murine – rodent

- pavonine – peacock
- piscine – fish
- porcine – pig
- rusine – deer
- serpentine – snake
- ursine – bear
- vulpine – fox
  I have made another one up. Galepine – shark-like.

18 avril

Today was really hot again. After about three weeks off due to her various family commitments I went to teach Madame Cocheteux. I love how she talks to me like the man that I will be rather than the boy that I am. When I arrived I am pretty much sure that she was topless in the garden, and quite possibly bottomless because I had to wait over a minute at the gate.

Told Monsieur Guy Rufin about my list, he asked me if I had 'eusuchian' – like an alligator. Amazing.

19 avril

Oh my God. Amelle is actually a complete and utter mentalist. Last night she started with a variation of the footprints in the sand in which Jesus carries you. Except in her version, unlike the one which adorns Nan's mantelpiece, the Jesus character is played by a spaceman! Her family are all believers in higher powers, all think astrology is real and go on family trips to see inspirational speakers together. Once she had me interested/frightened she explained to me how I could have my soul saved by Scientology as we sat in this pizzeria in Juan-les-Pins. She told me quite matter-of-factly about the hydrogen bombs they used to make souls cluster together. When she started telling me that she believed in Xenu, an alien ruler of the Galactic Confederacy I was genuinely scared.

I have been teaching the older students about the universe and told her the version I knew.[117] She probably pressed some kind of Scientologist

---

117 There are millions (*millions!*) of galaxies in the universe and that our own galaxy, the Milky Way, contains over *one hundred billion stars* as well as our sun, and that more than half of those stars have planets orbiting around them.

red alert button as next up we debated what would happen if a deranged evil scientist blew up the moon. Would we all die?[118] But Amelle isn't scared.

Keep distance.

20 avril
Why do we call the French 'frogs'?

21 avril
When I arrived at art class today it was explained to me that I would hold five or six short ten-minute poses in the first hour, the more athletic the better, and then one long 'reclining pose' for most of the second hour. I was asked to go and put my robe on. I reckon the correlation between being a 20-year-old male and the owning of a robe is pretty low. Also my 'dressing room', somewhat surreally, was a sheet hanging completely straight from string attached to the ceiling. It hung about a metre and a bit off the floor and I am about 1 metre 80cm tall. Standing behind it the material essentially covered my chest and shoulders, my neck and my head, but only if you looked straight at it. As no-one else was there I quickly stripped off and kind of just stood there, a headless naked torso. A few minutes later I felt even more silly – people were setting up and could clearly see round the sides, and the front...it was a sheet. I think I looked like an obscure art installation.

Wednesday afternoon is an afternoon off at Collège le Big Fun. On this one Wednesday afternoon, (the odds must surely have been heavily stacked against this), two teachers decided that they wanted to draw a human. The attractive, yet temperamental, Corsican Madame Muglioni one of them. She was with the lady who looked after Monsieur Rufin, Madame Haricot, the school secretary.

As I appeared from behind my Dalian tea-towel dressing room I was greeted almost immediately with the gaze of Madame Muglioni. Her eyes went straight from my face to my genitals. It would have actually been okay if I had been in a pose when I had first clocked her as it

118 I looked into it. Like a meteorite, giant pieces would rain down on us. It would be pre-empted by tidal waves and mass climate change. Or it might take thousands of years until our orbits came into collision course. It could stop you sleeping at night.

would have side-stepped the most embarrassing scenario which ensued. Small-talk. I stood there with my hands casually covering my crotch, for a good few minutes talking, desperately hoping for some direction from the teacher to break this situation we found ourselves in. At one point, desperate to keep conversation going, I actually asked her who had designed the Corsican flag. She didn't know. Then I kind of acted like I had to go and get in position but what really happened was that I just walked three feet over towards my tiny stage and stood there looking hopeless, my naked bottom about a metre from Madame Muglioni's face.

The athletic part of the modelling was one of the worst things I have ever forced myself to do. Weirdly the first pose I went for was the javelin thrower. After about two of the ten minutes I was shaking, struggling, sweating and desperately needing the toilet, terrified I was going to piss or, worse, shit myself. For my next one I got on the floor. I propped myself like a sprinter and after about 40 seconds I felt the numbness set in and knew I had made another error.

After that my fear of pain led me to experiment with a couple of variations on being cross legged, or bending over whilst kneeling down. Poses which were frankly pornographic. Particularly if you were standing on Madame Muglioni's side. At the end of the lesson the artists show their work to each other. But I noticed from the shelter of my tea-towel-in-the-sky dressing room how they didn't seem to be doing this today, the work no doubt deemed too shocking.

22 avril
I am reading Sarraute's *L'Enfance*. It was described as an 'easy read'.

23 avril
It is so not.

I went to my bank, *Société Générale*, today. As I have insufficient funds I have incurred a 200F fine. Rendering my two hours of naked humiliation pointless. Or a really smart move. Depending on how you look at it.

24 avril

Saw Madame Muglioni. She said nothing. I never heard anything from anyone about my performance back at the school. But I feel sure it had been discussed.

Met a girl called Aurelie.

25 avril

The Beatles are the key to my success with the Music Club. It seems all music can be brought back to the Fab Four and, my knowledge of them being Grade A A-Level standard, this is working well. The incredible international language which is Scouse Melody is proving a real winner. Kids are bringing in old vinyl owned by their parents, old French fanzines and even, in one case, a photo of one student's very hot Mum with George at Bercy in Paris in 1964. Today I made them all laugh by telling them about a comedy covers act which I had seen featuring Wrong Lennon, Paul McCan't Be, Erringo Starr and George Comparison. Translated surprisingly well.

'Zombie' by The Cranberries, however, is still number one.

Avril 26

Dear Sod,

Every now and then someone comes along who pushes you hard in the chest, knocks you off balance, musses up every single nape hair and reminds you just why chicks remain the most vibrant and energetic force on the planet.

In the meantime, I am having to put up with tediously mumsy, conformist girls like Aurelie.

My confidence not high, I met Aurelie through a teacher at school who suggested it. Aurelie is new to Cannes and wants to make friends. She wears giant jumpers and looks away coyly when you are talking to her in a way which suggests she knows something you don't.

I even think she might be a racist as I noticed that she talks about immigration a lot like she is gearing up for another conversation.

That is literally all I have to write today.

Me.

PS Aurelie is reading a novel with a drawing of a

medieval sewing machine on the front. When she talks about it I am so bored that I actually think about really awful things like decapitation. You see? You can judge a book by its cover.

PPS My favourite line in '50 ways to leave your lover' is "Just drop off the key, Lee. And get yourself free."

Rock n roll...Ram-a-lama! Or something. Apologies for the intense boredom that is no doubt reading this letter.

Peachy keen, jelly bean.

ZZZZZZZZZZZZZZZZ

VINGT-SEPT
Going bananes in Cannes

27 avril

Today I got a letter from Fannie. I think it might be the shortest letter ever. But it looks like a real letter. She told me that she is coming back to Cannes for the weekend but then writes, "*Enfin, tu dois t'en faire foutre pas mal de ce que je te dis.*" And then next the line, "*Je t'embrasse énormément.*"[119]

28 avril

Amazing day. Went to the Monte Carlo Open Tennis Championships with Jason Priestley.[120] Watched my favourite, and local resident/party boy, Boris 'Boom Boom' Becker beat Richard Krajicek in straight sets in the quarter-final. We bunked the train there (more crime written down) from Cannes. The Cannes-Nice-Monaco train line is so spectacular that they should charge extra for it. It was about 6 quid to get into the tennis and our seats were perched high up on a cliff top overlooking Monaco bay and its jade blue sea. I felt like the luckiest person in the world. Particularly when I turned to my left as I could see up an extremely attractive woman's skirt and her almost see-through white knickers. I think she knew.

---

119 "In any case, you must not give a fuck about what I say…I embrace you enormously."
120 The last time I had been to a tennis tournament was at Wimbledon last summer. It is worth mentioning as I had experienced one of the more embarrassing days of my life. We had been queuing all night on the pavement and in the morning, leaning on a crash barrier as we watched the pretty posh girls go past in their pinafores to work in the catering department, and at the exact moment that the queue we were at the forefront of started to move I realised that my knee was stuck in the crash barrier. Almost an hour later, and lying on the verge while St John Ambulance people massaged my leg with industrial Vaseline, I was untangled.

MONACO
OU MONTE-CARLO?

The whole Monaco/Monte-Carlo thing is obviously absolutely loopy. Before I went there my knowledge of the place consisted of racing cars, Herbie going bananas, rich tennis players habitats, a successful football team with no fans, Michael Jackson kicking his heels with inappropriate company around the hotels and Grace Kelly having a fatal car crash off the cliff face. Arguably that is not a bad review.

Monaco is a principality. A principality is a small mini-country which has a royal family, ruled by a Prince or Princess. This family is called the House of Grimaldi and makes it sound like a fashion label from Hungary. So a principality is a bit like a really small country, which makes up its own rules. Monaco is often called a city-state as it only really has one city – and that is called, er, Monaco. About 30,000 live there and, as it is a tax haven, upwards of 80% of these are wealthy foreigners. It is situated just about in France but a few miles away from the Italian border. Apart from the likelihood that they are absurdly rich the people who live there are also known as Monégasques, which is also a language spoken, although French is the recognised one. After Vatican City it is the second smallest country in the world.

Monte-Carlo is just a region of the principality of Monaco. But it is the bit most people know with the resort and the casino and the big flats with all the girls by the pools on the rooves, which they always show on the grand prix coverage.

Historically it used to be part of Genoa and the Grimaldis took control in 1297. It was part of a Franco-Italian tug-of-war for ages before settling in French hands in the late 1800s. It was completely independent until the 20th century when it decided to stand a shade behind France's defence and economic might, whilst retaining some independence. The really glamourous period came in the 1950s when Prince Rainier married Hollywood icon Grace Kelly, turning her into the real-life fairytale Princess she always was and conveniently deflecting from his un-Prince Charming looks and manner. She died in 1982 when she suffered a stroke whilst driving through the Monaco mountains with her teenage daughter, Princess Stéphanie. Her starry televised funeral effectively ended Monaco's period of worldwide media obsession. It is now more known for gala evenings which old people go to, big sporting events like football's grandiose-sounding but pointless Super Cup which old people go to and the grand prix at which it is impossible to overtake, making it appealing to old people.

29 avril
Today I taught 'Hey Jude'. A new high. They *really* sang it.

30 avril
Aurelie dumped me! I haven't spoken to her for a week! She said that she doesn't think it is "worth" her spending any more time with me! A kind of gentle but crushing humiliation is becoming my calling card this spring.

1 mai
There was a general election today. Jacques Chirac was elected President. If I am honest it will impact on my life in no way at all, I figure Chirac would not be any more interested in my rent rebate situation than Mitterrand has been before him. And he COMPLETELY ignored it. And I am less interested in French politics than I am in English politics. And I am not interested in that at all. I go with Albert Camus:

> "If there was a party for those who weren't sure they were right, I'd belong to it."

Boris Becker lost to Tomas Muster tonight in the Monte Carlo Open final having been two sets up. Pretty gutted. BB reminds me of Wimbledon, where I was born.

Loads of things are reminding me of home at the moment. Why am I thinking of home so much?

2 mai
Today I taught a lesson about John Lennon being shot. I am worried that I am getting into a comfort zone of rock stars, death and photography.

Still no rent rebate but did receive letter telling me that I am eligible for a pass to the Cannes Film Festival through my assistantship!!! Amazing.

I'm really drunk now. I have lots to say. But I don't know how to say it. The inevitable disappointment of being a drunken visionary. *En Attendant Godot* is amazing. I had to go though different doors in my mind to get there.

3 mai

Last night I thought *En Attendant Godot* was really amazing but today I don't understand it nor can I remember why I thought that.

Later

Madame and Monsieur Mordant are married to each other and both teach at Le Slab. They are proper Cannois.[121] This morning they asked me if I would like to spend a weekend with them at their daughter's apartment in Marseille. Would I?!! I have been fascinated by the lure of Marseille's legendary port and lively history from the moment I arrived and, in football terms, since I was eight. The football team captured my imagination when the husband of my Mum's French friend gave me a book called *L'OM, L'Amour*[122] and, whilst I couldn't really understand it, I particularly loved it. Slightly grainy 80s photos of the German defender Karlheinz Förster and the stylish French midfielder Alain Giresse stuck in my mind. The next year a Christmas gift of a pair of white OM football socks and pale blue silky adidas shorts cemented it. I loved it when he told me that the words '*Droit au But*' emblazoned on their team badge meant 'The Right to Goal'. Presumptuous. But wicked.

121 From Cannes.
122 'Olympique Marseille, My Love'.

PLANÈTE MARSEILLE
(PARTIE 1)

Marseille is sprawling and filthy and stinks. It is rough and aggressive and confrontational. The fact that the drink they all neck is the rocket-fuel-like pastis may well be a contributing factor. The main thoroughfare, La Canabière, is filthy and putrid. Behind it are alleyways where gangs and prostitutes lurk. You need to drink pastis just to be brave enough to leave your apartment. It's why morning drinking is so big there. Everyone is petrified.

But that's just the edge. It is also the most proper, working, living city in France. It's got massive *couilles*[123] and an incredible life and soul to it. Its crumbling beauty and epic, proud port makes everywhere else seem bland and lifeless. It is one of France's oldest multi-racial cities and a model for modern melting pot living.

A lot of what I had picked up about Marseille had come from the emerging hip hop scene. Groups like IAM[124] promoting a forceful message of Marseillan power (their first album was called '...De la planète Mars'), with their tongues often firmly in their cheeks. Hardcore Marseillans also wanted independence from France, creating an unofficial scene, which led to the area being generally referred to as 'Planète Marseille'. And when you tied all this spirit up with a passion verging on the hysterical for football you were in for one hell of a ride....

Oh yeah, they also have the national anthem named after them...

> *"Allons enfants de la Patrie*
> *Le jour de gloire est arrivé!*
> *Contre nous de la tyrannie*
> *L'étendard sanglant est levé*
> *Entendez-vous dans nos campagnes*
> *Mugir ces féroces soldats?*
> *Ils viennent jusque dans vos bras.*
> *Égorger vos fils, vos compagnes!"*

123 Balls.
124 Stood for *Invasion Arrivée de Mars*. 'Mars' being short for 'Marseille'.

4 mai

7 pm

Monsieur Mordant himself is a massive OM fan so the three-hour Citroën journey involved a lot of tales. We arrived at their daughter's flat in a very *La Gloire de Mon Père*[125] area of the city, all leafy streets and old houses. I have NEVER seen such domestic turmoil as when we entered that flat. Initially I was concerned that they had been burgled, such was the *bordelle* when we let ourselves in. Cats everywhere and also other animals like two massive rats in a cage, which look to me like two evil small dogs. There are also two actual dogs, one which is really ill with an awful skin infection. And their love of cats is excessive.[126]

But they are the most down-to-earth people I have met in France. Probably because a city like Marseille is not a bourgeois haven like Cannes. Down-to-earth is always good. I just wished they hadn't left the earth all over the floor. Literally!

Later

I am not a fussy guest but this is pretty full-on. When we sat down at the table I felt like I was actually inside a cage at the zoo. The table was liberally covered with fine animal hair and the whole flat smells of skin infection cream.

Their daughter seems cool and lives in the flat with her boyfriend, a doctor. He is also cool but together they have formed a kind of unified bond against cleanliness and are very much pro-animal rights.

Really late

And I have just discovered what it is like to be a cat as I ate what was pretty much a full hairball. We had sat down together, a large feast

---

125 Much-loved Marseillan book and film about growing up in the ideal family unit.
126 Some people think that cats are clever when it is widely ignored that they can't even talk. My money is firmly in the dog camp. Who don't pretend they are. Apart from guide dogs – which help blind people! You don't get 'guide cats'! Dogs value the company of humans, cats merely rip off peoples' good nature. Cats hunt like real predators and they kill some small creatures. Also, and the flat I was staying in was physical evidence of this, cats do not, as rumoured, bury their 'toilet'. The dim-witted, claw-slashing psychopaths have one thing I would give them – intuition. They know I hate them, and behave accordingly.

prepared in the middle of the table. Monsieur Mordant was quite taken with the presentation of it, exclaiming, "*Au début, on mange avec les yeux!*" The salad-type meal was served up and I put a forkful into my mouth. The hairball had been slightly hidden underneath some salad. I am retching as I write.

5 mai

Didn't get to see l'OM play live this weekend as the game started too late tonight, but I felt the OM spirit as Monsieur Mordant and I went to a bar on the port and necked *pastis* and watched them beat Rennes 3–1. When they scored the third one a group of sailors (yep, real ones) turned a table over and everyone acted like they had just dropped a beer mat on the floor.

PLANÈTE MARSEILLE
(PARTIE 2) LA BAGARRE, LE FOOT ET LES
FASCISTES. ET BERNARD TAPIE.

In order to truly understand the modern Marseille, you have to understand it in both political and footballing terms; as such it is important to understand the phenomenon that was Bernard Tapie. If you like your politicians on the more colourful side, then this was the technicolour-dreamcoated man for you. Tapie was a sometime businessman, champagne socialist, actor, singer, TV host and criminal, amongst other things. He was a mythmaker extraordinaire with charm and flair; he also had an entrepreneurial streak the size of Texas.

Painting a picture of blue collar hardship, he claimed that he grew up in the fierce La Courneuve estate in Paris when it is widely known that he grew up in a middle-class area up the road. An enthusiastic singer, he once changed his name to Bernard Tapy to copy the sound of the name Johnny Hallyday, and was even signed by RCA.

He developed a taste for business and after a successful foray into the US, he came back to France in his thirties and started buying and refinancing companies, culminating in his audacious acquisition of the failing Adidas brand in 1990. As the *"enfant du people"*[127] (his words) on his own TV show he baited the establishment and stuffy Parisian oligarchy with vigour. His calling cards were Porsches, corporate logo'd private jets and tiny hamburgers on cocktail sticks – this was the fun side to left-wing politics.

Football-crazy, he had become interested in the purchase of Olympique Marseille. "I'm not selling you a team, I'm not selling you a stadium – I'm selling you a public", Gaston Deferre, the late mayor of Marseille, had told him. Tapie didn't need a second invitation and whipped out his sizeable chequebook. The first goal was simple, make OM the most glamorous, sexy football club in France. Booming music, fireworks and lasers, an audacious attempt

---

127 Child of the people.

to buy Diego Maradona, the courting of the Maghrebin immigrants to come to matches again…it was one big multi-cultural show, the like of which Marseille had not seen. He reignited pride in the team, and this reflected on the city as a whole. Also on him, as a whole.

His fervour to help OM put one over on the elusive Parisian enemy elevated him to folkloric hero; he was a prized defector from the much despised capital. Tapie hyped the annual matches against Paris Saint-Germain, elevating them to Cup Finals with the whole of France tuning in to watch this sporting civil war erupt. Unfortunately, supporters of both sides loved a fight as much as they loathed each other which led to chronic crowd trouble and hooliganism in the nineties thanks to the ultras (the really hardcore fans) who populated Marseille's Velodrome's *Virage Nord*. The favourite songs were fierce anthems about Marseillan independence and the inappropriate insertion of the Eiffel Tower.

This burning rivalry was borne out of a history and bad blood running far deeper than football. Despite Paris being seen as a primate city of overbearing dominance by the rest of France (particularly in Marseille), the one thing the south always had over the haughty Parisians was their dominance on the football field. For a start PSG weren't even founded until 1970. It was only when TV station Canal Plus bought PSG that they were catapulted into the top bracket overnight. These arriviste tourist-pleasers infuriated the substantial, working men of Marseille, reigniting this hatred which went back centuries.

Within the city of Marseille itself, it was the OM under Tapie's watch who were credited with bringing the multiracial city together. The team was a precursor to the mondialisation of European football that followed, with a blend of international talent never before seen in France. It helped that they were very, very good: five successive titles between 1989 and 1993, two successive European Cup finals and exhilarating football…Tapie's dream realised. He had a team featuring star French striker Jean-Pierre Papin, the tough African defender Basile Boli, the Serbian Dragan Stojkovic, the Uruguayan midfielder Enzo Francescoli[128] and the one they simply called the 'Crazy Dribbler'.

The 'Crazy Dribbler' was Chris Waddle and he had signed in 1989 from Tottenham Hotspur, one of the first, and most unlikely, English players to seek fame and fortune overseas. As an enormous success he had single-handedly started something of a love thing going on between Marseille and the English. The man they called "Chrees". Chris Waddle was the Geordie who had served his apprenticeship working in a sausage factory and whose personality was largely based around sticking his tongue out, pretending that he was blind when he missed an opportunity and wiggling his fingers over his head like a bunny rabbit. The hardcore ultras of the *Virage Nord* adored him. In an era when English players stayed at home he was nothing short of a sensation at Marseille. Arguably he was the best footballer in Europe at the time. But it was his *joie de vivre* and his engagement with the hardcore fans, on a very softcore level, that won everyone over.

They won the European Cup in 1993 but Tapie's tenure was doomed to end in ignominy after he was found guilty of bribing tiny Valenciennes so that the best players could be rested for the big games. They were stripped of the French League title and sent to the second division in shame. Tapie ended up going to prison for corruption, served six months, then got done for tax fraud (in for a penny) before becoming a prominent socialist and left-leaning politician. Having been courted by Mitterrand's left it was the news that Le Pen would be standing in Marseille which forced him into action. Marseille was a political *sujet brûlant*[129] and National Front leader Jean-Marie Le Pen had made a name for himself in the papers talking about the 'Harlemizing' of France, managing to get himself a worrying 20% of the vote. Rallying primarily against North African immigration he displayed his trademark bigotry, bullying tactics and belligerence.

But Tapie was a bar-room brawler too and when the time came for

---

128 Such a hero to a young Zinedine Zidane that he named his son Enzo.
129 Hot potato.

them to go head-to-head on a TV debate Tapie went for the jugular.

> "Anyone who votes for Le Pen is *un salaud*.[130] Anyone who can call the Holocaust 'a detail of history' is *un salaud*....
> Le Pen calls weak members of our society 'handicapped'.
> And we know what the Nazis did to their handicapped."

France loved it. A role as a minister in Mitterrand's government was won and then lost almost straightaway due to his *armoire* full of skeletons. The mixture of business and politics would cost him dear but even then, in the early 1990s, more than half the country said they would have voted for him as president.

Now that would have been brilliant.

130 Bastard.

6 mai

Taught Madame Cocheteux again today. It is the third lesson in a row I have focused on 'The Beach' and what we do/don't take there. Think she has clocked this. If I teach her another 146 times I can buy the Lacoste windcheater.

7 mai

I have been told some brilliant news by Muriel. Jonno has been caught with his trousers down. He has been having an affair and the whole thing has come out. Somewhat disappointingly, having an affair in France does not necessarily lead to divorce papers. But I bet it doesn't make the Family Christmas Newsletter this year.

8 mai

Film Festival starts in two weeks. Quite excited. My brother-in-law, a long-distance HGV driver, is going to be staying two nights *en route* to Italy.

9 mai

I am O.F.F.I.C.I.A.L.L.Y. sexually frustrated. I haven't pulled since April 18. And she was a spacewoman. Last night I tried to pull a girl I didn't even want to pull. She blew me out. Girls can smell fear. I have started fantasising about President Mitterrand's wife.

More worryingly I am becoming increasingly homesick. Or just kind of blue. And I can't understand why.

It comes out of nowhere. I feel like I am constantly yo-yoing between being really happy and really sad. Either I'm completely on my own for what feels like days on end or shitfaced with a crowd of people so that I am intensely happy and then nothing. It's all or nothing but ultimately it feels more like nothing. And not any all.

I know I need to massively dry my eyes but I can't talk to anyone else about this. Am I homesick?

I hate the word, and I really hate it when people you meet here bang on about England all the time. I mean if you like it so bloody much then why don't you just piss off back then? Stop going down to *Chez Wayne's* and watching the footy match wearing your bloody Chelsea top and lying that you're a season ticket holder and that you haven't missed a match since Chopper Harris used to play. Stop going on about missing a "proper cup of tea" or talking about your best friend from home, Gareth, who's "mad".

I've been here for eight months and I've ticked almost every box in terms of making a life for myself – I have a job, my own place and new friends both French and English, I have even sort of had a bird; I have, not to put too fine a point on it, a life. I've even stopped reading English newspapers (not just because I can't afford them) except the odd *NME* which doesn't count because the French have NO CLUE about music.

Why do I get these bouts of crippling desolation? Are there some things that I will never get used to precisely because they are French and not English? It's difficult to explain and even more difficult to understand – maybe I'm just lonely. I don't know. How do you know? Perhaps I've only attained the veneer of a grown-up life and there's some component unknown to me that I need in order to be fulfilled. It can't be because I don't like France. Because I really do.

I don't miss specific people either, apart from maybe my Mum and Dad and Sod a bit, so maybe there is a part of my psyche that needs the known, the dependable and the familiar. That's totally at odds with my rock and roll aspirations, but I'm wondering if all these new experiences I'm arriving at somewhat erratically and haphazardly are too much for me emotionally. I'm fucking immature.

That's what it is. This constant bombardment of the senses is taking it out on me. Perhaps I need to look after my ailing body more in order to keep my mind in good health. I'm going to start running every day and I've decided I'm going to take baths rather than showers.

The girl with the cappuccino tresses

Dear Sod

I'm such a wrist. This is another life-changing letter. Are they getting more recurrent?

I think I might have met Meg Ryan, in Euro, my-age, form. With bigger lills.

I met Fabressa again in a bar about a week ago. This time it was personal. My approach that is. I couldn't have been any less personal than my previous performance when I quizzed her for 40 (long) seconds over what was in her fruit drink. This time we actually conversed, although I would put this more down to the fact that she was tipsy and bored. This in itself was progress of significant proportions. I was with Enzo and Jason Priestley in a bar in Juan-Les-Pins when I asked her quite genuinely if she was waiting to be served. As she turned I think I actually gasped and the 3 gin and tonics in my system gave me the confidence/front I had needed before. I greeted her as if she was the sister I thought lost in a scuba diving accident. She, naturally, did not remember me. As I explained where we had met and talked her through the entire 40-second conversation in real time she pretended to remember. It is always great when you tell someone you have met them and they don't believe you.

She is half Genoese and half Cannoise. Sounds pretty good but her Genoese Dad, who we were shortly to meet at the table for her sister's birthday, was no laughing matter (Genoa is scary, we went there pre-San Siro). Imagine Tuscany and go to the opposite end of the cute/television-series-about-bread and tapenade spectrum. Some of Italy is like the Third World. The Genoese are quite proud of this because they are so hard. Padre Fabressa looks like a small, fat Giovanni Agnelli and speaks in a kind of drunken Italian slur, but apparently in French. I felt as welcome at the table as a dog in a game of skittles. But I was drunk, so everybody liked me in my head. I didn't make up that skittles line.

When not teaching Italian to the lycée students Fabressa is at university in Aix-en-Provence near Marseille and she was back for the weekend for her little sisters' birthday. Her parents have a house high up in the hills in an area of Cannes understatedly known as Californie. Unbelievably I managed to get her number and with the debonair style of a young Alain Delon I waited until 10 am in the morning to call her, fully 8 hours after she had given me her number. We arranged to meet up the next night and I drove over on my Honda Hairdryer.

From the moment I got there Giovanni Agnelli scared the absolute shit out of me. Just by saying hello. Am not generally scared of people but this guy looked like he would have his people chop off my testicles if I tried it on with his daughter. He asked me if I had a helmet for his daughter. Too quickly I said yes and then, crippled with embarrassment showed him the SKATEBOARD helmet I have as a spare. I tried to explain that obviously I would wear that one. In a scene from my very own Antonioni film I was taken into the garage where her father proceeded to show me his collection of vintage motorcycle helmets. He had leather-lined Vespa and Lambretta ones, Valenzias, Alvorios and Modenas. It looked like a museum in there. Carefully selecting his daughter's favourite one he gave it to me as if passing me the elixir of life. If I dropped it I was dead. I went one better.

As we whizzed through the spring night and headed for Cannes' old town, Le Suquet, I felt like Serge Gainsbourg driving through Paris laughing to my Italian version of Jane Birkin like in the film Slogan, her neck scarf blowing playfully in the wind and us both finding it hilarious. I felt unstoppable. The hottest girl imaginable was on the back of my scooter and I was on the up. We parked up and I took the helmets and walked hand-in-hand with Fabressa to the restaurant I had picked, primarily for its excellent house rosé and its fiercely competitive pricing. When we left the restaurant 2 hours later I had been relieved of one helmet. Unfortunately for me the vintage leather fan had left me the new plastic one I had bought for myself and had chosen the irreplaceable vintage cashmere-lined Italian one instead. I was more worried when Fabressa started sobbing, swiftly returning inside to call her father from the landline. We sat on the wall waiting for his arrival, as I obviously could not drive her home sans casque.[131] His arrival was swift and brutal. He got out of his car and walked straight up to me. He shouted incomprehensively and ushered Fabressa in to the car. Coming back, I assumed to hit me, he told me to follow him.

On arrival at the villa he frogmarched me back in to the garage where he proceeded to lecture me for over half an hour in a dialect I could not understand. Every now and then a teary-looking Fabressa's mother would come out and then return back to console her daughter. It did all seem a shade over the top but I felt genuinely awful. I wanted to tell him that I am not a careless lad, I know right from wrong and I genuinely respect other peoples' possessions, but I couldn't get a word in. I really did feel awful and knew it was all my fault. Thankfully, somewhere between the 3 of them my bleary-eyed performance (the melodrama was infectious) won them over and we kind of all sat in the garage mourning, looking up at where the innocent helmet had hung, never having hurt anyone, just hours before. I eventually left after midnight, weirdly I almost felt we were all closer over the incident.

After that I almost managed to almost gain affection in the family, so much had the loss meant to me (?), and 'us' as a group. Fabressa and I have hung out twice since and

131 Without helmet.

got on well. Second time led to amazing tongueing sessions
on this viewing point overlooking Cannes. I hope we are
kind of dating. But don't want to ask for fear of looking
like a duvet-clinging sap.
    Peace. And I'm out.
    This is a good one. Isn't it?

10 mai

It is particularly hot (interspersed with heavy rain, apparently this is very common) and this afternoon was spent at the main public beach in Cannes with Fabressa and her collection of gorgeous French friends. After work Jason Priestley drove down as fast as his Peugeot *Poubelle* would take him to join me and the sirens on the beach. They all seem to only wear the bottom part of their bikinis. Swimming out to the little rafts they supply in Cannes with a coterie of beautiful topless girls will, I predict, become one of mine and Jason Priestley's favourite shared pastimes.

Later

The *1995 Palme d'Or Cannes Festival du Film*. My French cinema interests back at uni plus assistantship have brilliantly secured me a free pass to the festival. Not to all the gala screenings on the red carpet but it technically allows me access to every film showed in competition. I went down to the administrative centre to get my pass this morning. I fully expected to be sent packing. But no. My pass was ready along with a rucksack (!), stacks of freebies like t-shirts and caps, a guide and an actual lanyard with my accreditation card in it! *Allez!* I can't believe it.

I have used my brother-in-law's relaxed dietary habits as an excuse to eat at *Joannathanne's* three times in the 48 hours he has been here.

My Mum and Dad are coming out in six days. Gonna stay at Taba's. Must hide from Madame Cocheteux as she will think I am a child.

11 mai

This is getting better. Big discovery day. Fabressa has suggested that we visit a beach where we can get all over tans tomorrow afternoon. I have never been to a naturist beach before but Fabressa has Olympic-level experience. Her whole family are card-carrying naturists (again!).[132] They are nude junkies. A shade concerned. Will go for a run later. Too many Joannathanne's.

12 mai

Fabressa and I headed down to *La Plage de la Baterie*[133] this morning with just towels, suncream and a bottle of water. I was bricking it. She was wearing a kind of tissue-thin summer dress, which made it reasonably apparent (to my trained eye at least) that she was not wearing underwear underneath it. And it is Sunday. At the entrance there are rocks and there were a load of old pervs wandering around with just towels covering their bits, waiting for action in the shrubs that border the trainline. Fabressa seemed entirely unfazed by this in a way in which no English girl I could imagine would be, shrugging it off with a giggle as a greasy old Moroccan banged one out while laughing maniacally. I felt like I was in a Tinto Brass[134] movie. My desperation to see Fabressa's nude 'kiki' was overbearing.

Fabressa had explained before how Monsieur Paul, the unofficial beach owner, ran a small stall down there where we could get sandwiches and drinks. When we arrived he greeted her like a weird cross between his daughter (he ruffled her hair) and his teenage lover (he hugged her for about thirty seconds, his 14-inch penis pressed up against her leg). Even at 10 am it was already packed with naked bodies. Fabressa seemed to know almost all of them and we spent the first half an hour kissing naked people. Finally laying our towels down in a tiny spot between an old man wearing his cycling cap (and nothing else) and two women who I was sure worked in the Intermarché in Cannes, we stripped off.

---

132 She explained to me my misuse of the word 'nudist', as in 'beach'. Nudists are people who every now and then go to a beach where they might sunbathe naked, on holiday for example. Naturists are people who whole-heartedly believe in the 'ethos' behind being naked. They are at one with nature and in harmony with it. In other words, they get naked as often as they can.

133 Very hidden. The train track to Antibes and Nice above runs past it and if you are observant when you are on the train you can see the thin slice of sandy beach for a couple of tantalizing seconds.

134 Italian softcore director whose films include *Frivolous Lola, All Ladies Do It* and *Cheeky*.

Fabressa nonchalantly took the hem of her tiny dress and in one graceful move pulled the material across her body and on to the sand behind her. She put her hands on her hips and smiled at me. Just writing this is making me shake. It is already my all-time favourite moment of full-frontal female nudity.[135] Fabressa and I have not even had sex! She is a strict Naturist Catholic Girl. Having met her Dad I am in no rush to suggest changes to this chaste set-up. But lying on my back was impossible. Her body is perfect and all of it is golden brown. She seemed completely unaware of the effect her nudity was having on me. We messed about in the sea, my gaelophobia calmed by the spring-cool water's effect on my non 14-inch penis. We walked to the open shower together and smoked cigarettes but when she bent over in front of me to rearrange the towels I had to lay on my front and think about how I would go about the process of building my own jet engine with matchsticks.

There was a woman on crutches, and nothing else, her leg in plaster, a family with about five kids, including some slightly odd adolescents (sorry, at 14 I would not have been down with this), a couple of skinny girls with fake boobs getting all-over tans and then an attractive older couple. Him like a circus strongman, hands like…yep. Oh My God. It was her! It was Famille Cocheteux. I stayed on my front and wondered what the fuck to do. After a few minutes the inevitable happened and Monsieur Cocheteux saw me, pointed me out to Madame Cocheteux and she casually waved, got up and walked over. Here I have hit my head on the low ceiling of my own vocabulary as I literally cannot express how I felt at this moment as the woman of my dreams walked, totally naked, towards me. It was everything I had dreamt of. I introduced Madame Cocheteux to Fabressa whilst remaining on my front. The fact that this happened slightly behind me made for an awkward scenario as they kept talking, with me attempting to swivel at the waist whilst

---

135 My previous Top five moments of female full-frontal nudity were;
1. Amanda Donohoe stripping off for the first moment in 'Castaway'
2. Rebecca de Mornay's window turn to Tom Cruise in 'Risky Business'
3. The shower scene in 'Porkys'
4. Kelly Le Brock's accidental bedding slip in 'The Woman In Red'
5. Sharon Stone's uncrossing of the legs.

keeping my crotch rooted firmly to the sand, squinting in the sun as the two most incredible female specimens ever to have walked through my life stood, totally naked, before me in the sun.

It was flippin' agony.

> "*Quand le printemps fait éclater tous les bourgeons*
> *Mes vêtements me pèsent d'une étrange façon*
> *Et soudain, dans mon imagination*
> *Je me vois cachée, dans les rochers*
> *Complètement*
> *Nue au soleil*
> *Complètement*
> *Nue au soleil*"

13 mai

When you are in love you can forgive your lover's physical familiarity with another man's 14-inch penis. Right?

14 mai

Today I actually drew three of the scenes I have burned into my brain of Madame Cocheteux and Fabressa talking at the beach.

15 mai

Furore at Collège le Big Fun. They served a very plain penne arrabiata and about ten kids refused to eat it. You've got to have standards eh?

16 mai

Mum and Dad arrived this morning having driven from London. A load of people dropped by the bar near *La Croisette* I took them to for drinks. Felt very proud of my independence and the fact that I really am making it work. I am proud of the fact that I live here, proud when they met my friends (my ma particularly likes Enzo and Jason Priestley), proud of Fabressa (who my Dad particularly likes), proud of my exoticism (relative I know, but still) and proud of my scooter. The French friends they met tonight could not have done more to welcome them and I glowed every time someone arrived.

I am pretty proud of myself.[136]

17 mai

Fabressa and I took my parents on the train towards Nice, heading along the beautiful stretch which took in Juan-les-Pins and Antibes. It was Fabressa's idea to visit the horse-racing at the *Hippodrome de la Côte d'Azur*, in Cagnes-sur-Mer, which you can see on any train heading into the city.[137]

When betting involves horses my Dad becomes insatiable. But these aren't just horses and humans riding them. At the Hippodrome the French brilliantly go *en masse* to watch 'chariot racing'. It started in the 1950s and they could get over 10,000 people in there for one of the bi-annual celebrated European 'trot meetings'. My Dad unsurprisingly loved it, regaling us all the way home with tales of Hervé Filion who an old boy he met at the bar had told him all about.[138]

Later

Fabressa is well charming my Mum and Dad. In a way that avoids that precluded standard French-girl clichés like being aloof or inappropriately flirty in an annoyingly coquettish way. It almost seems to be going too well. I hope I don't get the FEAR.

The Film Festival starts tomorrow.

18 mai

Badaboum-boum!

The French really love the cinema and this is very apparent if you live

136 'Pride before a fall' was not a phrase I was familiar with at this stage in my life.
137 My dad would bet on the weather if he was offered odds. When we were younger and waiting outside Marks & Spencer for my mum to finish work he would bet with me on which colour cars would come round the corner first. Once he bet fifty quid with me on whether a burger place in the high street was a Wimpy or not. I KNEW it was a Star*Burger but he seemed pretty sure of himself. Halfway through dinner we drove up in his car to find out. I was 12. And right. To his credit he paid up. But my mum was livid.
138 Filion was to chariot racing what Muhammad Ali was to boxing. He once won over 400 'chariot races' in a single year. Then achieved this feat another *fourteen times*. He also received an eight-year year ban but came back to ride winners into his seventies.

in Cannes. In part because there are about five big cinemas on Cannes' main street, *La Rue d'Antibes*, alone.[139] This year Jeanne Moreau, the fun-loving tease of *Jules et Jim* fame is President of the jury, her *joie de vivre* giving the whole event an easy freewheeling sense of frivolity and fun.

And there's *La Haine*.

So Day 1. Already life-changing. Because I went to the 8 am press screening of *La Haine*. AKA 'The Hatred'. Pretty much the first screening anywhere in the world. Ever. I have definitely decided to take the French Cinema module next year, so with that in mind, here is my first attempt at a review/synopsis:

> *This is a visceral sledgehammer of a movie and the reason the 54th Cannes Film Festival has been hyped to even more dizzying heights than usual.*
>
> *This gave the screening an incredible frisson and urgency.*

---

139 It was Francois Truffaut the *Nouvelle Vague* stalwart, who once wondered, "Is the cinema more important than life?" Literally only the French nation would have then pondered this as an actual question. And the fact that in *La Nouvelle Vague* they have their own cinema 'movement'. It was a late 1950s/early 60s group of talented young film directors who came rolling out of France like a wave. Four of its major proponents, Truffaut, Godard, Chabrol and Rohmer came from the snooty review magazine *Les Cahiers du Cinéma* and others included Resnais, Demy, Rivette, Malle, Eustache and Lelouch. Aggressive jump-cutting and the director as *auteur* (dictatorial story teller/visionary) were the group's calling cards. ObsessiveAmerican crime thrillers often featured and often featuring particularly tragic and lonely characters. Generally a breath of fresh air and great fun. Occasionally cringeing and affected.

All of the urgency was centred around one recurring theme or experience, that of "la banlieue". In this milieu, the meaning, unequivocally is "ghetto".

La Haine is a ticking time bomb of a movie complete with ticking time bomb clock-effect, which tells the story of the aftermath of a riot in response to the police killing of a young North African immigrant on one of the estates and the subsequent search for a missing police gun. It is inspired by the real-life case of Makome, a black teen shot in police custody. Filmed on location on a real estate outside Paris (the entire cast and crew moved in for a month with director Mathieu Kassovitz recruiting extras and technicians from the flats), the three main characters are played by relative unknowns – for now. They are Jewish, North African and Afro-Caribbean; Vinz, Saïd and Hubert respectively. It is rumoured that the Prime Minister, Alain Juppé, instructed the whole French government to attend a special screening of it pre-release last week, particularly when Kassovitz said defiantly, "La Haine is an anti-police film and that is how I meant it to be understood."

Kassovitz invited the cream of French hip hop to write songs inspired by La Haine. The musical response to the cinematic exhortation was ferocious, wild and savage but above all absolute and vital.

Like the film itself.

As a first attempt at cinematic criticism, I think my effort is pretty vital.

I am worried my relationship with Fabressa is becoming almost totally based on my fear of her being unfaithful to me.

19 mai
Biblical rain.

Told my Dad about the Lacoste rainsheeter and it being 300 quid. He said something about his first house costing less than 300 quid.

Quite pissed pre-bed.

I articulated how I feel like I have started to really love the French to my Mum quite well tonight. It's like an album you may not like at first, e.g. The Rolling Stones' *Exile on Main Street* two summers ago. I liked the Stones but wasn't mad on them, but knew how acclaimed it was. I bought it but didn't really 'get it'. I listened to it and thought it sounded pretty cool and looked nice but I didn't really bond with it. I read a brilliant book by Stanley Booth about hanging out with them just before they recorded it and I loved that. But there didn't seem to be anything I could really get hold of in there. Summer 1992 on a lads' holiday the opening strains of 'Rip This Joint' suddenly made sense. My Walkman seemed set to 'mind-blowing' and every track on 'Exile' sounded like the only music I would ever need to hear again.

It's like that with the French.

I am quite drunk.

20 mai

I am supposed to be reading Mme de Lafayette's *La Princesse de Clèves*. I tried to but I understand literally one word in twenty. I am doing a French degree. This is not good. The word I understood today was '*chaise*'. 'Chair'.

21 mai

Today I watched Johnny Depp's *Ed Wood* and Larry Clark's *Kids*. *Kids* was like being repeatedly spat at in the face.

This gradual liking of things being more substantial also applies to olives. When I was younger my Mum and Dad having people round for dinner meant that the next morning, if I rose early enough, there would be left-over peanuts and crisps on the coffee table. A bad morning meant only olives would be left and olives are not an appealing food to the average seven-year-old's palate. Throughout my teens I started to try and like olives, my efforts finally paying off around the age of 16 when on a school exchange trip I bit into a black one whilst staying with a family on the outskirts of Paris and, to my delight, found it non-disgusting.

Cannes has been transformed by the festival with any available space transformed into an advert. Prices hiked even higher and all the roads within about a mile of the beach are closed. Like when a pipe bursts and your school gets shut down, or when it snows heavily, I love the mayhem it is causing. Seeing as I don't eat in expensive restaurants anyway or drive a car it doesn't really affect me.

Later

Tonight we all went to watch Cannes play in a *pelota*[140] match. It managed to be both dangerous and boring.

I have also decided that Johnny Depp is a dick.

22 mai

I went to Monoprix today and they are selling dark blue rainsheeters like the Lacoste one for 110 francs – about 11 quid. True sartorialists do not compromise. I will wait or I will have nothing.

2 am

One of the strangest nights I have ever had. Jason Priestley and I got in to a party for some movie studio in *Jimmyz Club*, part of the *Palais des Festivals*. The evening started with Fabressa getting chatted up by a cheese-o Italian in his mid-20s wearing, with no hint of irony or sartorial precocity, a cable-knit rowing sweater tied round his shoulders. I mean what the fuck is it with Italians and Brideshead? He didn't give a shit when I made my boyfriend status clear. I didn't know what to do. Enter stage left Michelle, the kindly Vietnamese Oxford student-landlady from the world of textiles and tapenades. I have not seen Michelle since the day I left her flat, which seems a bit rude but kind of isn't. Couldn't quite believe my eyes when she staggered over to our table, shedded, and giggled through a half-French, half-something resembling English, spiel about her year. It was like a weird film. No sign of any Oxford Blues in her party, but there were a load of Cannois players fawning all over her.

We couldn't understand what she was talking about as she was slurring and employing a strange dialect. I wondered whether she was suffering from foreign accent syndrome.[141]

---

140 *Pelote Basque* or *pelota* is an old game based on tennis and with a nod to the Greeks which involves hurling a ball against a wall with a kind of woven ice cream scoop. The Basques in France live in the south-west, and there are a whopping 300,000 of them. They get quite feisty sometimes.

141 When a migraine sufferer went to bed with a terrible headache and woke up speaking

She was chatting away in this kind of mountain French then suddenly stopped and just looked at the wall and cracked up laughing for literally no reason. Briefly comprehensible, she asked me about my year but laughed like a drain when I said, "I found the teaching really rewarding." It was like she was on PCP. I told her that I had been to see *La Haine* and she looked at me for a second, like we had some little secret, before doubling up. She became weirdly lucid and started talking as if she had just necked a *demi* of truth serum, telling me about the teachers she had slept with and slurrily asking why I had never fancied her. She then asked Jason Priestley if she could have a fag, walked off with the whole pack, her bunch of blokes in tow. The End.

23 mai
My 21st birthday.
Brilliant night tonight at *Brun*, Cannes' best seafood restaurant. Just my Mum, Dad and me. The best food I have ever tasted. But I haven't tasted much. I tried to teach my Dad French, and touched on the connection that the Geordies and the French have. I explained how emphasis on liking something in French could be stressed by the addition of "*moi*", or "me" at the end. For example, "*J'adore les films de Godard*" = "I love Godard's films" could be made more emphatic by the addition of a "*moi*" at the end. So, "*J'adore les films de Godard, moi*", was more emphatic, i.e. you really loved those films. In much the same way as a Geordie might add emphasis to "I lov' Jackie Milburn", by saying, "I lov' Jackie Milburn, me."

24 mai
Bought the 11 quid rainsheeter in Monoprix.

25 mai
Mum and Dad just left. It was brilliant having them here. Kind of miss them today. I feel really proud of them. They're so cool. I never really noticed before.

in a French accent. Only a handful of people have ever had it. Triggered by minor brain damage to the part of the brain linked to language and pitch. Brilliantly… there is no known cure!

Alistair has a new girlfriend and she is called Hetty (short for Henrietta) and they are coming to stay tonight. Weirdly she drives an army green Land Rover Defender.

....Woah, Hetty is mental. And I am a bit too pissed to write.

26 mai
Found a poem called 'My name is cocaine' in one of my files and figured it might make for quite a good lesson with some of the older students. It's a bit like a wet version of 'White lines' by Grandmaster Flash. Makes it sound quite rife though, with schoolboys and renowned speakers all in on it.

That's not right though is it? I've never even seen real cocaine.

27 mai
Another weird night racked up. Went to see *To Die For* which I quite enjoyed but not massively. Early evening I left Alistair and his posh girlfriend Hetty, who has massive frizzy hair, in the flat whilst I went to an early screening of *The Usual Suspects*. Alistair implied they would be having lots of sex when I left. When they met me later on Alistair was smoking A LOT and Hetty was banging on about BLUR (?) to some random in *Le Chelsea*. By the time we all staggered back to the flat at 1 am Hetty was walking miles up the Boulevard Carnot on her own and Alistair was dragging his heels. I was in the middle. It was like a really shit version of *Jules et Jim*. Outside the flat they broke up. Then they agreed to be friends I think as they came up and got into my bed. Me by the wall, her between us. She took her top off and even though I was pretending to be asleep I was impressed to see that she was not wearing anything at all on her top half. She kind of snuggled up between both of us, her pendulous posh breasts dominating the sleeping area. I feigned sleep but I opened my eyes to look at her breasts. I was terrified to see her face just in front of mine, staring, like a vampire queen. I held her stare and she broke out to a suggestive smile. I feigned more sleepiness and turned over and in no way went to sleep.

One of the classes wanted to do Frank Sinatra's 'My Way'. I hate that self-aggrandising song. "I've travelled each and every highway." No you haven't. "For what is a man? What has he got? If not himself – Then

My Name Is Cocaine

My name is Cocaine -- call me Coke for short
I entered this country without a passport.
Ever since then I've made lots of scum rich
Some have been murdered and found in a ditch.
I'm more valued than diamonds,
More treasured than gold,
Use me just once and you too will be sold.

I'll make a schoolboy forget his books.
I'll make a beauty queen forget her looks.
I'll take a renowned speaker and make him a bore,
I'll take your mother and make her a whore.
I'll make a school teacher forget how to teach,
I'll make a preacher not want to preach.
I'll take all your rent money and you will be evicted,
I'll murder your babies or they'll be born addicted.
I'll make you rob and steal and kill,
When you're under my power, you will have no will.

Remember my friends, my name is "Big C"
If you try me one time you may never be free.
I've destroyed actors, politicians and many a hero,
I've decreased bank accounts from millions to zero.

I make shooting and stabbing a common affair,
Once I take charge, you won't have a prayer.
Now that you know me, what will you do?
You'll have to decide, it's all up to you.
The decision is one that no one can straddle,
Listen to me and please listen well,
When you ride with Cocaine you are headed for HELL.

Reprinted from The New York Christian Times, June 21, 1990

Inappropriate.

he has naught." Egg!!!!

Alistair still staying over – confessed that I think Hetty is a real wrong 'un. Didn't tell him about the staring.

28 mai
Film Festival ended. One of Fabressa's friends I know quite well was working the door at a party and she displayed some Cannoise attitude, which I feel sure will serve her well for her future life as a super-bitch. Clutching a clipboard outside an empty party she looked Enzo, Taba and I up and down, acted like she had never seen me before and asked for our names – she totally knows mine – she's been to my flat – and said, "*Desolé, c'est difficile pour moi.*"[142] She may as well have just said, "Sorry, I'm Just Really Bad With Names And Faces Of People Who Can't Help Advance My Shallow Career." When Fabressa arrived she didn't seem quite as aggrieved on my behalf as I thought she might.

29 mai
Jason Priestley and I tried to get into the Monaco Grand Prix yesterday. We couldn't even get into the QUEUE.

Alistair and Hetty got back together. Oops.

30 mai
My Mum's birthday. Alistair appears to have moved in permanently.

31 mai
Fabressa has taken to calling me her "*Pirata*", or her pirate. Like, "*Viens, pirata*". I quite like it. But it makes me feel like a little boy.

---

142 "Sorry, it's difficult for me."

Pass the hemlock

juin 1

Dear Sod

    This is a weird one.

    Having read both Le Voleur and Papillon I have a pretty clear idea what the French penal system is like. It seems strange now that this hasn't happened sooner. Not getting ourselves into loads of trouble in the south of France, but a few scrapes. New surroundings, cheap alcohol and a group of host people famed for their feisty temperaments though you can see where it might go wrong. There is a clue in there as to what has happened!

    Friday night we had drunk a lot. Jason Priestley and I had met for some apéros in town after work and then Taba and Enzo came over to mine for a pre-big night out music, crisps and Supersonics[143] session. We headed out, with spliffs and booze for the 30-minute walk, to a Cannes club, which we rarely do as they are pretty naff, called Palm Beach, which is right down the far eastern end of the Croisette, past all the big hotels and on a bit further. By this point we were obviously very, very loaded.

    Supersonics kicking in we strolled (very slowly) along the Croisette. Then became fascinated by a huge pile of white sand, which had been dumped in the middle of the public beach. Enormous. The most obvious thing to do in that moment was clearly not to throw a couple of the blue chairs set out to sit on onto the pile of sand, so obviously that was what we did. Someone told me that Cannes ships in sand from the Sahara to give its seafront

---

143 Gin & Tonics.

that special sheen, a kind of large-scale nip and tuck. So it wasn't even their sand.

It's eerily quiet here post-festival and it is also home to loads of old bourgeois women who probably used to be married to collaborators and who walk their dogs before they go to bed at night. Also home to a sizeable French National Police station, the harder bastards who look after the big towns and about as far away from the goofy gendarmes of folklore as possible. They act like the scarily named 1st RPIMa, (France's equivalent to the SAS). A kind of urban French Foreign Legion. I have no idea why they have such a big station in Cannes, they must have little or nothing to do. But Friday night they did. In their minds.

Someone must have reported our chair-throwing because as we swaggered our drunken path towards the club, two unmarked squad cars pulled up and four or five cops, not all in uniform, rushed out to grab us. Enzo and I were bundled into the back of one car, Taba the other. As we sped, pointlessly, through the empty backstreets the incredibly aggressive police twats shouted down any questions. We were cuffed in the back of the car and after Enzo had a hand raised at him for daring to raise his voice I went one better when I demanded to see their ID cards. The guy in the passenger seat leant round and smacked me across the bridge of the nose with some kind of truncheon!!!!! Both slightly shocked, and me seeing stars, we realised that we were in a spot of bother. (I was also shocked by seeing a truncheon, as I thought they only existed in cartoons and porn films.)

At the clink the 5-0 got even worse. One guy knocked Taba's glasses off his face and he was made to pick them up...how low is that? Then we were breathalised? What for? Drunken walking?

We all saw each other again in the basement of the police HQ, right in the heart of the Cannes intersection. We were read some kind of rights and repeatedly shouted at by the 8 or 9 of them there, including a woman typing notes and another senior lady. Unable to offer anything by way of explanation Enzo started shouting that his father was a prominent policeman in the UK, which earned him a crack across the nose too. It was getting worse and reached its nadir when we were uncuffed and stripped. To our pants, everything off, in front of two women. I said I had no pants on. I didn't. They didn't give a fuck, so I was completely naked. This public nudity thing is getting pretty commonplace. Recuffed — with hands behind our backs. Nice look. Started just saying whatever — thanks for the hospitality, all your mothers are whores etcetera.

Outside in separate corridors I was hit 4 or 5 times, this time with a fist by two more junior cops, each time I insulted their sexuality to a greater degree. Gin, weed and adrenaline coursing through my veins I now had practically no fear. Utterly pointless, but we were all in a state of shock. There must have been a moment of self-regulation as at one point they tried to be nice to us (possibly realising that they may actually get in trouble for this), but that just enraged us more. We were feeling aggrieved, concussed and boisterous. And as Sartre said, "I hate victims who respect their executioners."

We had an opportunity to give statements, but I think none of us, bearing in mind what was happening and that we had searing headaches kicking in, were probably at our most eloquent. From what we could make out there was a criminal damage one (the chairs), something to do with affray and also an insulting a police officer one. We all agreed to point out in these statements that all of this came after being hit in the face repeatedly. We were given back our clothes, hilariously minus belts and shoelaces — suicide was not high up in any of our plans — and informed individually that we were being charged. Taba and I were told in no uncertain terms on establishing that we were being employed by the French state to educate their children that we would not be teaching again and would most likely be leaving the country with immediate effect.

We were then led to separate cells where we all spent the next 12 hours with no water, no bedding, nothing but a grey plastered box and a hole to piss in on the floor. I was repeatedly visited by a really sympathetic lady from some kind of other department. By her third visit I liked her so much that I was worried I was developing Stockholm Syndrome[144] Mid-afternoon and the door opened. A woman gave us some kind of signed affidavit but knew nothing as to what our charges were. The 3 of us, slightly delirious and feeling a bit rock n roll, went straight to the bar opposite. It seemed like the right thing to do when you have just done your first night inside, aged 21.

I did my bird. Every man has to do a night inside, eh? I feel like crap.

I have been listening to The Scream's 'Jailbird' a lot. Is that too obvious?

Me

PS Why do people say 'gaol'? It sounds cooler than 'jail'. Like something from a Hank Williams song.

PPS

Scratchin' like a tom cat
Got a monkey on my back
I'm gonna push and pull
And howl like wolf
And drive my cadillac
I've got medication, honey
I've got wings to fly
I've got horse hoof tea
To buzz you like a bee

---

144 Stockholm Syndrome was made infamous by US rich kid Patty Hearst who not only got on like a house on fire with her kidnappers in the Symbionese Liberation Army, but changed her name (to the less than out-there) "Tania" and joined their gang, getting filmed robbing banks. The syndrome occurs when a captive is isolated, cannot escape and fears they face death. Small acts of kindness on behalf of the captor become overplayed and the captive becomes obsessed with keeping the captor happy. A psychological shift creates a warping of the psyche so that the captive identifies with and sympathises with the captor. Named "Stockholm Syndrome" after a 1973 case in which a botched bank robbery in Stockholm resulted in four hostages being scrobbled. Six days later, they actively resisted rescue, then refused to testify against their captors, raised money for their legal defence, and rumour had it, one of the hostages eventually became *engaged* to one of her jailed captors. The success of mass religious cults is linked to the same thing.

Gonna blind the evil eye
Push and pull with me
Funky jammin' free
Walk it like you talk it, honey
Strut your funky stuff

   PPPS "O! It is excellent, To have a giant's strength, but it is tyrannous, To use it like a giant."
   O! that, is a good fuckin' quote.
   Increase The Peace.
   Gaolbird.

2 juin

Fabressa came over last night and wasn't buying much of my rock 'n' roll thing. We are still together. It is getting a shade tricky, what with her being at uni in Aix, and me being the human equivalent to a Bichon Frise[145] on heat. She tried to get me to go the hospital as she thought I was slurring and talking funny because of the concussion. I knew it was because we had been drinking whisky in that bar opposite. And because I haven't eaten a meal for about three days.

2 hours later
I am slightly concerned about my teaching career.

---

145 A small, toy-like dog owned by women and very camp men.

Before you slip, into unconsciousness… I'd like to have another kiss

3 juin
I am developing extreme agoraphobic tendencies. It is far better to stay in bed as much as possible. Fabressa's presence, never wearing more than her tighty whiteys, is a bonus. I saw the music video for Céline Dion's new number one (yes, it will be there for a while), '*Pour que tu m'aimes encore*' enough times to start noticing inconsistencies with the production values. Céline Dion smartly records songs in both English and French, guaranteeing her acceptance from the French in the form of buckets of money.

4 juin
Got to school at 7.30 am this morning, eager to catch Monsieur Rufin before he caught me. I really look like I have been beaten up. His immediate concern was my welfare, which was a relief. Got me to explain exactly what had happened in my words, asking his secretary, Madame Haricot, to come in and get it all down. The last time we had seen each other had also been quite revealing.

I can't wait to get home to England where throwing chairs is the norm.

5 juin
As it turned out someone from the National Police had already contacted Monsieur Guy Rufin. He stood up behind his desk and said,

"*Benjamin, je suis très, très desolé.*"[146] Like a giant French lion. As far as he understood it they would not be pressing charges, but had filed some kind of official complaint document. He appeared extremely cross. And for the first time in ages, it wasn't directed at me. I was linked, but this is different.

I feel a bit embarrassed and slightly ashamed at what has happened today. He is pretty sure that they had no right to lock us up for the night if they were not going to press charges but all the deportation stuff is apparently nonsense. He told me that I have been a credit to the school and that everyone is firmly behind me in this bullying behaviour.

As I left his office he told me with a wink that you weren't a real man until you had spent a night inside in a manner which made me feel very much like a man. Like a real man.

The run up to my 21st do has been slightly overshadowed by the events. I had a little school do held at Fran's house and the absence of Jonno made it even better. I still have the card they gave me, it said, "You're not as old as you once were, but you're not as old as you will be." Then some weird kids from the village who may have been members of a cult sang 'Happy Birthday' to me in French. I bored half of the gathering by explaining the origins of the song's tune.[147]

6 juin

I feel happy, sad, angry, calm, emotional, cold. Homesick.

My delayed 21st do started early. The *Chelsea* opposite the station has been our Cannes watering hole since that first weekend we all had here. We generally sit there for hours on end, playing sets to each other on the VideoJuke (no-one else listens, that's for sure). Hanson's 'M-Bop' is a particular favourite. In the six months we have been drinking there we have not once been acknowledged by the owners or the bar staff as having been there before. It is a PMU, a working men's bar which you see all over France.[148]

---

146 Benjamin, I am very, very sorry."
147 Part of my teaching classics collection I knew that two sisters in Kentucky wrote it in the 1920s and it was originally called 'Good Morning To All'. One Robert Coleman then added the second verse we all know, the world started singing it, but the sisters sued and won.
148 PMU means *Pari Mutuel Urbain* – a kind of Ladbrokes with beer. They are cheap,

Started at midday and drank in there until 6. Watched an international France were playing in, racked up a small fortune in bar receipts stacked up on our spike in the middle of the table. By mid-afternoon there was Enzo, Taba, Jason Priestley plus a few of his friends, Pollyanna Peters, Andreas, Alistair and mad Hetty,[149] some friends of mine from Montpellier and Rhiain and her new French boyfriend. Fabressa is in Aix.

Headed back to my flat at 6 and Enzo promptly fell asleep on the floor for four hours. Lucas and *les Hards* soundtracked the party with a record player wired up to my tiny speakers and Enzo woke up in time for a game of England v France midnight beach cricket. No one got arrested and no one got shouted at. *Le Bonheur.*

smoky and a bit rough. It is also situated directly opposite the train station and in France that means that it will be full of schizoids. They show football and serve *pastis* and *demis*. Period.

149 She bought me Blur's 'Girls & Boys' on cassette single (because we both liked it), which everyone found weird, especially Alistair, who didn't know we had our own in-common things and I was a bit embarrassed.

What fresh hell is this?

7 juin

It gets better.

Enzo and I headed in to Nice for a night out. Took some 33 Exports, *chips nature* (no, this is not *déjà-lu*), my portable CD player, speakers and 'The Bends' and headed down to the pebble beach. 'Fake Plastic Trees' drifting across the empty beach made us feel like we never wanted to leave this corner of the world. 'The Bends' is a true masterpiece. I predict big things.

Couple of hours later we were in the mayhem of Vieux Nice. Andreas is now something akin to the Cypriot Crown Prince of Nice, at least in his eyes. The eye of the storm was the best place to be and getting elegantly wasted was a given. We stumbled out of the last bar at something like three and Pollyanna and some of the other girls peeled off in front as we fell into fountains and bushes on the long walk across *Place Massena* on the way back to kip at Andreas' flat. I thought I was elegantly wasted.

Andreas' gobby friend from home, Jim, passed a big group of Algerian lads sat chatting on a wall. One of them asked him the time and he sensibly rolled back his sleeve and told them that it was "quarter past fuck you o'clock". So the guy punched him hard in the face. We all saw this and drunkenly ran towards the action. The girls told us afterwards that all three of us went down with the first punch, which was no doubt impressive. The last thing I remember was lying in a pool of my own vomit and blood while some guy held my hair and repeatedly kicked me in the face and, way worse, the Adam's apple. "*Arrêtes…*" was all I could plead. Enzo found me and we hobbled back to the flat. Broken men. I thought that wisdom came from suffering. Not more suffering.

8 juin

Fabressa came over. To dump me. I asked her to pick up Enzo from the hotel on the way as he couldn't see out of his black eyes to drive. When I opened the door, once more bloodied and bruised, I don't think the decision was made any more difficult. We went on the balcony and she said loads of grown-up dump-talk things about being at life stages, which made it sound like school. And my increasingly regular habit of drinking to oblivion.

I am pretty sure that the 26-year-old cheese-o who was chatting to her whilst I was talking to Mental Michelle at the film festival party had something to do with it.

Note to self: enough with the bloodshed.

9 juin

If I was in a film, and I like to think that a lot, 'Fake Plastic Trees' would play over the slo-mo scenes of us being brutalised by these giant Maghreb warriors...like the Layla scene in *Goodfellas*.

Called Fabressa. Her and I is what the French call *un projet de fichu*. Out of the window.

> "She lives with a broken man
> A cracked polystyrene man
> Who just crumbles and burns
> He used to do surgery
> For girls in the eighties
> But gravity always wins
> And it wears him out, it wears him out
> It wears him out, it wears..."

Odi et amo

10 juin
I need to sort my life out.

I am stumbling over the finish line covered in blood.

I have tried to ignore the fact that my last few lessons as an English language assistant are looming. As are my leaving parties. I feel pretty honoured that I will be having a party per year, so one for the *sixième*, one for the *cinquième*, one for the *quatrième* and one for the *troisème*. I feel pretty close to a lot of the kids now and, in exactly the way that you are not supposed to but, as a human you can't help doing, I have my favourites in all the classes. Saying goodbye will be odd too in that I know I will probably never see a lot of them again. I don't need the Language Assistant's Programme to explain to me the inappropriateness of collecting 14-year-old French girls as penpals. Some of the families of the kids I have been teaching privately have become kind of friends but I reckon the majority will go off and lead lives I will never know about. The teaching has been incredible and has made me mature at a rate previously beyond me (despite recent lapses). I have had a taster of what it must be like to get attached to, and then let go of, students under your guidance. It's making me feel a bit forlorn.

11 juin
I think I am getting a kind of pre-emptive homesickness for France, whilst still here.

12 juin
UN-PUTAIN-DE-BELIEVABLE.

I received a letter through my door.

From the French state. If nothing else my lack of financial aide has forced me to be more entrepreneurial in becoming a) a private lesson guru and b) a thief and c) a kind of stripper. At the back is a perforated bit and a cheque for 10,500 francs!!!! This equates to over a grand! I have been paid the maximum rebate of 75% on a 2000 franc-per month rent. I am the richest man in Cannes.

Went straight over to the local shop to buy some rosé and a family bag of Haribo.

Fermé.

13 juin

Pivotal, almost epiphanical day. I took the Honda up to see Enzo at the hotel this evening. Enzo is doing a French and Spanish degree so although he doesn't want to leave France any time soon, he's got between now and October to get fluent in Spanish as well as French. Pollyanna is itching for them to go Mexico City and stay with her family so his days here are numbered. Enzo's problem is that when he took the job, he lied and told them that he would be in France indefinitely and he doesn't want to leave the hotel in the lurch after a few short months. It is pretty much the crappest job in the world (porno festival time aside) so the chances of finding someone else to do the job at such short notice are slim to none. Before I could help myself, I opened my mouth and said that I'd take over his role as *veilleur de nuit*. Enzo told me not to be such a dickhead, but I told him that I'll join a video library and make my way through all the major œuvres of French Cinema in preparation for next year so that he'd be kind of helping me out. On paper, it's a bad move but with my rent rebate ending along with my teaching jobs and the summer rent hike that comes into effect at the end of the month, I can't afford to stay at my place for much longer anyway. All the other assistants are leaving now that the school year is over and although I could easily do the same, I just can't go home. I don't feel as if I have achieved whatever it was that I set out to accomplish – I feel I have unfinished business. Or maybe it's because I shall soon be homeless and jobless. At about midnight, after all six of the guests had gone to bed, we lay in silence on the sun loungers outside by the empty pool and stared at the stars as we gorged on crisps and hotel beer. By the end of Enzo's shift we were pretty pissed, the heavily salted crisps had kept our thirst up all night and since the beer was technically *gratuit*, there was only one logical outcome. I could barely see, let alone try and ride home, so I kipped with Enzo in his bunker underneath the hotel. The absurdity of sharing a creaky camp bed with his size 12s in my face made me laugh. I am definitely not ready to give this up for the comforts of home; it may be dark and smelly but at least I'm still here.

On my own terms mostly.

juin 14

Dear Sod,

Which book do you think is better, 'The Lord of The Flies' or 'The Catcher in the Rye'?

Do you think that that is a pretentious way to start a letter? It's not, it can't be, because I am not pretending.

Fabressa said she thought my drinking was getting too much and called time on it. In actual fact she said, "Can I say something to you?" So of course I agreed to her plan. Then she said, "Don't take this personally but I think that you are drinking too much these days." I feel really bad as she is so nice (and right) but I asked her how I could not "take it personally" as we were the only people in the room. It was a direct observation.

I hope these letters aren't too boring. They are very self-indulgent. I quite like reading them back myself. It's a bit of an excuse really.

Enzo's job, mine two days a week as of next week, consists of starting work at 9 pm when we man the phones, take bookings and deal with late arrivals. In the advent of people hanging around by the bar we serve a few drinks, maybe knock up the odd late-night croque monsieur[150] if we are lucky. The whole job kicks into life 2 hours before we finish though as at 5 am the ovens in the kitchen have to be put on and the breakfast preparation begins with a whir of action. Woo-hoo! You have to take the pain au chocolat and croissants out of the freezer and brush them with egg yolk. Then tables have to be set. When there are less than ten people staying at the hotel this can

---

150 Ham, cheese and maybe *béchamel* sandwich favoured by children.

take literally minutes. But for the majority of the time the business customers from the nearby Sophia Antipolis industrial park are super low-maintenance and we often have literally nothing to do from 9 pm all the way through to the brushing of the croissants and the placing of the forks. 9 aching hours to try and stay awake through.

Enzo is about to leave France with Pollyanna Peters for 3 months in Mexico. They're doing French and Spanish and Pollyanna has family in Mexico City. University visits planned in 4 short months. 4 months, it feels like another world. I thought about the Lower Precinct shopping centre in Coventry and the record shop Spin-a-Disc, sausage rolls from the pikey bakers, Golden Wonder crisps, a pound a pint at the Dog & Whistle and 99p CD singles in Virgin Megastore. The distance is under 1000 miles but I can't get my head round how it is existing in my absence. God that's self-absorbed.

The hotel is owned by an old colonel, who is like something out of a slightly twee French film about a family-run hotel and the japes they get up to when the Germans come to visit. Sounds quite good actually. A kind of Fawlty Towers meets Jean de Florette. He regularly gets up in the middle of the night wearing his boxer shorts and a vest, shotgun on his shoulder, and insists that you follow him on one of his missions to find the invading enemy he has heard in the nearby scary forest.

There is nothing much to do during the night other than watch the extensive set of Arc'Otel videos (there is no cable or satellite in the hotel) and desperately try to not fall asleep. The entire collection consists of 4 VHS video tapes:

Innerspace: A k-ray-zee Meg Ryan movie about a naval aviator shrunk and injected into a rabbit. Yes, a rabbit!!!

Four Weddings & A Funeral: The newest film in the collection film follows the fortunes of Charles, a cardboard cut-out of a bumbling English toff, and his friends as they wonder if they will ever find true love and marry. Charles thinks he's found "the one" when he meets an American oddly called Carrie, sharing her name with the demonic

telekinetic schoolgirl. On the way the cheery bunch attend
4 weddings and one funeral, where they all bump into
a whole plethora of exes and gay people. The cliffhanger
comes though when serial buffoon Charles has to choose
between second best and a woman named after a horror
character. What do you think will happen? Marc, who
also works here, seems genuinely surprised each time he
watches it. He watches it frequently.

Scrooged: Weird watching a Christmas caper in the
middle of a Med summer but I have seen it about 4
times. Starring Bill Murray as Dickens' anti-hero. In the
company it is keeping on the shelf this felt like watching
La Règle du Jeu.

Overboard: Goldie Hawn and husband Kurt Russell
in a wacky maritime rom-com. Memorable only for a
scene in which Goldie Hawn walks around on a boat in a
kind of extreme string thong swimming costume. I could
locate the scene in under 2 minutes from a starting point
anywhere on the tape with a decent remote control.

Also there is the campest straight man I have ever met.
He is called Marc du Jardin, which translates literally
as Mark from the Garden. He is from Belgium. He speaks
French (not his first language, he is from the Flemish part)
like someone hamming up an impression of a really gay
French gallery owner. He jumps at the slightest sound,
literally if someone unexpectedly says "Bonjour", and
draws his very limp wrist across his neck in mock horror
when he realises it is just another human being. Giving
him the impression of someone with something to hide.
He is great company as he is always so animated. Rubbish
at drinking though.

I'm so tired I haven't slept a wink, I'm so tired I'll have
another drink, and write a letter to my main man.

Really bored here in this job.

It's now tomorrow, Enzo leaves tonight. All farewells
should be sudden, eh?

Rolled a zoot and smoked it out by the swimming pool
tonight which is probably a sackable offence. Brilliantly
the colonel joined me and I had to hide it under the

sun lounger. I live in what can only be described as a dungeon, under the ground, no natural light. I have made a decision that life is too short to stay here in this palace of boredom, the world is going on around me and I am missing it. I am working tonight and tomorrow and then when I finish work on Mon morning I will grab my bag and head down the coast in search of the holy grail... St.Tropez. I am going to find a job. Like Dick Whittington. I am done with Cannes.

Later...

I feel like I am waiting for something to happen here when I could go and look for it for myself.

I might be starting to eat myself. Why don't I go to St.Tropez now?

Over and out.

Me

PS There is a bit in 4 Weddings when a guy says "I was at school with his brother Bufty. Tremendous bloke. He was head of my house. Buggered me senseless. Still, it taught me about life." What????!!!!!!

15 juin
Today I received the weirdest letter ever written. I assume from a student. She didn't leave her name but I miss her, apparently.

16 juin
Enzo and Pollyanna left. Got told off for my crisp consumption today at the hotel. I was going to counter by saying I only eat the ready salted. But I couldn't be arsed.

17 juin
Bored.

18 juin
I am going to St.Tropez.

A le Cannet

le 3/09/95

Hello Ben!

Like I've promissed you before your departure,
I'm writing to you on a Sunday Night.
I know that we haven't often spoke together during
your stay but I'm sure of one thing I
estimated you like a very good friend. Yesterday
I heard a song of Otis Redding on the radio,
and at this moment I've thunk to you and so
today I've decided writting to you. I made a
lot of mistakes in this letter and I'm sorry but
I will try in the next letters not to do a lot
of mistakes like in this one. You miss me.
I remember the first time I've seen you,
I'he found you ugly and after several
encounters, your lovely blue eyes, your hair,
your face hadn4 let me indifferent. I've

* to made

leant to know you and when you looked
at me my heart beat more and more
quickly. Don't worry it's not a decloration of
love. Every times I've seen you I wanted
to ask you your phone number but I
hadn't the courage. And after each meeting
I told myself that I was a stupid girl.
I wished going out with you but each times
I'm resigned not to ask you. I told me
at his eyes you are just a little girl, and he
"doesn't give a fuck" of you. Stop there this
"mother fucker" ("love story"). I think that
the next summer holliday I will come to
London during three weeks to see you and to
look around your country

Big kisses.

WRITE me soon.

Slightly scary.

19 juin

The OJ Simpson trial is the only interesting thing in my life. It is trash manna from heaven for my starched brain. The murder of Nicole Brown-Simpson and her special friend Ron Goldman has shocked the entire world. One, because the slayings with a type of kitchen knife were so brutal (one of the bodies was practically decapitated); and two, because of the ludicrously you-couldn't-make-this-up-even-in-America nature of events – OJ being a cuddly football legend-turned movie star caught with a, er, suicide note, whilst trying to escape in his friend's jeep, carrying $8,000 in cash, a change of clothing, a loaded .357 Magnum, a passport, family pictures and a fake goatee and moustache? Talking to a news station from the car and saying that he was "just gonna go with Nicole". *J'accuse le Jus d'Orange Simpson*!!!![151]

20 juin

Three and a half days. I can't wait. I will come back for the Lacoste rainsheeter.

21 juin

Alistair has taken up formal residency in the corner of my room. Tonight is the *Fête de la Musique* in the whole of France in which loads of roads are closed and everyone has an all-night party based on anything to do with music. Brilliant. Alistair is going to make a killing.

22 juin

Alistair lost most of his money after we got hammered in Nice and missed the last train home. Slept on some grass by Nice train station til 5 am and then got on the train to Cannes. Fell asleep and woke up in St Raphaël, having slept through Cannes. Got next train back and, panicking, actually managed to get off a station early, at Cannes La Bocca, near Le Slab. At 7 am we started walking. At 7.15 we both went

---

151 The trial rolled on all year. When OJ tried on one of the gloves found at the crime scene, (despite the fact that it had been frozen and unfrozen loads of times and OJ was also wearing a rubber glove already the prosecution went ahead and asked him to try it) he couldn't get it on. His defense attorney, Johnnie Cochran, summised, "If it doesn't fit, you must acquit." It was gripping stuff. He was also acquitted.

to sleep on the beach. Got in at midday.

OJ trial on live this afternoon. There is a scene in one of the *Naked Gun* movies where his Detective Nordberg character rides down the stairs in a wheelchair at a ballgame and is flipped out as it hits the wall. And this is a little bit like watching that happen to his life in really slow-motion. Great analogy by me.

Television doesn't get much better than this.

23 juin
A funny thing happened last night. Alistair and I were sitting on the beach by the Palais at the end of the day. We got quite stoned and were just about to leave about 7.30 when suddenly the whole beach started filling up with people again. We started pissing ourselves. Now dark, there started what can only be described as the most incredible firework display I have ever seen. Things we have never seen happen before. After half an hour we asked a guy behind us what it was all for. He told us that it was the closing party for the world fireworks convention. Fell about.

24 juin
I'm outta here.

L'Eté

Pampelonne Babylonne

25 juin

I am on the train heading to St. Tropez. Right now my French is 'good'. It is strong and fluent. But it is not good enough for someone who has been living here for this long. Footballers who move abroad can pick up a language in that time. Warwick is extremely tough on the language side and we have been told in no uncertain terms that our final year will push us in terms of the progress we should have made during the year out. I also have a vague concern that my French is somehow morphing into Italian, my tutor in a phone call at Christmas having said that my newly sing-songy French was a direct consequence of living so near the Italian border and hanging out in Nice. I like the way it sounds.

Being bilingual is pretty much the point in choosing a language degree.

So here I am. Cannes was beginning to feel like the stadium after the game. Pop once told me:

> "The pessimist complains about the wind,
> The optimist expects it to change,
> The realist adjusts the sail."

The sail it is. Yesterday I went to Decathlon sports shop to buy a tent and rucksack. The tent I have purchased appears to be made of rice paper but the sales guy informed me that it is very modern and effective. I chose it 'cos it was the cheapest.[152]

---

152 John Ruskin said: "It's unwise to pay too much, but it's worse to pay too little. When you pay too much, you lose a little money – that is all. When you pay too little, you sometimes lose everything, because the thing you bought was incapable of doing the thing it was bought to do. The common law of business balance prohibits paying a little and getting a lot – it can't be done. If you deal with the lowest bidder, it is well to add something for the risk you run, and if you do that you will have enough to

I am skint again, scooter debt ruined my windfall.

Cannes to St Raphaël must be one of the best stretches of train track in the world. Through Mandelieu, La Napoule and Théoule-sur-Mer we then dive head first into the terracotta red of the Esterel mountains, staying in darkness for 30 seconds at a time before coming up for air as the train slides round a headland to reveal an enchanted hilltop villa or breathtaking chateau.[153] St Raphaël. Scene of my near-fatal, near-actually-happening great white attack in October. Seems like a while ago.

From the port at St Raphaël, from June until October, you can take one of the bright blue boats, which ferry people back and forth to St.Tropez. It is a crossing I have made the last two summers and boarding the boat now all my sun-drenched memories of St.Tropez have come flooding back. I know right now that however I do it, I have to move further down the coast, here, to the spiritual home of summer fun.

An hour on

We are rolling in to the port at St.Tropez. I am about to walk the 20 minutes to the edge of town where the snaking *La Route des Plages* weaves its way all along the back of Pampelonne beach. Little arteries every half mile with names like *Route de Tamaris*, *Route de l'Epi* and *Chemin des Moulins* are signposted with the names of the different beaches you could find if you took that little track. I am hitching up to the camp site I know so well. Kon Tiki Beach Club. If in doubt, go with what you know.

Allons-y, allons-o.

Waited for ages by the roadside. Amazingly a middle-aged woman stopped.[154] She was driving a Mini Moke, and had wild hair and a slightly loopy manner. I wonder if she knows Brigitte Bardot?

I wonder if anyone will ever read this diary?

Kon Tiki is the grandly named caravan park where I have stayed in a

---

pay for something better."

153 The area was immortally described by novelist Jean Rhys as she passed through, La Napoule stopping her in her tracks and suddenly feeling complete happiness for the first time in her life, "I existed no longer…I was the wind, the trees, the sea, the warm earth, and I left behind a prison, a horrible dream of a prison."

154 The hitching fraternity consider her type to be one of the least likely to stop.

tent both the previous two summers with family friends, next to their mobile home. It's strange being here in June and not August. I know no-one. I don't tend to adapt well to intense isolation and am prone to extreme shyness attacks.

Now at the beach by the campsite. I have set up my tent, put my trunks on and headed down here, armed only with a scraggy towel, a *La Vache Qui Rit* and crisp baguette and three boiled eggs, which I pilfered from the hotel kitchens at 5 am this morning.

Now what?

PAMPELONNE: LA VIE À LA PLAGE

Pampelonne beach is a stretch of white sand roughly five kilometres long. It was first made famous when Brigitte Bardot got her dress all wet and was found lolling around in the damn thing right in the middle of Pampelonne when making a movie (she had previously got attention by flashing her knickers at the Cannes Film Festival – a juvenile, if wildly effective, stunt). Whilst the area of about two metres in front of the surf line is public property, and much of the beach is in fact 'public', there are about thirty private beach clubs along the whole of Pampelonne.

The most famous of these was the first one, *Club 55*, or simply, *Cinquante Cinq*, which opened in, yep, 1955 and now sits in the middle of the area known as *Boulevard Patch*.[155] Legend has it the crew from Bardot's movie had stumbled upon some fishermen who agreed to knock them up some food and *pastis*, moonlighting as a catering arm. They kept up the trick for the next two weeks. (Nowadays *Club 55*, the biggest of the private beach clubs, is an A-list scenester-paradise. Bono, Beckham, De Niro, Nicholson…the list is pretty much everyone.) Like all of the 'private' beaches anyone can go there. If you don't mind paying upward of thirty quid for a couple of mattresses and an umbrella you can have your place in the sun. The restaurant is humidified with Evian spray from above you, the food is great and, whilst hardly cheap, not as expensive as you might think.

Each of the beaches has its own reputation, although hedonism is high up on the list for many. *Tabou* and *La Voile Rouge* were eighties powerhouses of nobility, nudity and nonsense, a tradition the decadent *La Voile Rouge* (naked women being bodypainted yellow while you dine and having actual champagne showers) has carried on. Particularly with its very popular topless female boxing evenings. Ask at the St. Tropez tourist information office about those ones. *Aqua Club* and *Coco Club* are for the gay market, *Liberty* and *Neptune* are for those who like to sunbathe, eat and drink at the bar

---

155 It was named after the US general Alexander Patch who was at the head of the Allied troops, which landed here in August, 1944 as part of Operation Dragoon.

in nothing more than birthday suits, *Bora Bora* you can imagine, *Nioularguo* is a kind of yacht club… the list of names is cheesy but *très, très TROP*…[156]

- *Bar du Soleil*
- *Tropezina*
- *Tropicana*
- *Cherry Beach*
- *Les Bronzes*
- *Epi plage*
- *Key West*
- *Le Lagon*
- *Maison Ocoa*
- *L'Orangerie*
- *Les Palmiers*
- *Polynésie*
- *Tahiti*
- *L'Esquinade*

An influx of bling (as opposed to the more artistic crowd of the sixties and seventies) seems not to have affected the charm of most of the private beaches. The shabby chic ethic of most of the beach clubs creates a bubble of the Côte d'Azur many older observers say has remained untouched since BB and the great discovery.

---

156 *TROP* is a word which in French means 'too much'. St Trop is a shortened way of saying St Tropez but has the slight play on words of making it the place of 'too much'. Clever, eh?

25 juin, 13h00

I sat at the beach for ages and nothing happened. Apart from it getting really hot. I'm not sure what else I expected to happen. I have been spending quite a bit of time on my own lately and I am beginning to tire of my own company. No water, a scorching beach, waiting for Godot, quite introspective, then eccentric, and then I started to eat myself. In a psychological way.

15h00

An Arab-looking man just walked past shouting "*Beignets! Beignets abricot, beignets Nutella, beignets pomme?*" Giant sugar-covered doughnuts the size of a standard housebrick that look like they are made from car seat foam. Piled up on a wooden tray above his head, in full glare of the burning sun, but he seemed to be doing quite well, considering that it is far from high season. One of the many brilliant contradictions in the French sensibility is the fact that they love things like these giant doughnuts. Happy Shopper would turn their noses up at them.

Oh Nutella, pommes et abricots.
Beignets, Beignets!

Like the Child Catcher in *Chitty Chitty Bang Bang*, dancing along the sand with his tray of foam briquettes, sniffing out the vulnerable and under-nourished children.

"Come along…kiddie-winkies!!"

Then I noticed another guy dragging an anvil along the beach. It wasn't an anvil but a giant coolbox. His sales patter was less slick but he seemed to be shouting, "*Boissons fraîches!*" followed by a more comfortable, "Ice-cold drinks!" In French he sounded like a very tired and slightly camp Dudley Moore.

I feel a little bit like I have been let out of an institution, such is my carefree current mode of living. I signalled to *Mr Boisson Fraîche* and he came over, relieved I think just to put his coolbox down. His name's Lee and he's from Leeds. I asked him if he knew my friend Brad from Bradford. He has also been teaching up near Grenoble and decided to come down to St.Tropez to work the summer before going back to university in Manchester. His evident desire to not move physically led to us getting quite chatty. He stumbled on his job from an English guy he met in a bar. The deal is simple, you got the drinks from him at 11 at a pre-agreed station along the beach, but hidden from the bar and snack bar owners. You work from 11.30 til 6.30 going up and down a one kilometre stretch of beach. You sell the drinks for 10 francs (about a quid) per can, you keep 5 francs, you give him 5 francs.

I told Lee that I am actively (sort of) looking for work and if he hears of anything to let me know. They will all be in a bar on the campsite (they are all living in caravans here) tonight and he has invited me down for a beer. Brilliant, I avoided another Nottingham scenario. No-one to not knock for me.

Also bumped into a leggy Dutch girl called, brilliantly, Yolita. She worked here last summer when I was here. She is getting hotter as she gets older.

Having a few beers in my tent and then heading down to the bar. This is going VERY well.

26 juin

Oh my God. What just happened?

It is now 5 pm and I have finally got my head and my body going in the same direction again.

Left tent last night and sat in a bar on my own. Mastered my 'I am so fucking cool sitting in a bar on my own' look with the Roses' 'What the World Is Waiting For' playing in my head. I am shockingly self-absorbed. The beachsellers are pretty full-on. Pretty relieved when Lee spotted me and came over, proffering a pint of some red happy hour cocktail. Pointed out the brains (and no small amount of brawn) behind the whole covert operation, the self-appointed Maharishi of the Beachsellers, a man called Mobby. He's ancient, about 40, intense-looking, with long blond matted hair in a ponytail. He supports West Ham and has been working these beaches for ten years. The nickname 'Mobby' is a kind of linguistic tribute to his love for England's World Cup-lifting Bobby Moore and his own real name of Mick.

I was encouraged to hear from one of Colonel Mobby's lieutenants that if I pop back down next week I can probably get a trial working Tuesday to Thursday. The rest of the evening was alright. Felt pretty wasted after the first cocktail then they just kept coming. Quite a few girls around. English though. I need French. Stumbled back to my tent at about 3 am, my head massively ringing, suddenly really pissed.

About 4 am I truly understood the value of a good tent. I had wisely pitched on or close to St.Tropez's centre of all things creepy and crawly and so found myself trying to empty my small, sweltering, loose-structured rice paper tent of various cockroaches and endangered giant stick insects.

Drunk, nervy and dealing with extreme entomophobia, the rain started to hit hard. I desperately needed a piss. The wind and rain started to puff and pour.[157] And they blew my house down. The legendary wind picked it up and redeposited it by the fence. I managed to drag some sodden bits of my insect-filled tent over to a hedge where I covered a plastic bag containing my beloved Walkman. Then I just laid there in the pouring rain as the early stages of an intense rosé-sangria-cheap cocktail-tobacco migraine kicked in.

This morning the sun rose and got straight on with the intense heating. The *cigales* started singing. Like the morning after an epic row between your parents the night before it acted like nothing had happened. From my vantage point under the hedge I could see a watery yellow pool of cheap nylon and some crisps covered in ants. As if I wasn't wet enough I had also pissed all over myself. Lying there on top of a plastic bag, covered in my own discharge I could not even muster up a hello when the young Dutch family next door unzipped their sturdy tent to start a fun day of healthy activity.

And now I need to get back to Cannes.

Toto… we're not in Pampelonne anymore.

---

157 The *mistral* is a torrid, spiteful, cold wind which tends to hit in the spring and is a result of air piling up in the less clement Alps and rushing down into the Rhone valley. I had heard it could blow for days at a time, and St Tropez' position meant that it often bore the brunt as it rolled over the land before hitting the Mediterranean. Apparently trees in the region are bent over in one direction because of the wind. Local mad women will also tell you that the *mistral* arouses the restless gene in local children and drives local animals and Brigitte Bardot mad. It also dries the atmosphere out and contributes to the scorching summer weather.

The Master and Large Margarita

27 juin

I got the coach back to St Raphaël, then a train back to Cannes then another bus inland to the Arc Hotel in Mougins last night, scraping in at two minutes to nine. Then had to stay up for the next ten hours with no-one but Hugh Grant for company. Marc was there for the first hour so I told my story of poor tent purchasing. He told me that in Russia they have a saying; "We are not so rich that we can afford to buy cheap things." At the time I didn't get it because I was in a state of mild delirium. Now I think it is pretty clever.

I really hate this place now.

Despite the stormy start I need to get back to St Trop.

28 juin – 2 pm

I feel like I have returned for one last goodbye to a former girlfriend, and will say my adieus and resign. I have only been in this job a month.

28 juin – 2:07 pm

So that went surprisingly well. Almost too well. They were lovely.

Like they didn't care.

29 juin

I went to put all my worldly possessions in storage at Fabressa's house (her offer), print some CVs (in case I need them) and a quick drink to say goodbye at the café opposite, before hitting the three-hour scooter drive back to St.Tropez on my hairdryer on wheels, ready to start work today. A pleasant farewell, very grown-up. She seems about ten years older than me. I had rolled a spliff[158] and we sneakily smoked together

---

158 Stupidly strong.

round the corner from her house. Rumbled by Fat Giovanni Agnelli who screeched up in his vintage Lancia halfway through. Reeking of Mary Jane he slapped me on the back and forcibly pushed me towards the garden to have a 'drink and a chat' with me.

The grappa was about 50% proof and its biting, crabby taste slipped slowly and painfully down my throat. After three massive shots, and with the smoke still in my lungs, I began to feel the most enormous whitey coming on. His conversation would not abate, his cigar smoke in my face. Fabressa had disappeared and I became embarrassingly aware that I would not be able to drive – I could barely see. I tried to leave, telling him I had to get back for my job. He asked what it was and I meekly told him that I was becoming a beachseller. A beachseller! He roared, and then he seemed to get angry. He said it was like working on a fairground, dismissing it as if it was simply not going to happen. He went on to regale me with tales of summers in the seventies (I can barely understand his accent at the best of times, at one point I thought he was speaking Turkish) and then he took his shirt off and wandered over to the barbecue. His giant dark brown belly looked like it was going to burst, his giant greasy sausage hands all over me. My drug-addled brain was for some reason paralysed by the thought that he was going to seduce me.

He wandered into the kitchen, returning with another bottle of grappa, this one was for some kind of special occasion,[159] and some kind of protoplasm-and-gristle sausages which he would barely show to the barbecue before serving up to me on stale French bread, washed down with the industrial strength paraffin. When he went inside (possibly to get a sledgehammer to slug me with) I summoned up the co-ordination to throw part of my sausage into the bushes but my effort fell short and the lump of gristle lay limply by the water fountain. Another five minutes and I was sick in my mouth. In one rushed move as Berlusconi went for more food I stumbled from the garden chair, deftly (and incredibly) managed to sidefoot the gristle into the garden like a young Tardelli and, without the ability to explain my own actions, dashed up the stairs to the spare room and fell full-length onto the bed.

159 My imminent heart attack perhaps.

In the morning I woke at six, my head clanging (I am really not trying to get so intensely drunk all the time, but it seems to follow me like a spectre, people seem to like me more in that state), and remembered that I had to be at St.Tropez at eleven. Embarrassed, I left the Famiglia Fabressa a note on the kitchen surface and I was gone. All farewells should be sudden. Again.

30 juin

Waited on the beach. No work for me today. Went to the bar with Lee, only for an hour. Mobby was holding a kind of court in one corner of the bar. He has not yet acknowledged my existence. He is part Colonel Kurtz, part Howard Marks and part Jacques Tati. He is like loads of characters in one. Like in Dante's *Inferno*, Mobby presides over his corner of the beach bar, one head and three faces. All I hear is him talked about in hushed voices. Everyone else was downing carafes of margarita in a competition. Hope I get a day beachselling tomorrow.

"Never confuse charisma with a loud voice"

1 juillet
Day one. My achievements could be described as 'slight'. Twelve cans sold.

2 juillet
Better, sold 16.

Amazing night. Yolita the girl from last year turned up at the bar with a friend. Damn she is fit. She has a body like Elle MacPherson. We both acted a bit like we knew each other better than we do really. The only thing we laughed about was some kickboxer guy who was obsessed by her last year. Raymond Van der Roundhaus used to follow her around like a proper stalker. I don't know what I said right but what she did behind the pedalos at 2 am was mind-blowing.

3 juillet
Merde. Back to 12… 12????

Fucking hell. Raymond Van der Roundhaus is back on the campsite.

4 juillet
Ten. A new low.

My four-day career as a beachseller is not going well. I am being outsold by pretty much everyone. I am confused. Most of them can't speak French. I am selling on average 12 cans of drink a day across my stretch to the west of Pampelonne – a sizeable area of public beach plus a massive public/naturist beach. At 10 francs a go (about a pound) I am taking 120 francs back and pocketing a not-very-cool 60 francs – about £6!!!!!! £1 an hour. This is supposed to pay my rent and my rosé. I can't get near a pizza. My other rebate cash has gone on the final payment of scooter, which is a weight off my mind. But my own weight is plummeting. Other guys are picking up 50 sales a day. I am going to trick my own head with the notion that 'only the mediocre are always at their best' and keep fighting on. I am not even mediocre though. I am dreaming of mediocrity.

As Fabressa's Dad once said to me in a slightly scary moment, "*La derrota no es una opcion*".[160]

5 juillet
Last night I got to chatting with Emily, she works a patch much further east on Pampelonne. She told me that my stretch is known as being quite a tricky one (YES!), largely because of the area to the west, which is St.Tropez's largest naturist beach. Emily told me that French naturists looked down very much on *les textiles* (non-naturists) and that the wanderings of a clothed beachseller don't wash well. They would rather put a sarong on and wander down to the snack bar. She told me that the previous summer she had doubled her *beignet* sales on the same stretch by whipping off her bikini at the entrance to the beach. "I became one of them," she said, with a twinkle in her eye.

And mine.

6 juillet
This nudity thing is becoming quite the norm so I have no qualms about giving it a run out today.

7 pm: 24!!!! The removal of shorts has had a vast effect on my performance. Not, I should be clear for any great wonder inside the shorts, but I think for the fact that I am 'joining in'. I am showing willing. And willy. About 20 or so nude regulars commented on it and I was offered sandwiches, sweets, even a night out based on my newly-found *au naturel* business flair.

7 juillet
Twenty-six.

---

160 Defeat not is not an option.

I am getting slightly obsessed by Mobby.

He has had me working every day on the three stretches of public beach. Although he has yet to actually talk to me directly, he drives the van from which one of his crew delivers me the drinks at 11.30. This is always the dangerous bit as the Ramatuelle Beach Police (that's what they think they are) cruise up and down on beach buggy-bikes looking for dodgy dealings. This could be gay sex in the sand dunes, straight sex in the sand dunes, drugs, or our chosen felony; the notorious trade in illegal Fanta. You have to be constantly on the look out for the dune bikes. Like crazed Manson Family members they appear over the dunes, at which moment you drop your icebox and stay still. You are also under attack from the occasional snack bar owner. Those guys understandably don't take well to our little trade, what with it killing theirs. At the end of the day we all gather in the lair of colonel Mobby, hoping to be chosen. Or something.

8 juillet

Twenty.

Still drifting around in the mediocrity waiting room. I am reading Colette's *La Naissance du Jour*.

I hope none of the other sellers see me doing it.

Had sex with Yolita.

Watching Mobby tonight I see him as a highly decorated British Army SAS officer who has gone renegade. He now runs his own operations out of the Pampelonne bamboo fields and is feared by the French military as much as the local beach owners, monopolising his position as a demi-God amongst the loyal yet confused beachsellers under his zen-like control. This former God-like leader of men, cursed by his dark actions and tortured by the rising supermarket prices on Orangina.

The horror...the horror....

9 juillet

Raymond Van der Roundhaus must have had a good view from his sniper's lair behind the sun loungers. Minutes later he kicked my head in as Yolita plaintively wailed beside me. Massive shiner.

Third time in a few weeks.[161]

Later

Thirty-two!!!!!! Oh happy day. A black eye is no barrier to selling stuff.

Some brilliantly flirty chats with Emily along the lines of her popping up to see me in action and off with the shorts.

The other sellers are all pretty mental and generally seem to be running away from something/somewhere. One of them is a cool, but slightly psychopathic guy called Yorkie. Today I learned that he is called Yorkie because he looks like the Yorkshire Ripper. There is a rumour that once he had a row with a punter and actually punched his dog. Last night he told me that he shared his birthday, April 20th, with Hitler. He thought that would freak me out a bit. It well did.

10 juillet

Twenty-six.

Adam is 19, so younger than everyone else. His brother is one of the more established seasonal workers. Adam is the brightest of Mobby's young stars. The primary reason for that is his status as St. Tropez's very own Iron Man.[162] Adam is the favourite to retain his title cos he drinks everyone under the table.

This afternoon I saw another girl from last year just arrived for the summer stint with her family. Alessandra was and is the cream of the crop in the looks department. I met her last year when she pleased the dads on the family function I was on no end by making the walk from

---

161 She probably married him years later like Agnetha in ABBA did to her stalker – giving hope to mentalists the world over.

162 St Tropez Ironman: A competition (entirely unlinked to the official athletic competition of the same name) invented by Mobby himself in the eighties and which takes place in August every year on Pampelonne. Simple in structure but legendarily difficult to complete. The contestants (over 30 last year when Adam won it in his inaugural attempt, aged 18), have to stand on a line at midday in the beating sun and when the whistle blows down half a litre of rosé. From there they have to run 200m to the next line where they down two pints of lager before being spun round five times by a race official. Head spinning they then run the 200m back to the first line where another carafe awaits them to be downed. The return sprint was followed by ten full rotations before they run the 100m to the sea, swim 100m out to a buoy and back before a pint and a 200m run complete the race.

her family to my beach locale in nothing more than a tiny pair of white bikini bottoms. Half Italian and half French. Her level of prettiness is pretty intense. It is kind of infuriating.

11 juillet
Fourteen. Bad.

Last night was worse though.

Mobby himself was offering up a giant carafe of rosé to all of us beachsellers exchanging stories. Without thinking[163] I held my glass up too. Like Joe Pesci in Goodfellas it started off almost comically with something like, "Are you holding your glass up to me? Me who pays you, you who has never bought me a fuckin' drink?" Some people laughing, me embarrassed and not really saying much, hoping it would blow over, Mobby getting louder, people laughing less, everyone else getting quieter.

University and Cannes and 'You are my Sunshine' felt very far away. It must have gone on for a full five minutes but it kind of got worse as he kept sort of walking away and then coming back, his face about two centimetres from mine, his spittle in my eyelashes, the smell of cigarettes, cheap booze and *moules marinières* being blown like a red hot hair dryer into my face. My loyal friend Lee looked vaguely concerned and Emily even intervened, only, rather worryingly, to be shrugged off by Mad Dog Mobby. I was genuinely scared and slightly numb. At one point he went nose-to-nose with me and screamed about five times in succession,

"Who. The. Fuck. Do. You. Think. You. Are?"

It only ended when the bar owner came over and pulled him off, looking at me as if it was my fault. A few seconds passed and Mobby paused, threw his carafe of rosé into the hedge and erupted with laughter. People were jumping on me and getting me in headlocks and saying things like, "welcome aboard". I smiled and joined in but inside I was raging. I still am. I felt so humiliated and angry, I actually wanted to glass him. Which I have never done before. Or cry. Which I have.

A few minutes later and Mobby came over to me with a new carafe

163 It didn't really require it.

of rosé and offered it up. I refused point blank and apparently looked at him with such hang dog eyes that he felt compelled to hug me. As we talked he explained to me about his "need to keep his mystique" and how it was "all about respect".[164] I was also kind of relieved. He then ushered me to his lair where he sat me down and told me a story. I can hear every word. A scorpion wants to cross a river so he asks a nearby frog to carry him. "Are you mad?" says the frog. "If I let you on my back you will sting me and that will lead to my death." The scorpion shakes his head and says, "Why on earth would I do that? It's illogical. If I sting you, you will drown and therefore so will I!" The frog could see his point and so bends down and lets the scorpion on to his back to paddle across the water. About halfway across the river the frog feels an excruciating pain in his back and realises that the scorpion has stung him. "But it's illogical!" wails the frog as he begins to slip under the water, taking the scorpion with him. "I know," says the scorpion, "but I can't help it – it's my character."

He just grinned and slapped me repeatedly on the back. We drank on and even had a hug. I winced inside as I had just made my first Faustian pact. Glasses raised and smiles all round. In reality I was sure he was drinking to something other than my rude health. And me his.

> "I've seen horrors... horrors that you've seen. But you have no right to call me a murderer. You have a right to kill me. You have a right to do that... but you have no right to judge me. It's impossible for words to describe what is necessary to those who do not know what horror means. Horror... Horror has a face... and you must make a friend of horror. Horror and moral terror are your friends. If they are not, then they are enemies to be feared. They are truly enemies! I remember when I was with Special Forces... seems a thousand centuries ago. We went into a camp to inoculate some children. We left the camp after we had inoculated the children for polio, and this old man came running after us and he was crying. He couldn't see. We went back there, and they had come and hacked off every inoculated arm. There they were in a

---

164 I had seen *Goodfellas* about 40 times and I know the bits he lifted, but I was drunk.

pile. A pile of little arms. And I remember... I... I... I cried, I wept like some grandmother. I wanted to tear my teeth out; I didn't know what I wanted to do! And I want to remember it. I never want to forget it... I never want to forget. And then I realized... like I was shot... like I was shot with a diamond... a diamond bullet right through my forehead. And I thought, my God... the genius of that! The genius! The will to do that! Perfect, genuine, complete, crystalline, pure. And then I realized they were stronger than we, because they could stand that these were not monsters, these were men... trained cadres. These men who fought with their hearts, who had families, who had children, who were filled with love... but they had the strength... the strength... to do that. If I had ten divisions of those men, our troubles here would be over very quickly. You have to have men who are moral... and at the same time who are able to utilize their primordial instincts to kill without feeling... without passion... without judgment... without judgment! Because it's judgment that defeats us."[165]

165 *Apocalypse Now.*

ST. TROPEZ: CAUSE CÉLÈB

St Tropez hit the headlines big time in 1956 when Roger Vadim made a film called, *When Roger Vadim Created Brigitte Bardot* AKA *Et Dieu Créa la Femme*.[166] The place went mental and the whole world wanted a bit of it. In the sixties the Stones and The Beatles hung here, Priscilla Presley bought a villa there (though her and Elvis never actually came) and in the early seventies Jagger even married Bianca at the town hall with Bowie, Clapton, McCartney and Ringo in attendance. Bianca would later reminisce, "My marriage ended on my wedding day." As incorrect as it was mournful.

Throughout the seventies and eighties every single starlet to ever make a name for herself in the world of French film, from Romy Schneider to Béatrice Dalle, came to the beaches to take their clothes off while being filmed in the act. Sometimes they pretended that they didn't even know the camera was there. The *beau monde* from all over came to play with wild tales of Greta Garbo arriving by night with an Empress, Richard Burton and Elizabeth Taylor bickering in a villa, Liza Minnelli in no way being normal and Madonna being Madonna. All the super cool French stars like Serge hung around and sunbathing with your top on was officially banned on pain of public flogging. Elton John, George Michael, Giovanni Agnelli, Eddy Barclay, Pink Floyd and Pierre Cardin all had houses here.

The eighties saw things almost get out of control, as a controversial novel dished the dirt on the seedy underbelly of the sunshine strip. *Les Hauts de Ramatuelle*,[167] by Françoise Parturier exposed the underbelly of the bay from high up in the village of Ramatuelle, looking down on a place that was seedier than a pomegranate. The English photographer David Hamilton played his part in this scene by repeatedly photographing and filming young nymphettes in the all together on the beaches of St. Tropez. His wildly popular choice of girls in their early teens in soft-focus shoots involving muslin led to him

166 *And God Created Woman*
167 The Heights of Ramatuelle

being labelled a child pornographer, an accusation which never seemed to bother his adopted French nation as much as the rest of the world.

Elton John rocked up and filmed the video to 'I'm Still Standing' in the main square, *La Place des Lices*, prancing around like he did when he was still fun. Grace Jones took up summer residence at the beaches, where Charlotte Rampling, Amanda Lear, Cher, Boy George, Jack Nicholson and er, Bonnie Tyler all came to show face. Possibly the only big name who didn't appear to come was Michael Jackson. His über-producer Quincy Jones was chummy with ooh-la-la producer, Eddie Barclay (in St. Tropez if you weren't, you may as well have been Belgian) but he appears never to have made it to the beach himself.

The port's car park even got in on the celebrity act hosting a world lightweight championship boxing match. The undercard featured a young light heavyweight by the name of Evander Holyfield who would go on to international fame as Mike Tyson's *amuse-bouche*.[168]

By the 1990s spraying Cristal was enforced rigorously and St. Tropez also became camp as Christmas. It took on the moniker of 'St. Trop' (pronounced TROP, like DROP), meaning the Saint of Too Much. As appropriate as it was linguistically clever. It was like an Andy Warhol wet dream...Rod Stewart, Michael Hutchence, famous people in brightly-coloured Villebrequin shorts, Claudia Schiffer, Gerhard Berger, wrap-around shades (again), Vanessa Paradis, Helmut Newton, Robert de Niro, Giorgio Armani, Henri Leconte, Magic Johnson, Elle McPherson, Alain Prost, Flavio Briatore and Michael Schumacher.

I arrived in 1995, in the midst of St. Tropez at its most wanton and overblown. The Too Much thing was never more apparent than in the fashion. The Tropezien look was being described as "ultra-chic jet-set gypsy". Irritatingly I had left all my designer jerkins and moccasin-fringe boots at home. Late spring had seen a Vadim–Bardot reunion in town to celebrate one hundred years of cinema and that summer the whole place went into overdrive. Flashier, trashier and brashier than ever. Unashamed conspicuous consumerism was very much the order of the day, washed down with a methuselah of pink bubbles.

---

168 A bite-sized *hors d'œuvre* served before the main event. In this case, Holyfield's ear.

Cabane

13 juillet

Just spoke to my Mum at length.

Didn't want to sound down but she drew it out of me. She pointed out that I have been living successfully on my own for eight months and that there is no shame in coming home if St. Tropez doesn't work out. I am pretty much the only one left out here anyway. And in August alone I can make some cash gardening or in a telesales job, which will make next year easier at uni. But we kind of agreed that this is pretty shit. I am selling fucking Fanta. Really badly.

Have moved out of my tent and into a mobile home with Lee, his mental girlfriend Suze and flirty Emily. The living arrangements are a bit full-on and everything you would expect from four people living together in that situation. The sharing of girls, weed and wine in the whole group gives the place a weird hippie vibe, soundtracked strangely by Lee's live Prodigy bootlegs.

My membership in Mobby's firm of mentalists is now confirmed. I have started to get a bit bored by the mind-numbing seven-hour beach day plus seven-hour rosé session to follow. I have also hit my head on the ceiling of my own talent with the icebox.

Much more of this and I will be back to English-speaking square one. I want more, and I am ambitious.

Later

If I am honest, this is shit. I am not just hanging out with Brits but I am hanging out with the kind of shitbox, thick, slightly racist dicks I thought I had left behind in Sutton and Croydon.

14 juillet – Bastille Day

Lee's mate is heading to Toulon tonight from where I can get another bus direct to Cannes tomorrow afternoon.

Found the CVs I printed out, going to hit all 28 private beaches. Last chance. CVs written in French? Not that much of a novelty if you actually are French.

15 juillet
EVERYTHING HAS CHANGED.

I need to get this down fast. So much to tell.

I literally walked the length of Pampelonne beach, going into each private beach and saying,

"*Salut, je suis anglais et je parle très bien français, vous n'avez pas besoin d'un saisonnier?*»[169]

Was politely declined by the first 23. Beach 24 of 28, *Cabane Bambou*. Particularly picturesque. As luck would have it I timed my entrance as the Don Corleone-esque 'Monsieur Louis' was firing a guy at the bar. The guy being fired had kind eyes and as he walked past me, clutching my last few CVs in my grubby hands, he said, "*Bonne chance*".

Sensing my opportunity, I reeled off my spiel. He interrupted me as I was speaking to say, "*Tu l'as fait avant?*"[170] I told him how I have worked in many restaurants and bars in London and that I come with a lot of experience.[171] He told me to come back at seven and they would give me a trial, to ask for the head waiter, "Bernard". Legged it back in time for my afternoon shift of disappearing shorts and Lipton Ice Tea delivery.

Being Bastille Day[172] we were booked out to maximum with a mixture of St.Tropez folk (*les Tropeziens*) and tourists. I was informed that this was the best way to learn a new job. Quite clearly this is a complete lie.

An intense guy with a misleading name, called 'Sennet' (it means

169 "Hi, I'm English and I speak very good French, you don't by any chance need a seasonal worker?"

170 "You've done this before?"

171 My actual experience includes washing dishes for a catering firm my Mum works for, and clearing the table in our dining room at home.

172 Bastille day is a big deal because it celebrates the 1790 *Fête de la Fédération*, held on the first anniversary of the storming of the Bastille prison which took place on 14 July 1789. Bastille was a fortress-prison and very much seen as a symbol of the uprising of the modern nation.

'wise'), explained the order of the 32 tables to me in a way which it was literally impossible to remember. Then he explained that my duties would be opening water and wine in ice buckets at tables, and clearing finished plates. It actually didn't seem simple enough for me as I found him nigh-on impossible to understand.

> "Forward, the Light Brigade!
> Was there a man dismay'd?
> Not tho' the soldier knew
> Someone had blunder'd:
> Theirs not to make reply,
> Theirs not to reason why,
> Theirs but to do and die."

Within half an hour I served a few drinks (also corked my first bottle of spenny wine, nice) and then I started to *débarrasse* my first table. The table of eight all finished and I carefully removed their first two plates for the long walk in the sand to the back of the kitchen where the *plongiste* gets them clean.[173] Bernard is pretty much bilingual (very rare) and politely asked me to accompany him to an area at the back. He then said,

"I am going to ask you a question and I would like you to be honest with me. Have you ever been a waiter before?"

I blurted straight out,

"No, never. I don't know what I am doing."

Obviously this could have gone either way and Bernard looked at me in silence for ages. Then he just turned round and walked off.

About a minute later he walked back out with a stack of plates and told me that I had passed the honesty test. We went out onto the deserted public beach where no-one could see us, a stack of plates in his arms.[174] He said that he should kick me out, but he was going to show me how to carry numerous plates and how to clear and carry at speed. Enough, he hoped, to get me through the night. He told me that he would be watching and that I had better pick it up quick sharp.

---

173 I learned later that everyone watched me with amusement as Bernard followed me out to the back of the kitchen.

174 This is sounding like a kind of restaurant version of *The Karate Kid. Assiette Enfant.*

"*Oui. Monsieur.*"

As they say, if you want to improve, be content to be thought foolish and stupid. Tick.

I got through it and it was a massive rush. It is exactly what I wanted in that it is tough, demanding, fast and best of all, very French. I love it. We hung out afterwards and smoked a few joints and had some beers. I punched the air inside when Bernard asked me to be back at midday today. Didn't mention anything about my performance. Sennet drove me back to my caravan on his speedway bike all along the beach. In the caravan Emily was having sex with a beach hat seller in our shared bedroom. Didn't care. I have a career.

I am a waiter in San-Fucking-Tropez.

"BB" – BRIGITTE BARDOT ET DIEU CRÉA LA FEMME

It is crucial that we establish the basics for any understanding of St. Tropez. A crash course in the town's spiritual daughter, the personification of the place, the high-priestess of *Tropezienne liberté*, both its heartbeat and its pouting glare. The Unstable Sex Kitten was either the world's eighth wonder or the world's biggest attention-grabber, living perpetually in her own purgatory; between the 'fans' who idolised her but made her miserable and scared her and the men who desired her.

In many ways Brigitte Bardot is the perfect embodiement of St. Tropez in that she is a riotous mass of contradictions, not very hard to look at and sometimes incredibly stroppy. Her story is both generic (model/actress/whatever – although she was possibly the trailblazer) and latterly interesting, not always in a good way.

She was born in Paris into a pretty nice upbringing, became a model when barely a teen, decided to give acting a go, hit the big time with the incredibly rude (for the time) *Et Dieu Créa la Femme*, thus kicking down doors everywhere for women who had a healthy fear of both wearing clothes and being seen as just a sex symbol. Developed a fairly impressive acting CV over the years but remained staunchly a French language starlet, shunning the attention of Hollywood (apart from bedding Warren Beatty, almost a rite of passage for any woman in the 60s/70s who could carry a headline).

Tabloid fodder extraordinaire, the infuriatingly coquettish Bardot left a trail of men in her wake and enjoyed sunbathing nude (often within shot of the permanently stationed paparazzi) at her Tropezien home on the coast, *La Madrague*. Almost 40 years ahead of her time she both bemoaned the constant attention yet seemed unable to live without it. Four marriages came and went and a life devoted (after an early career conversion) to saving animals became her foremost role after quitting films in the 70s.

This devotion to animals has divided France with many seeing her anti-immigration, anti-other-people and generally dour demeanour as proof that if she cared as much about humanity as she did about parrots she might enjoy her life a little more and even rekindle a smile every now and then.

Her most recent marriage to Jean-Marie Le Pen's right-hand man (and far right stalwart) Bernard d'Ormale has cemented this view.

Her legacy as an enduring fashion icon is more than apparent in everyone from Kate Moss and Elle Macpherson to Vanessa Paradis and Laetitia Casta. You just can't help feeling, as with another of her inspired fans, Madonna, that if she could just lighten up, stop hating so much and enjoy it a bit she might find life a shade less painful.

The Glimmer Twins

18 juillet

I have not been able to write because my life has gone mental. I will get used to it.

I went to see Mobby in his lair and he seemed weirdly quite chuffed for me about the job. They have a waiting list for beachseller work but I reckon I displayed incredible sagacity in this visit, considering the amount of bad decisions I make in general. Still. Another resignation, another joyous acceptance of my decision. Best not dwell.

19 juillet

Cabane Bambou has a gently sloping beach into a kind of lagoon of azure blue water before a large sandbank. The beach is one of the largest on Pampelonne with white mattresses set on dark wood frames and a hundred striped green and white parasols. Behind that is the restaurant, also in the sand, which can serve around 200 covers at peak times and is a white linen and dark wood oasis set amongst a real-life bamboo forest. Clients enter the beach through a massive bamboo walkway, emerging through the last part into the beautiful white sand oasis as if through the fur coats and into the crunchy white snow of Narnia. There is also a triple bamboo shower at the back of the beach and a massive kitchen. At the heart of it all is a large square bar, a till and an office for Louis Corleone. The *capo dei tutti capi*[175] is not to be messed with and is definitely capable of venality on a Sicilian scale. I am vowing right now never to cross him, or even look at him in the eye if I can help it. I don't think that I would cope well with finding a horse's head in my 30 franc sleeping bag.

---

175 The boss of all the bosses.

20 juillet

I have a break for half an hour. Louis Corleone is the most imposing, while Patrick and Bernard are the two most important people at *Cabane Bambou*. Patrick is the head barman and Bernard is the head waiter/ *maître d'*. Louis owns the business and his yappy nephew, Romain, manages it. But Patrick and Bernard are its heartbeat. They seem to be the reason people come and spend all day and night and thousands of francs here. They have just joined having spent more than ten years at legendarily full-on *Tabou Beach*. Their transfer was not, it appears, a particularly happy one for them and there still seems to be a lingering political[176] edge to their appearance at the *Cabane*. Their two big selling points are charisma and respect. They are brilliant at their jobs, incredibly talented at dealing with people and social situations and they know and are liked by all of the local movers and shakers. Patrick is a proper barman.[177] He knows about drinks, and I reckon he knows about people.

21 juillet

The rest of the staff, almost to a man (there are only two girls) are all from *Planète Marseille* and so they talk about three things; l'OM, weed and *les Carolines*.[178] I have elaborated my Marseille trip to such an extent that you would think I had been elected onto the local government during my 48-hour stay. I am being viewed with a kind of cautious affection. My idolisation of Chris Waddle helps enormously as do all my English Eric Cantona anecdotes.

My sartorial look is not going to be well-received. I feel like I am creating my own St.Tropez fashion – a kind of ultra-cheap back-pack gypsy.

23 juillet

Our caravan is like a big human ashtray.

---

176 In Tropezien political terms, not French ones.
177 Not one of these fly-by-night, look at your crowded bar and say something like, "So who's next?" types.
178 Chicks.

24 juillet

Today I was offered the job. I will start at 8 am every day when we have breakfast as a team then we clean and set the tables, according to bookings being dialled in, from land and sea. At 11.15 we all have lunch together for half an hour whilst the first people arrive at the beach and then at twelve the first sitting in the restaurant starts. The second sitting starts at two. They finish around 5.30. Work permitting we can all go out for a swim using the speedboat or we can take an hour off. At 6.30 we have to be showered and back, in Thai uniform (baggy Thai trousers and a white branded tee), ready to clean and set the tables for the evening bookings, when we become *Thaï Bambou.* We are one of only seven beaches which are open day and night. At 7.30 we all eat our Thai meal together as a team (there are about 20 in total) from earthenware bowls, sitting on the beach at sunset, and at eight the guests start to arrive, leaving by about 12.30 for us to clear up and finish by 1.30 am. By this point everyone appears to be so wired that we stay for a drink. Or eight. This will be my schedule for 13 days. On the 14th day I get the evening off, when I am advised to rest. Then the next 13 ½ day cycle starts again.

25 juillet

This type of work schedule very much contrasts with most people's day plans, who are here for the summer. They are only really getting up at midday and get themselves together by three to come down to the beach for lunch. I wonder how they are all so tanned when they seem to spend most of their time avoiding the sun. *Apéros* at eight and then dinner at ten or eleven. A club at two and tucked up in bed as the sun rises.

26 juillet
Glimmer Twin No. 1.

Chatted to Bernard last night quite a lot. He is in his mid-thirties and is from Geneva. He's been in St.Tropez since he was 16. He is about six-feet tall and has the calm, yet stern, demeanour of a kind of popular senior military man. He is also, without a shadow of a doubt, the most charming and popular human being I have ever met. All the men in

St. Tropez want to be him and a lot of the women (and some of the men) want to be with him. I have never met someone with such an effortless aura around his own self. Quite literally anyone could walk through the bamboo trees at the entrance and be seduced by his tongue-in-cheek, yet old school, class. He is, in a nutshell, the French Cary Grant.

27 juillet
Terrible skunk-induced hangover. Headache boring a hole in my temple.

28 juillet
Glimmer Twin No. 2.
The other half of the double act is Patrick. Patrick is probably one of the more formidable human beings I have met. Tough enough to skate on. He is like a bear, made of oak, er, other sayings. He chain smokes Gitanes, can drink anyone under the table and has the most incredible silent charisma of anyone I have met in France. The world. Everyone is kind of scared of him, even though, like a kind of French Aslan, he never roars. Well he hasn't yet. He is respectful to others and demands respect in return, whether that be a cocky *Nice Matin* beachseller (he regretted selling his wares without asking first), the *plongiste* out the back (who was rude to the old dear who washed our clothes) or a Hollywood movie star (who invariably he won't recognise). In a place as vacuous and superficial as St Trop can be, I think that's pretty cool. That's balls. He has already told me stories about Pink Floyd playing in town but no hotels being willing to take them in case they trashed it,[179] about a young Zinedine Zidane and about mass swinging scenes amongst the rich Swiss families. But most of all he is all about the respect.

29 juillet
Last night I saw Alessandra in St. Tropez. I am pleased to report that she has added some new skills to her sizeable repertoire. She has added the knack of doing every single normal thing in a sexual way. Licking coffee

---

179 Weird story. I am sure the hoteliers had them confused with someone else. What were they going to do, put their lava lamps everywhere?

foam from her biscotti, twisting her burnished hair into a kind of Euro top notch with her sunglasses arm, tying it messily on top of her head and finishing by letting it cascade back down her exquisite face like waves crashing all over her. We met up at the El Loco *banditos* bar in town and she was all over me in front of Adam and a couple of people from the beach. The fact that she was drunk mattered not. Minutes later a dude who looked like he was at once a millionaire, hilarious and a model, rolled up in a Maserati and asked her if she wanted to go for a drive. She asked me if I minded, acting all like I was her boyfriend. I said of course not (anything else would have looked less confident), it was all good fun. I laughed to my friends, displaying the knowingness and experience of the 21-year-old and winked, "The looser the grip, the tighter the hold."

30 juillet

Patrick today taught the very important lesson that, in France, if you don't smoke enough, you don't get a break. As an overall this is pretty on the money but also in the most literal sense. If you are given a quick 10-minute *repos* during service you had better well spark up or you can guarantee that the next person who walks past will shout at you to do something. *Maintenant.*

31 juillet

The job is really floating my boat. I love the intense speed of it, the smell of buttery rich food cooking in the sun, the sound of popping corks, the taste of ice-cold Badoit in the walk-in fridge, the taste of a Lucky Strike cigarette with a double espresso at 8 am as the sun comes up over the bay, the whirring sound of speedboats, the clinking of glasses, the buzz of a celebrity arrival, the smell of the suncream, the Orangina sunsets on the beach every night. I have discovered a giant world of fun, and everyone is invited. I can't understand how back in England all the journalists are obsessed with writing about finding the 'real France', when the plastic one is so good. St. Tropez, for all its exclusivity, right now feels like the most inclusive place in the world.

1 août

Today I slightly miss white bread lightly toasted with butter and then Bovril on it. Also toasted sandwiches with cheddar and ham. But it'll pass.

2 août

Last night we were winding down with 50 or so people left in the restaurant at around eleven when I found Patrick sitting on his own in a chair, feet up, by the kitchen door, staring up at the stars. He was smoking a cigarette and lost in his own world. He looked troubled.

"*Ça va, Patrick?*" I ventured.

Without saying anything he pulled up a chair and gestured for me to sit. He handed me a cigarette. I took it, he lit it in my mouth. Staring up at the sky he said, to no-one in particular,

"*Le soleil se lève tous les jours.*"[180]

I am living most of my life in a daydream that I am actually in a film so this is one moment when I actually feel for real that real things are happening to me in real-time. Never before has anything ever felt so intense, so urgent, so quiet. We sat there, a kind of awkward silence hanging over me (not him), but knowing words were not really necessary. Patrick entirely comfortable with the dead air.

"The mass of men lead lives of quiet desperation."

180 Every day the sun rises.

L'Année des Méduses

"This is what we would sing:

> Mama was queen of the mambo
> Papa was king of the Congo
> Deep down in the jungle
> I started bangin' my first bongo
> Every monkey'd like to be
> In my place instead of me
> Cause I'm the king of bongo, baby
> I'm the king of bongo bong"

3 août

When I was 11 I saw a film called *L'Année des Méduses*.[181] I really shouldn't have. I snuck downstairs when we were staying with a French friend of my Mum's in Paris. It wasn't even on that late (we were in France, full-frontal female nudity was on daytime TV) but the racy tale of clothes-fearing nymphettes[182] running around Pampelonne beach pursued by men aged between 16 and 60 (with pretty equal success) stayed with me. From early signs at *la Cabane* I think I may have walked on to the film set.

I have also progressed from drinks as today I took my first dessert order.

4 août

1. Sophie Favier
2. Vanessa Demouy
3. Vanessa Paradis (she would hate to be included on this list)

---

181 *The Year of the Jellyfish.*
182 Primarily the libidinous Valérie Kaprisky.

4. Ophélie Winter
5. Cachou
6. Mallaury Nataf

Mean nothing to people in England. But they are crucial for my final year French knowledge. These are the Top Six of my early evening/late-night viewing fodder. Sennet told me that Cachou and Favier come in all the time.

5 août

I had an idea today for a film called 'Desire' in which the protagonist will be a paranoid schizophrenic and the last scene will involve a swinging camera following him down a busy street after his girlfriend leaves him as the strains of the Lovin' Spoonful's 'What a Day for a Daydream' plays and we see that he is crying uncontrollably. I need to work on the start, the middle and the story.

6 août

So Sophie Favier is extremely polite and mad for seafood.

7 août

France is obsessed by what they call *les top models*. There is a magazine called *Casting* dedicated to it and everyone on TV refers to *les tops* and *les castings* as if we are all going to give it a go. Karen Mulder is pretty big and she came in with her Monégasque boyfriend today. Even ate a reasonably normal (it had carbs and stuff) meal. I served her as 'Dessert King of La Cabane'.[183] She was very fond of our *crumble aux fruits rouges*. We joked that the next time she comes to London she should come to my Mum's house as her apple crumble is out of even this league. I was deadly serious. Perhaps too serious. Which may have come across.

8 août

It's relentless.
   'Nagui' is the single-named[184] presenter of the mega-popular French

---

183 Admittedly I was the only one who used this title.
184 See also Bjork, Beck, Cher, Donovan, Enya, Pele, Kylie, Lulu, Madonna, Moby, Pink, Prince, Sting. And Sartre.

version of Chris Evans' zoo-TV classic, '*N'Oubliez Pas Votre Brosse à Dents*'.[185] He has been coming in off and on a fair bit and I have gotten quite chummy with him and his band of friends, producers and hangers-on. Today he gave me his details on a piece of Marlboro notepaper and suggested I call him the next time I am in Paris if I am interested in working any more in France.[186] Wicked.

9 août
Four words.

'The Muscles From Brussels'. Jean-Claude Van Damme arrived today and apparently stays most of August. He is extremely polite, quite small and very intense.

10 août
Sometimes you get on with someone just 'cos you like being around them, and not because you like playing squash together or something. I like that about Patrick.

11 août
Got a nice letter from Mum today. She sent me some newspaper cuttings of Wimbledon tennis. She wrote "Be careful out there" at the end like they used to say when she watched Hill Street Blues. I've got a pretty cool Mum. It's pretty true at the moment too. She has also extended my travel insurance. Think I might need it.

12 août
The level of celebrity down here has never been more apparent than when today one of the other waiters took a call on the main beach line. Laughing afterwards he told us that some joker had called in saying he was Robert de Niro. Everyone laughed until Sennet piped up, "Er, what if that was Robert de Niro?"

185 'Don't Forget Your Toothbrush'.
186 I didn't, and still regret it.

13 août

Such is my progression up the performance chart that I am now actually in charge of desserts across the whole restaurant. This is quite a big move for me and I have grasped the opportunity and am running it with aplomb. Didier, AKA Chou-Chou (The Cauliflower), is the stoniest of the kitchen Marseille boys, but also (not connected), the one I get on best with. He is the dessert chef. When he isn't being read the riot act by someone for being too stoned to speak properly. As the dessert waiter I am forced to work closely with my constantly baked wastoid compadre who one night forgot the difference between *fraise* and *framboise*[187] with disastrous consequences for the *coulis de framboise*. Stress and weed are not great companions and Chou-Chou is on about his fifth last warning.

14 août

Massive day at the beach today. Bank Holiday. Work is going brilliantly, every day brings more stuff. Whilst I am just a small-time waiter in a beach restaurant I am pretty chuffed with what I am starting to achieve. My French is improving massively. The sink or swim nature of the work is helping no end. *Veni, vidi, vici.* I am the big fish. *Je suis le grand poisson. Le grand requin blanc.*

Minor aside. Cachou came in. I definitely had eye contact.

15 août

Got particularly bombed last night.

I went through the dessert list with 'The Muscles From Brussels' and his partner today in incredible detail. He is so intense and serious he looked at me as if I was a US Fed from the future explaining to him how he must travel into the past to arrest and detain time-travelling bandits.[188]

16 août

Bad Starlet Day. Mallaury Nataf is very moody. She is starring in a new

---

187 strawberry and raspberry.
188 *Timecop*, 1994.

sitcom set in St. Tropez called *Sous le Soleil*. She is notorious this year for appearing on a TV show called *Club Dorothée*, aimed at 5 to 12-year-olds. Wearing a fairly inappropriate knicker-skimming skirt with white socks pulled up mid-thigh she performed a particularly energetic spin when the cameraman[189] had her full screen, revealing to the nation that we needn't have been worried about the knicker-skimming. She wasn't wearing any. She denied she had done it deliberately. I think she had.

189 Who knew more than us no doubt at this stage.

PHRASES FAMILIÈRES ET PARFOIS IMPOLIES QUE JE N'AURAIS JAMAIS APPRIS AILLEURS QU'AU RESTAU

Either taught to me or learnt by me due to gross misunderstandings…

Allumé. Drunk. *J'étais allumé*.

Balcon. Literally balcony, also breasts. *Y'a du monde au balcon*. There are people on the balcony/She has large breasts.

Je bande pour toi. I have a boner for you. Informal.

Bander comme un cerf / un tigre. To have the hard-on like that of a deer / or a tiger.

Tu es betes comme tes pieds. You are as smart as the bottom of your feet

Bite (bitte). Penis.

Bloblos. Literally milk, but really it refers to big pendulous boobs.

Vous sentez comme le boeuf et le fromage. You smell like beef and cheese. Not a compliment.

Boudin. Literally a bloody sausage, but really a slim woman. Also drunk. *Je suis boudin*.

Bourré. Pissed, drunk.

Branler. To wobble oneself or to masturbate.

Branleur, -euse. Wanker, insignificant or stupid person

Casse-toi. Fuck off

Costaud. Solid or robust. For most of the summer I thought they were saying Cousteau. As in Jacques, the underwater explorer.

J'ai les bulles. I have got the arse.

Tu me fais chier. Literally you make me shit myself but really you annoy the shit out of me.

Ça-va ça-vient. Sexual intercourse, literally, "it goes, it comes".

Vous avez le cerveau d'un sandwich au fromage. You have the brain of a cheese sandwich

Chatte. A she-cat, or a pussy cat. Or a woman's bits.

Cheval. A tall and slim woman or girl.

Chinois. The Chinaman. Penis.

Chiottes. Bogs.

Fumer le cigare. To smoke a cigar or to give a blowjob.

Con, conne. A metrosexual insult; arsehole/bitch.

Connard, connardee. Bastard. Insult for both sexes.

Connasse. Bitch.

Couilles. Balls. *Tu me casses les couilles*, you break my balls.

Cul. Arse, bottom.

Doudounes. Tits.

Drague. Dredge, or on the pull, looking for sex. *Je fais la drague*, I am on the pull. Although not one to lead with.

Fiche moi le paix. Get the fuck away from me. The opposite to drague. Perversely this one may work with some French girls.

Que tu es emmerdant! You really piss me off!

Quel enculé. What a bastard.

Va t'faire enculer chez les Grecs! Go get fucked up the ass by the Greeks! (What with the ancient Greeks being renowned for their appreciation of homosexual relationships.)

Femme publique. A public woman or a prostitute.

Fils de pute / putain. Son of a bitch.

Flic. Cop.

Folle. A mad woman or a gay man.

Va te faire foutre! Go fuck yourself!

Les Anglais ont débarqué. The English have landed. Or she is having her period.

Mange de la merde. Eat shit.

Vouz avez plein de merde. You are full of shit.

Merdeux, euse. Crap(py), shit(ty). *Cette soiree est merdeuse*. This do is crap.

Ta mère! Your mother! Shortened from *Nique ta mère*! Fuck your mother.

Meuf. Woman.

Pédé. A homosexual man.

Faire une pipe. To give a blowjob.

Poilu. Hairy, shaggy. Also a man who is a stud.

Poupée. A puppet. Also a young girl or woman who is an object of sexual desire.

Putain. A prostuitute or bloody hell! fucking hell!

Cette putain de machine. This fucking machine.

Pute. Whore, bitch, cowtart, hooker.

Queue. A tail, also a prick, cock.

Salaud. A worthless person, trash.

Salop, -e. A worthless, trashy woman.

Souris. A mouse or a young girl or woman as an object of sexual desire.

Tringle. A rod. Or a hard-on, erection. *J'ai la tringle*, I have a hard on.

Vache. A cow. Or a woman with big boobs.

Je suis vert. I am green. Or I am gutted.

Je suis vert de chez les verts. I am really gutted.

Zizi. Male or female genitalia.

Zob. Penis.

Living dolls

17 août

Agathe is a permanent fixture at the bar. She is about 60 and has dyed red, scraped-back hair, which would look severe on a 19-year-old Russian supermodel. Sort of like Lorraine Chase, but madder. She wears long, flowing kaftans and silver ballet shoes. She is from Belgium and as such she is something of a figure of fun. The Belgians are to the French what the Irish used to be to the English. So in essence they are punchlines at the end of jokes. To make matters worse for the Belgians the word '*belge*', as in 'Belgian' has become commonly used as a descriptor for a stupid person. In the sense of, 'what are you, Belgian?!!!' A particular favourite is,

"*Tu savais, la Ministère de transport belge a introduit un nouveau signage?*"

"*Oui, c'est marquée 'Fin de Rond-Point'.*"[190]

Some of the beaches, and thank the Lord the *Cabane* is one of them, have daily fashion performances. These fashion shows take place at lunchtime and involve two girls (one of them normally Scandinavian) who work for Agathe. Agathe dresses them up like dolls on the beach and then sends them out beaming like showgirls as everyone eats.

This has the double bonus of showing the women what lovely bathing apparel is available this season, as well as showing the men what a 19-year-old Swedish girl's arse looks like in a thong bikini. It is a genius idea. But there is an even better bit to the show for all of us workers. When the girls have done their bit in one ensemble they walk to the side of the beach, handily near to where we congregate to collect the bottles of water from the walk-in fridge. It is well-known that if

---

[190] "Did you know the Belgian Ministry of Transport has introduced a new sign?" It reads 'End of Roundabout'."

you can time your orders right you could be back there every time the two girls slipped out of one 'collection' and in to the next. The world's smallest thong was all that stopped you having everything, and the girls seemed to quite enjoy chatting while wearing the fashion equivalent of a postage stamp.

18 août
Good shows today. We have a girl called Ilse from the Netherlands who is petite and curvy and we have Katherine, who is from Sweden and pretty much your average smack-me-in-the-stomach, we-have-a-winner sunshine blonde. Ilse and I get along well. I pay her an obscene amount of attention (a trick I have mastered not doing with French girls) and she allows me to. Sometimes when I am talking to her I feel like I am interviewing her on a Euro TV show, such is the one-way nature of the conversation. I have lost my shame. Today I started to ask myself questions, cheerily answering them while Ilse just sat there.

19 août
I have a night off tonight, Madame Agathe, whilst sipping the blood of young virgins at the bar in her white shroud, fixed me with her whisky glare and beckoned me over. Straight up she insinuated that I may have the hots for young Ilse. She is intuitive; you have to give it to her. She kindly suggested that, as she is driving to Cannes tonight in her 'jeep', and is aware that I need to pick up more stuff from said town, why don't I jump in with her, she will invite Ilse and we can all go for dinner *en route*. Amazing. I have agreed hastily and liaised with Ilse, who seemed reasonably OK with it, too. Indifferent, if I'm honest.

Later
At 6 pm last night we left the beach, Ilse long gone, and got in the car. It is not a jeep but a kind of pedal go kart with a vacuum cleaner engine called a Mini Moke, a British relation to the Mini, with which it apparently shares many parts. 'Moke' is also an old term for a donkey. When I asked Agathe where we were picking our third guest up she announced that Impervious of Amsterdam had had a change of heart. As we hurtled (relative) towards the motorway which connects Cannes

to the St.Tropez area I felt the icy creep of her hand on my knee. It would have been funny, had it not been happening to me. I tried to laugh it off but it just kept coming. She made it in to a kind of childish game as every now and then she would kind of tickle me or playfully pinch me. This would have been easier to ignore if she wasn't trying to tickle my genitals. By the motorway I was almost literally fighting her off and had to raise my voice. She cackled and all I could see were stripey socks and flying monkeys.

Thankfully Fabressa was out when we went round, she would have been unimpressed with my new female companion, and we picked up a big bag of clothes and started the return journey back. Trying to convey a sense of gratefulness, yet not wanting to let go of my other sense of extreme defensiveness, I agreed to stop at a pizzeria on the way back with her. I ordered a pizza, she ordered wine and champagne, largely for her. I paid, making the trip something of an expensive one.

21 août

I spoke to Ilse today and she said that Agathe had told her that the trip had been cancelled. I overreacted in an attempt to make us seem like some kind of star-crossed lovers, cruelly denied our time together, the evil witch tearing us apart. Ilse looked entirely unbothered to have missed the trip. All my colleagues think it is brilliant and use the term TOY BOY every 30 seconds as though they have just come up with it.

22 août

I read in the paper that John Major has successfully retained his leadership of the Tories. It feels like a long way away.

Dear Ben,

I hope you're well – I imagine you freakin' are!!! Just spoke to your ma and she said you had moved to San-Tro-fucking-pez!!!?? How did this happen??? I imagine that the beach in St Trop is marginally more exhilarating than L'Arc Hotel Mougins. I'm going to hazard a guess and suggest that it may well be. You need to fill me in.

Mexico City is properly mental, Mano. Mano is short for hermano, which means brother. It is, as you can no doubt imagine, very different here. The people are as friendly as they are short and everything is incredibly cheap.

Fags are the equivalent of 20p a packet if you smoke the local Pacificos which although tasting like sucking the exhaust fumes from a 73 bus, lend you an air of knowing. Plus they are filterless which is well Belmondo in A Bout de Souffle. What else? Oh, the locals put chili on or in everything. I do not exaggerate because I really do mean everything; Corona (no-one drinks Sol here) with lime and chili in it? Way better than it sounds.

So. Emotional turmoil at this end. Pollyanna, after all her pushing for an early exit from France to Mexico, decided not to join me straightaway here, but rather she wanted to "just hang around Guilford for a bit". I mean, how gash is that? What the fock does she want to hang around that shithole with her gash mates for? C'est le trahison! In another brilliant move (I'm not sure a career in diplomacy is on the cards for this girl) she decided to get to Mexico the day after my 21st birthday. I mean how hard is it to get a flight in time for my birthday? Incidentally I spent my 21st birthday at work (up at 4 am to get in for 6 am) then got home to, er, Pollyanna's auntie and uncle having left me a note saying they were out for the night and that I had missed a call from my friends in England. Great.

Anyway, she gets here to great fanfare from her family like she's Maria Madre de Dios or something, and I'm doing my best to not act all pissed off. The reunion between she and I wasn't exactly how I imagined, in that she wasn't that pleased to see me. She gave me a sort of sympathetic look, followed by a kind of wet hug and then went to bed for six hours while I waited patiently downstairs with her auntie. I knew something wasn't totally kosher, I could properly smell it.

I said nothing until about a week later when under duress from me, she confessed to feeling "like our relationship was going nowhere". I hate it when people use cliched phrases because they feel they kind of fit a cliched occasion. How can our relationship be going nowhere? We were three hours into a 27 hour coach trip across Mexico on our way to Cancun. That I chose to interrogate her at that point was not necessarily the smartest thing I could have done, but she was doing my head in. Our year abroad, just as our relationship it seems, is coming to an end, and as our lives unraveled on that bus, all kinds of home truths and confessions (yes, indiscretions of a carnal nature on her part) unfurled from one another's lips. There were few surprises. It did at least make the time pass more quickly, and for the record, I have, as you know remained faithful in body, if not in mind, through the relationship. In the face of great provocation, I hasten to add. Fuck it, Ben. Although I'm totally depressed, I can say the following about myself... I have:

Discovered and rejected drugs in a big way.

Left home.

Suffered clinical depression.

Received counseling.

Lived in Cannes, Monaco, Nice and Mexico City.

Punched a mirror like Bruce Lee, with the difference being that I had to be rushed to emergency to have my hand sewn back together.

Become fluent in three languages.

Fallen in love.

Had my heart well and truly broken.

Oh and did I mention that my job here is being some mobile phone mogul's personal bodyguard? I have no self-defence skills let alone the ability to defend someone else.

I have been listening to Rod Stewart's first solo album a lot which although you may find this very hard to believe, is totally amazing. there is a cover he does of The Temptations' 'I know I'm Losing You' which makes me feel pretty chuffed about all of the above, and makes me forget about the shit stuff with P. The way I look at it, this is merely the end of the beginning...

Must go now, I hope all is well with you, especially on the ladies/porno front and that you have found somewhere in St Trop to replace Joannathanne's and Le Chelsea.

Con mucho amor y un abrazo,

Enzo Cilenti - Rey del Districto Federal de La Ciudad de Mexico.

You got the client you always wanted...

23 août

Today we were all given *Cabane Bambou* t-shirts with LIFEGUARD printed on the back. I hope no-one thinks I am an actual lifeguard.

Really racking up the good days. Today Patrick introduced me to Olivier – a man from SONY Paris. Today he summoned me over to his boozy lunch table to ask my English view on a new band which have landed in his lap, called OASIS. FUCKING HELL. They have kind of landed in France now. I told him that I have some very strong opinions on the subject. He liked my front I think. Tomorrow he has promised to bring in a 'surprise'. The way things are going it will probably be Liam, asking me to join the band.

24 août

Olivier didn't show.

Sometimes French women, when talking about other women, say this:

"*Elle est trop sympa…elle est trop!*" This literally means "She is TOO nice" but is said as a compliment. As if she is so nice that our earthly compliments are not enough for her. But it just makes them sound really phoney.

All of the French girls I meet at the beach are in relationships. I tried chatting up an Italian one last week, but conversation was an uphill struggle and Patrick has put me off, constantly telling me to look at any Mediterranean girls' mothers to see what I am getting myself in for. I didn't want to marry her.

25 août

"Come at the car," he instructed, in the English of a ten-year-old French boy. A very drunk Olivier walked me to his very tidy Porsche in the car park and I sat in the passenger seat while he rolled a joint. He then proceeded to play me four songs from the new OASIS album (not released until October) at full volume while we both got pretty loaded in the late afternoon sun. The last song was the singalong-a-hymn-like 'Don't Look Back in Anger' and I was quite transfixed by its anthemic chorus.[191] Phoned Sod in London straight away (pay phone, the only one at the beach), and made it sound a bit like it was Liam's car.

26 août

It's 8 am and unbelievably I am up as I did not get pissed last night and came home and went to bed. Haven't seen enough of the mornings here. First thing you get the different tempo of *les cigales*, and at night you get their chums *les grillons*. A woman who comes to the beach is a specialist and she told me all that last night.[192]

27 août

Like a cigale I have started to react to the heat and this is primarily linked to changing sartorial codes. My experience and enjoyment of taking off my clothes is increasing with direct proportion to the amount of time I am spending in France. We frequently have the serious distraction of serving topless women at their tables in the restaurant, either tops

---

191 NB I also remembered a song about champagne containing the lyric "Slowly walking down the hall, faster than a cannonball, where were you while we were getting high?" In hindsight this may have been a warning sign as regards their future. They are no Stone Roses.

192 The two insects are pretty much the best ones as they play beautiful music by day and night, dig hot weather (so you get them largely on holiday), and they love humans and don't bite us. The *cigales*, cicadas in English, are the owners of one of nature's finest pairs of lungs, displaying astonishing acoustic ability. Their noisemakers are called 'tymbals' and when you really listened (I occasionally had a lot of down time) you could tell that they were different in their style from insects like crickets. They love a scorcher and tend to sing during the day. Only male *grillons*, or crickets, chirp and they only do it at night. They have wings, which are a kind of pair of hair combs and they play their tune by rubbing one wing against the other. They sing pining love songs of different types to the females and sing faster the hotter it is.

which came off as wine was consumed or just because they could. The classy ladies think it terriblement gauche. We think it is ace.

Our sizeable beach is covered with around 200 bodies in July and August and a lot of these bodies are barely covered. Sometimes as the restaurant empties mid-afternoon one of us waiters is called upon to help out with the beach service. This involves spotting your clients from the restaurant and seeing whether they want any more drinks taken out to them on the beach. If your clients are gorgeous supermodels and they are discreetly housed in the booth-style area of the beach you can almost guarantee that they will be wearing nothing or as near as damn it. Having served them kind-of-clothed a few moments before in the restaurant this switch is a shade erotic to someone like me.[193]

Last week I had a group of German models who made no attempt to hide their complete nakedness whilst ordering ice-cold rosé from me with cheeky smiles. It was the first time I have seen a completely naked woman, like completely! No hair at all. Not even a landing strip.[194] Pretty amazing. Reminded me of my Dad's Two Ronnies' book *Sauce* from the 1980s with the airbrushed women from Victorian times.

---

193 By this point I was finding girls wearing flip flops erotic, to give you some kind of marker.

194 This was before the days of Brazilians, Hollywoods, moustaches, hearts, Playboys, Bald Eagles, Beavers or German Waxes.

Postcard from the edge.

Dear Sod,

The postcard only tells half the story. The top half.

It is 7.45 and I just have to get this down before we start work. The 5.30 trip out on the speedboat to the small lagoon round the headland is always one of the best bits of the day. Normally it is all blokes who go and we dick about and take a frisbee and it is a laugh. Tonight was different. Vanessa is one of only 2 girls who work at the Cabane where she is also a waitress. She is in many ways the archetypal French girl in that a. she has a boyfriend of about 8 years and b. she likes being naked. Tonight it ended up being just her and I and we took the boat out for a quick swim. Weirdly she was wearing shorts and a vest. Arrived at the jump off spot where I was pretty shocked/ ecstatic to see Vanessa whisk everything off and dive in as though it were the most normal thing in the world. As she stood there on the lip of the boat, her pear-shaped naked bottom at my eyeline, the side of her sizeable breast bathed in evening sunlight she was as undressed as anyone I have ever seen. Intensely flirty yet at the same time intensely innocent. That magical Gallic mix. Her boyfriend is an idiot (theme). I don't feel bad.

QUARANTE-ET-UN

Le cri

29 août

It happened over nothing. I have been thinking that everything is almost going too well at the restaurant. As basically the only non-Marseille member of the 15-odd-person kitchen staff I should have realised that a good knowledge of football and fluent French won't wash with everyone. And the head chef Pascal was the obvious one I haven't feared 'cos I don't deal with him that much. I misordered, a genuine and common waiter's mistake, but quickly dashed back to the *chef de partie*'s[195] line of orders to rectify the error. The order was way down the line and the *sous-chef* hadn't even seen it by then. Coming at me like Gallic steam train, wielding a kitchen glove, which to me felt like a machete, Pascal tore into me like the mistral. For what seemed like an hour and a half, but I think was only two minutes, he questioned my likely parents, my sexuality, my right to be in France, my haircut and my general chances going forward of existing on the same planet as him. It was pretty bad.

---

195 This is the shortest ever guide to the world of chefs: The Executive Chef manages the kitchen and is responsible for actually creating the menu. A bit like a headmaster who doesn't teach much anymore, he might not chop many onions these days. The *Chef de Cuisine* sounds a bit obvious but this is the one who really is standing the heat and getting grease on him. Might be in charge of a few restaurants but this guy, to the outsider, is running the show. The *Sous* is second in line in the kitchen and picks up the reins when one of the big boys is off sick (this never happens). A bit like Paul McCartney in any band he can do all the other chefs' work probably better than them. The Expediter or Announcer is the messenger who frequently gets shot or shot at. Primarily working between the dining room and the kitchen they announce orders as well as checking dishes before they are taken into the dining room. Then there is a *Chef de Partie* or a Line Cook, a *Sauté Chef*, who can sauté probably as well as anyone else can but had a patronisingly-administered nickname, a Fish Chef, a Roast Chef, Grill Chef, a Fry Chef, a Vegetable Chef/Cold-Foods Chef, a Butcher and the frankly embarrassing Pastry Chef. Dessert waiter doesn't actually count as a title. But Dessert King of *La Cabane*....

Got worse when he called me a "*putain de touriste*"[196] and I remember almost standing outside myself, and this whole kitchen, and thinking, "that was a bit low". The stunned silence around informed me that, in case I didn't realise, this was a big one. When it was over he threw the giant kitchen glove into a stack of fruit pallets and stormed out leaving me standing there alone and shell-shocked. I'd love to say that I did something really cool like laughed but that would be lying. The silence was replaced by a subdued chattering and a return to the extreme pressure of lunchtime in a restaurant in the south of France. Pascale's *sous-chef* walked over to the order queue, pausing briefly in front of me to say, with a glint in his eye, "*Bienvenu*". I am so over the initiation thing.

30 août
Failure is not falling down, it's the staying down. I have picked myself up (metaphorically) and am going at it again. I took it on the chin like a man.

Vanessa has become my naked cohort on this voyage of self-discovery. Last night we wandered over to the (open) bamboo showers, neither of us thinking anything of just showering in front of each other.

PS That's totally not true. I was thinking all sorts of things.

Later
I am reading a book on Bob Dylan and it has quoted a Hank Williams lyric.

> "Hear that lonesome whippoorwill
> He sounds too blue to fly
> The midnight train is whining low
> I'm so lonesome I could cry."

I hear you, Hank.
That's how I feel.

---

196 A fucking tourist.

Middle of night.

I wonder if this is going to happen to me once every few weeks for the rest of my life. Why do people keep screaming at me?

What if I have become an unbearable asshole who everyone apart from real idiots hates?

31 août

My relationship with Vanessa is clearly getting out of hand. Although nothing has happened. Last night we went to the naturist beach next door in our hour off and she brought a bat and ball game with her. As she casually rubbed suncream into her breasts she informed me that the ancient Greek athletes always performed nude. The word 'gymnasium' derives from the Greek word '*gymnos*', meaning naked.[197] I desperately tried to think in philosophical terms as a completely naked Vanessa bounced across the sand opposite me whacking a small pink ball into the blue sky.

I have reached a stage in the summer whereby I am practically a hippie. In that I smoke loads of weed and seem to be wearing clothes less than normal people. As opposed to rejecting established institutions and values or particularly expanding my consciousness.

1 septembre

Still keeping my head down.

But since, and to quote someone else, "at every moment of our lives we all have one foot in the fairy tale and the other in the abyss…" I will just wait until I get my balance back.

Patrick told me the origins of the expression 'OK'.[198]

---

197 A gymnasium in those days also housed the philosphers and they were naked too, in imitation of the Gods they revered and pondered. The very father of philosophy, Socrates, advocated nudity as a form of honesty.

198 In the American Civil War soldiers returning from the trenches would want to know how many people had been killed that day. Officials would write the number of deaths on a board followed by the letter "K", standing for "killed". No deaths would mean that '0K' would go up and 0K came to be seen as a pretty good thing.

2 septembre

My libido is out of control. French girls are very much living up to the hype. The golden triangle of unshakeable self-confidence/extreme femininity/love of casual nudity has captivated me. I have also developed what I think is a healthy obsession with Sophie Marceau. It has been growing a while and I have begun to see it as something of a progression in my own personal development.[199] My obsession with Bardot had always felt a little juvenile. Even to me.

But I genuinely believe that if I meet her we will click.

3 septembre

I am increasingly immersed in French culture. Except for the fact that I don't have a girlfriend. But that's because they all have boyfriends. The odds of any French girl having a boyfriend are so astonishingly high that she may as well have been planted there by my own inner insecurity.

4 septembre

There is one girl called Emilie. She is Parisienne and she is the classiest girl I have ever met. She is about seven miles out of my league. When she didn't respond when I said *Bonjour* I knew I was a few miles short.

But the interesting/nice axis has come into play again with the beautific Manon. She is half-English, half-French and to my disappointment she is desperate to converse only in English. She is so nice it is painful. Her bottom is so perfect they could use it to design peaches. She looks like she has just walked out of a NIVEA ad or one of David Hamilton's softcore St.Tropez photo shoots of 18-year-old nymphettes. Last week

---

199 For the uninitiated, Sophie rose to prominence in France in teen fayre like the film *La Boum* and its sequels, kicking off when she was just 13. Born Sophie Maupu she renamed herself after Paris' grandiose Avenue Marceau. She then became unfeasibly stunning, made loads of films in which she took all her clothes off, became the darling of *Paris Match*, sending sales through the roof every time she is on the cover, but still manages to be the kind of girl you could imagine introducing to your Mum and Dad. If you have a tendency to daydream. She is also smart and funny and adored by the French. She is from a working-class background, married a Polish director about 25 years older than her, gives great interviews, she is curvy and real and once aggressively turned on a foolish interviewer for questioning her shape, *"Je suis ronde, et alors?"* (I am curvy, so what?).

I was serving at a table and she walked to the showers on the beach in her bikini bottoms and, looking up like some kind of buddy-dreamgirl mix she winked at me and waved…. I think I actually mouthed, "I do."

Her family are like a family from an idyllic cinematic ode to the wonder of family life.[200]

5 septembre

My first date with Manon last night on a 14th night. She came to the campsite with her Dad. There is something about really hot girls when they kind of dress down and wear secondhand plain Jane-style gingham baby doll dresses. We met in the bar and I got there early, smoothly ordering a carafe of rosé. "Here you go," I said, taking her glass to pour.

"Oh no," she said, "I don't drink alcohol." I ordered her a Coke.

"I like your campsite bar," she said.

"It's basic, but it seems to please most people."

The conversation didn't improve.

We headed into St. Tropez and to my horror she was one of a very rare breed of girls who think that you are supposed to talk to the driver of your scooter as you hurtle down the treacherous *Route des Plages*. It didn't help that I had already drunk half a litre of wine. I was taking her to the jewel in my own crown I wore as the Prince Regent of St. Tropez. The Hotel Sube. A first-floor bar of the picture-postcard harbourside hotel of the same name. This was the perfect locale for my *Pagnoliane Princesse* to flourish and where, I had no doubt, she would become the future *maman* of my children after I persuaded her to down a few glasses of blush rosé and had loosened her beautiful tongue.

If anything the drink made the conversation worse. I didn't think it was possible. At one point we were actually talking about flannels. At about ten I gave up the dreamchasing and came to the conclusion that it was most likely me. I am not in tune with the kinds of girls who

200 The films *La Gloire de Mon Père* and *Le Château de Ma Mère* at the French cinema in South Kensington left an indelible mark on my Francophilic psyche in my early teens. In essence I desperately want to live *in* those films. Seeming about a thousand light years away from my own life at the bottom of the Northern Line the tales of mesmeric summer days in the blazing hills of Provence literally used to keep me awake at night.

feature in classic French films. And thus I will die unhappy. *Tant pis.*[201]

6 septembre

There is an episode of 'The Simpsons' in which Lisa desperately wants a pony. After much badgering Homer breaks and buys Lisa a pony called "Princess". In dire need of more cash, and in order to pay the rent for Princess' shelter, Homer takes a second job working nights for Apu at the Kwik-E-Mart. When he gets in from the night job he turns his alarm clock on and rolls over, the alarm clock instantly goes off and, in a daze, he gets up, gets dressed and goes to work.

My life has, I feel, become like this episode. When I am not working I am working at something else (female attention normally) and the gaps for sleep are getting smaller and smaller. The addition of more grown-up alcohol is not helping. I read in an Orson Welles biography that whilst working on his theatre production of Macbeth he was working solely by night, recording his radio programmes by day. He was apparently so taken over with the frenzy of work that he completely neglected sleep. People working with him noticed that he would take 20-minute catnaps, stoked up by enormous meals and a steady drip of alcohol and barbiturates.[202]

I have gotten into a little thing with Patrick whereby after 10 pm every time I walk past the bar, if either of us sings, or hums The Doors' 'Show Me the Way to the Next Whisky Bar' we drink a double JB (Gee-Bee) and Coke. It is great, but it is killing my insides.

7 septembre

One of the few hiding places when the heat/booze/tobacco combo gets too much is our walk-in fridge where we keep the wines and, more importantly, the one-litre glass bottles of Evian and Badoit. The sensation of the ice cold Badoit as it slithers down your scratchy throat

201 Oh well.
202 My habit of comparing myself to legends continued into my later years. I was increasingly troubled in my late twenties, not by the onset of my thirtieth birthday, but by the fact that John Lennon had had fifteen number one UK albums (nineteen in the States) and seventeen number one UK singles (twenty in the States) by the time he was thirty.

is one of the greatest (non-sexual) thrills of the summer.

8 septembre
My homelife is becoming something of a health hazard. The problem is that by the time I scooter home it is often 2 am, but my beachseller pals don't start work til 11.30 the next day and never have plans for any kind of normal night. Some of the more hardened sellers, led primarily by Lee, often don't even start until after lunch, such is their ability to work sales on their patch. The caravan is getting worse. Two nights ago, at Patrick's suggestion, I slept in the mattress shed on the beach. Like the bed in *The Princess and the Pea* as the mattresses actually have a ladder up the side so they can be stacked high. Wrapped in the cotton coverings, and with only the sound of the sea I can sleep like a baby until the *plagiste* wakes me up at seven. Slide down the side, a run and dive into the Med, followed by bamboo shower (ideally next to Vanessa) before a double espresso and a Lucky Strike and I have the perfect morning routine. The cure for any hangover, too.

As the saying, er says, "a hangover is the wrath of grapes".

In the club

"There were a hundred different beach clubs along the three-mile bay. Waffle fences separated them from one another, and every morning the sand was meticulously raked by the lithe, tanned plagistes in brightly-coloured shorts. Beach mats were arranged in rows, little tables and umbrellas placed beside them. It was the best part of the day. The sky and the sea were white as the morning humidity slowly evaporated. A speedboat buzzed back and forth, pulling a parachute out of the water into the air. It sounded like a faraway bluebottle battling with a window pane. The workers lunched early, when the beach was pristine and ready. Everything changed as the holiday crowd began to trickle in. The sea turned a deep Mediterranean blue. The silence was eaten by the screams of the Arab planchistes in the kitchens, the waiters flying around the restaurants, the clatter of plates, the popping of corks, the holiday hysteria and the din of a thousand outboard motors."

Rupert Everett

9 septembre
Club Cinquante-Cinq (55) is the best-known of St.Tropez's beach clubs. The clientele have been described as "the beautiful and the tanned". It's a massive beach with weird wooden frames all over it, a restaurant where you eat practically on the lap of the person next to you (at another table), a bar, a shop, a photographic studio, a PR heaven, St.Tropez's Cathedral of Self-Publicity and a whole way of life. It's also really simple in that the alpha males are alpha because of all the money they have and the alpha females are alpha because they are beautiful and they are wearing really small bikini bottoms.

I read somewhere that visiting St. Tropez is not so much people-watching but "watching salmon swim upstream". It's a brilliant analogy. Unlike a lot of similar places *Club 55*, and a lot of St. Tropez in general, is a particularly accessible stream. You can have fun here if you don't have tons of money. A lot of Pampelonne beach is public and if you take a packed lunch, like you would to a lot of beaches in the world, it is a day out like anywhere else by the sea.

My introduction into the high-life really came yesterday. We've been hosting a sizeable family group from Switzerland. They are polite and unassuming, easy to look after and I enjoyed their presence at their block-booked corner table. I thought it somewhat classy that they requested no bills to be brought to their table during their stay but it wasn't until Patrick told me to look more closely at their wrists that I understood that they were bona fide Swiss royalty. Of the horological variety.[203]

This afternoon the Dad asked Romain if they could take me out for an early lunch one day to say thank you for being their primary waiter. This was a great honour. Well pissed off the other waiters as it guaranteed me a couple of hours off, and it was paid.

10 septembre
Lunch at *Club 55* was memorable for two things. One, I unwittingly arrived looking like it was dress-down Friday in a meat-packing plant in Metz. And two, the moment the father of the family insisted that I choose the wine for the table. I know less about wine than I do about how a combustion engine works, or even how paperclips are made. In France you are loosely expected to drink the local wine with your food and I know a few of the names as ones which we serve at the *Cabane*. Not wanting to go too high, and not wanting to look too low-rent I went for the middle ground. When the rosé arrived at the table I was given the honour of tasting it. Not knowing what a seventy quid bottle of rosé tastes like I smiled approvingly and the waiter poured everyone else after my approval. Glasses raised and thanks received we all sipped. A second later Papa Timepiece spat his mouthful into the sand. "*C'est*

203 One of the big three.

bouchonné!"[204] he yelled. We all laughed heartily (at my divvy lack of nous) and whilst I laughed along I felt like a very small boy from south London.

11 septembre
I am going back to uni soon. I still have to read…17 out of 18 books.

12 septembre
The upper echelons of society are much easier to handle at the beach. The worst are the arrivistes and the snobs who really make it hard. I know that the word snob originates from the Latin *sine nobilitate* – without nobility. This is exactly what they are lacking, along with basic manners. I have had my accent mocked by Parisians dripping in gold and learnt that the most vociferous crybabies are normally the ones with the biggest status points to prove. One nouveau riche couple, perfectly pleasant on their first day were so insulting on their second that Patrick almost physically removed them from the beach. They complained to the *plagiste* and I over their position on the second row of mattresses. When their lack of manners quickly demonstrated itself Patrick unemotionally strolled over and told them, "*Cette plage n'est pas pour vous.*"[205] He repeated it three times to their protestations as we stood behind him like children watching a fellow pupil getting dressed down by a teacher.

13 septembre
This is a good one. Barbecue at Patrick's last night. Everyone wasted. As per normal me up there with the worst. Left at about three. Patrick followed me to my scooter. Apparently wasn't sure I was alright. Got on scooter and tried to drive off. Couldn't. But bickered with him over it. He has now, unbeknownst to me, decided to go and get his motorbike to follow me as he thinks I am too drunk. As I drive out of the road he lives in near Ramatuelle I see a car pulling out ahead. I don't know what happened but I was literally incapable of stopping and I really slowly hit

204 Corked.
205 This beach is not for you.

his front wing. I fell off. He went berserk. Patrick rocked up. I said I was sorry, he looked like he was going to go for me then I had to go to my bike to get my papers. To everyone's surprise I got on my bike and drove back to Patrick's. Both follow me at speed and I wind up having him (it turns out he is Parisian) swinging at me as Patrick got in his way. Patrick sent me inside and locked the door. Stayed on the sofa. Now morning. Patrick not speaking to me.

6pm. Went out for another naked swim with Vanessa today. Brilliantly, as a functioning galeophobic, I have managed to keep it under control. It helps when Vanessa is swimming naked next to me. But I still feel incredibly ill at ease when the water goes colder. The Carcharodon Carcharias loves the cool water.

Later
Patrick's neighbours turned up at the beach and he made me apologise to them for all the noise I caused last night. I did. But they give me hugs and make jokes about how I wound up a Parisian. Brilliant. Bought me two glasses of champagne, too.

14 septembre
Today we had a real twat come in on the world's biggest floating metaphor. A massive ugly dark grey speedboat that looks embarrassingly bigger than the others. Party-goers circled his boat in speedboats, waiting to be thrown scraps. Are these people really the 'jet set'? They look more like the dick set.

Turns out the man with the biggest yacht is a loathsome Parisian commercial greengrocer who we watched jamming his tongue in some 19-year-old's mouth all afternoon and giving 'booby massages' to whoever went near him. He is such an enormous loser.

15 septembre
It turned out after they left that the Swiss family's cumulative bill for the two-week period was doubled with the proceeds going directly to us waiters. Now that I find classy.

septembre 16

Dear Sod,

Plus ça change.

We need to go back 2 weeks. An afternoon when a girl walked out of my wildest dreams and into my wildest fantasy. She could not have been more different. She is Sophie Marceau.

First off she acts like she can't even hear me when I speak. As the chats became more frequent the incredible suddenly started to seem credible, I swore inside that if I ever got a shot at that title I would not let go for the rest of my life. At the end of the day she topless (she is always topless) strolls along the beach on her own and I started to bound over to join her like a cocker spaniel. She is arty and musical and lives on her own with her dad in an old townhouse near Versailles. Any spare moments in the evening before the shift (even in the place of naked swimming with Vanessa) we started to spend sitting and talking. She listened to my thoughts about 'Exile on Main Street' like I am the world's leading music critic. I listened to her thoughts on her favourite book, 'Le Petit Prince' by Saint Exupéry, like I don't think it is wildly overrated and that I was not at all looking at her breasts.

Sometimes in the middle of talking she smiles and then sort of looks off into the distance, as though she has heard the howl of a mountain wolf hundreds of miles away. It is disconcerting and I had to sort of sit there waiting for her to return. When she isn't half-naked she behaves like she wants to be, tugging at her clothes and cupping her breasts in a way which makes it impossible to focus on whatever deep and meaningful is coming out from the space between her plump cherry lips that day. I never even showed fear when one day she started talking about her ex-boyfriend and actually referred to him as "beautiful". I felt no fear when she told me that the over-sized cashmere jumper she drapes over her breasts on rare occasions belongs to him.

I know you have heard this before this year pal but she is the ONE.

To prove it when she played me her favourite song it turned out to be 'One' by U2. I have been listening to it around fifteen times a day. I told her how we also "carried each other" and she took it very literally by actually asking me to carry her along the beach one night while she gazed out to the horizon. It was really hard, I am not physically strong enough and had to put her down. But I can think of nothing else. I fear I may be becoming a dreamer, in the worst sense of the word.

One night last week when I could barely take any more of the proximity of our lips and her pert breasts we kissed as the sun set over Pampelonne. Over the last week or so she tends to stroll over from the caravan she shares with her father for most of the summer and lolls around at the bar late at night, usually on her own (Patrick scares off the many interested Tropezien suitors), reading a book, ruffling her mane of hair, barefoot and precocious. Occasionally she gazes at me as I work, which drives me crazy, and makes me think I really am in a coming-of-age Marceau movie. Two nights ago after closing she turned up at the mattress hut I was sleeping in with two chocolate yoghurts and proceeded to initiate me in the art of culino-sexe involving mouthfuls of rich chocolate goo, tongues and other areas.

This is the bad bit thought. She left 2 days ago and I feel completely heartbroken. She left me a letter, which begs me to come to Paris when the season is over. I have read it about a hundred times. She says in one bit that she would show me the "alentours". I asked Patrick what it meant and he told me it was slang for the clitoris. He said it so believably that I didn't question it until later when him and Bernard were laughing about it. Based on where she lived in Paris Bernard told me that it was the equivalent of saying she'd show me round Southall.

Yesterday morning I got up early and wrote 'Je t'aime Emilie...we carry each other' in giant letters in the sand next to our beach. I have photographed it and when I get them developed next week on my night off I am going to send it to her along with the world's longest letter I am 18 pages in to writing her. Long letters are not, as Patrick suggested, an excuse for someone not being arsed to write a shorter one. This is the real deal.

Everything.

Me

PS I need to find a fault and there is one. You would find it really annoying too. She uses air quotation marks when she says anything in English. Either she is secretly as dumb as a box of rocks (she's not) and thinks that's what you do in a foreign language. Or it is a massive "affectation". She couldn't be perfect.

From Queer to Eternity

17 septembre

The last 24 hours have been hellish. Not 'any' hangover can be cured by that mattress/sea thing. The grapes have turned out to have a lot of wrath. Yesterday was some national or local holiday thing so late and heavy work night. Patrick and Bernard rounded everyone up for the short walk to the next private beaches along, *Coco* and *Aqua Club*.

These two Pampelonne powerhouses are both very, very gay.

They are a priapic bunch, the owners of the two gay beaches next door to ours in St.Tropez, and it can be quite dazzling finding oneself immersed in the hedonistic nightlife of the Gods of *Coco* and *Aqua*. Pretty great fun for a night out but definitely not for the faint-hearted. The gay scene in St.Tropez is far more promiscuous than the straight one, and that's pretty full-on. We arrived on foot to be greeted by scenes from *Caligula*. Knowing most of the staff from our own place the drinks and relaxants were free. This consisted of shots, carafes, champagne, stuff with leaves in it, stuff with powders in it, just powders. About an hour in I told Patrick that I was in trouble. Really wasted. He laughed and carried on dancing with a post. I found myself amidst a group of naked men dancing on a pedalo with what I was pretty sure was an actual woman attempting to fellate all of them at once. It was like the last days of Romatuelle. I saw circle jerks and daisy chains and even a *trajet en train*[206] which involved about eight men looking like they were pretending to be train carriages pressed up against each other. Except they were all naked apart from the odd pair of cowboy boots and the carriages were bumping very violently against each other. At one point I stumbled upon a mattress shed where some kind of bacchanal was taking place with two men wearing giant animal heads and a woman

206 Train journey.

somewhere between them, enjoying the company of a bottle of Sancerre in a way which did not involve glassware. I can't really remember all that much more as my vision was getting hazy and I kept literally falling to the ground, surfacing and realising I had to find my colleagues or I may never find myself again.

I remember having a play fight with Sennet in the shallow surf and then I don't remember anything at all apart from someone digging and water being all over the top of me. It's never a good idea to fall asleep on your own in the sea. Apparently they hauled me out as I was dragged under by the surf. I have just been told that the last thing I did was order a half pint of vodka and milk at the bar, in a display of largesse to some girls to whom I had boasted that I would drink anything.

Apparently they dragged me most of the way back but left me lying on the beach at the *Cabane*. At about 8.30 am this morning I came to, water lapping around my ankles. I was lying full-length on the wet sand as waves gurgled gently around me. Still dressed in the night before's clothes I made to stand up but collapsed pathetically. Nothing in my body worked and as the early morning sun beat down on my matted, sandy hair all I remember is seeing loads of the staff laughing up at the restaurant. I have never experienced such intense thirst but horrifically it was coupled with the overwhelming sensation that I would be violently sick if anything went anywhere near my mouth.

"Water, water, everywhere,
And all the boards did shrink;
Water, water, everywhere,
Nor any drop to drink."

Everybody was laughing except Romain. I was half an hour late and he'd been looking for me everywhere. He forced me to get up and pretty much single-handedly dragged me to the shower, where I sat for a further ten minutes, sobbing inside, and almost out. I have never had a hangover, even an illness, like this before. I was sick in the bamboo shoots as I came out of the shower and violently sick at the back of the beach. I was now over an hour late.

I thought back to when I would want a day off school when I was younger and my tennis-loving Mum would gee me up with a "What would Jimmy Connors do now? That's right, he'd dig deep."[207] Nothing. By the time I had been cleaned up properly it was almost ten. One of the other waiters had shouldered the extra work and I was lying on a mattress at the back of the beach, desperately trying to get the will together to stand up. Before eleven Romain implied that I would not work there again but he at least expected me to be *costaud*[208] about it.

Managing to stand straight at around 12.30 I had my first table to clear. Somewhat inconsiderately, the eight of them had all shared some rather large fish on the bone so the table resembled a kind of aquatic Père Lachaise,[209] with bones and death everywhere, like a gothic restaurant. The beating midday sun was not helping and as I cleared the fourth or fifth grave on to the holding plate I felt a bolt in my lower stomach. Pausing only to put the plates back down on the table I ran through the kitchen and projectile vomited across the back wall of the outhouse.

I got somehow to 5.30. I still feel dreadful. Romain took me to one side just now and told me that I still have a job, actually complemented me on my hardiness but told me in no uncertain terms to get a grip, there will be no second chance.

At least I have got a night off in twelve and a half days.

---

207 I can't stand Jimmy Connors.

208 Robust.

209 Père Lachaise is the strangely romantic cemetery tucked away in a corner of north-eastern Paris, often referred to as *la cité des morts* (the city of the dead). Effectively a town of its own you get a map when you go in in order to navigate its rolling hills, small woods and elaborate sepulchers and tombs. Its position as the world's most beautiful resting place is reflected in its inhabitants who include Chopin, Proust, Colette and Jim Morrison.

Tigers play too rough

18 septembre

More diners, wilder parties and the temperature just keeps rising. I fear my hedonistic lifestyle is becoming a bit too much. Violent crime increases with the heat in cities then hits a peak at 90 degrees. This is similar. My violent chasing of fun has hit 90 and my young body has started to strain at the seams. We all have regular weekly visits from a kind of backstreet doctor (a lot of us are not 'declared' for tax dodge reasons) and today he found me in a state of disrepair. I am a broken man. One of the guys has started to call me a *roué*, which translates as a man dedicated to a life of sensual pleasure. A week or so ago someone dropped a tray of glasses on the way into the kitchen and, despite the near obsessive response in terms of fear of the floor from all of us (we are all working barefoot in the sand/kitchen area, a bad cut can end your season) I have managed to get a sizeable shard lodged under my big toe. The inevitable sand/dirt/grease/bronzing oil/cream sauce/fag ash has got in there and my whole foot is beginning to really flare up.

19 septembre

On top of this I have stupidly picked up something which is making another, more sensitive area, flare up, a decidedly more unpleasant experience which Bernard is taking me somewhere this evening to get treated. I also have mild exhaustion. It is hardly surprising, I still live in the campsite version of Villa Nellcôte[210] and my 13 successive 17-hour days, mixed with clubbing, heavy drinking and drug consumption has curdled with my extreme libido and floored me.

---

210 A 19th-century Côte d'Azur mansion once inhabited by the Nazis and converted into a libertine den of squalor in which the Rolling Stones recorded 'Exile on Main Street'.

Later

Tonight it got even worse. Bernard took me to more of a side-street doctor, so kind of a rung up from backstreet. He recognised signs of imminent death. The pernicious effect of alcohol, tobacco, marijuana, amphetamines, and the excess use of painkillers. I didn't tell him about the other drugs. He also suggested that sleep deprivation was not a great plan.

My foot was sliced and diced, then carefully dressed (you have to be really careful it doesn't look like you are hurt – we are in the fun-in-the-sun holiday restaurant business, nobody wants gangrene with their *gratin dauphinois*. My exhaustion treated with some full-on hydration tablets and some antibiotics for a kind of overall numbing. Bernard told me something that sounds like Pop says when he talks about how you can't squeeze the toothpaste back in the tube. But the word squeeze makes me want to hurl. My increasing enjoyment of casual nudity is more limited to female company and standing there in an office while *Mr Médecin* fiddled with my poisoned penis was no fun at all. The worst was that there was so much infected gunk up there that doc took out a metallic implement which looked like a giant needle and actually said, "*Je peux pas mentir, ca provoque une douleur aiguë.*"[211] It was the biggest understatement in the history of medicine. The steel rod (or 'steel umbrella' as I now know it is known was inserted into the eye of my dick, all the way up before he turned the end and a steel 'umbrella' opened inside me and he scraped it back down the inner wall. I am gasping just writing this. It is the worst pain I have ever known. I have promised not to drink for a week and went back to work.

10 pm

Had my first drink at nine.

As Oscar Wilde said, "Everything in moderation, including moderation."

---

211 "I can't lie, this will cause you extreme physical discomfort."

VOICI JOHNNY!!!!

Johnny Hallyday was and remains France's number one living icon. He is kind of like a cross between Cliff Richard, Eddie Cochran, John Lennon, Elvis Presley, Mick Jagger, Bob Dylan, Jon Bon Jovi, Rick Parfitt, Shakin' Stevens and Barry Gibb with loads of garlic round his neck. To the French he is, *tout simplement*, "Johnny" or, at a push, "*le rocker national.*" Or possibly to the rest of the world, "the biggest rock star you've never heard of".

Born Jean-Philippe Smet he was, according to his own legend, raised by an American man in Oklahoma with a made-up sounding name, Lee Ketchum. Unable to pronounce the word 'Jean' (this was Oklahoma in the 1950s), they called him Johnny. Lee's father's life had been saved by a doctor called Mr. Hallyday, little Johnny liked the ring to that and so changed his name. And the whole course of Softcore Franco-Stadia Rock!

He launched his career as a massive Elvis wannabe in 1960. More accurately he was a kind of mix between Elvis and a brooding Jimmy Dean, his film-star good looks making him the only real front-runner in the search for France's first rock star. To be fair no-one else was really trying. France at the time was Jacques Brel, Charles Aznavour, Maurice Chevalier and Edith Piaf. He was not in the *chanson* tradition of French culture. The *chanson* tradition (from the Latin word for song, *cantio*) is essentially any lyric-driven French song, normally a kind of mopey collection of *chansons*, even going back as far as the late Middle Ages and Renaissance. It would come to be pretty highly-rated over time but greasy young people hated it. They loved *Le Rock n Roll*. And rock n roll is not French, and Johnny was neither Piaf, nor was he Bill Haley.

Jack Lang[212] described Johnny as expressing "liberation...it was

---

212 Jack Lang was an extremely popular French politician. He founded the International Festival of Student Theatre, joined the new Socialist Party in 1972 and began a rapid rise. He was a very high-profile and long-serving Minister of Culture, working closely with his close colleague President Mitterrand. He attacked American cultural imperialism, gave the arts a clear and coherent

the De Gaulle period, very moral, Johnny expressed the aspiration for a free society". He followed up his early promise with the song '(Do the) Mashed Potatoes', a blatant riff on the how-to dance craze of the time and other songs like 'The Mess-Around' and 'The Hucklebuck'. His story was so derivative of other pop stars as to be almost worthy of Spinal Tap. A kind of Diet Elvis, one of his early singles was a cover version of 'Love me tender', translated word-for-word into French and called *Amour d'Eté* (Summer Love). There was the footage of him getting a sackload of fan mail doing his national service, there was the near fatal car crash, there were the rock royalty chums, the dinner in 1966 at the Marquee in London with Otis Redding, which saw him 'discover' a young Jimi Hendrix. They became buddies and Hendrix started opening Johnny's shows for him. He had an uncanny ability to roll with the punches of change, and, a bit like Zelig, he also appears to have been present at most counter culture and hipster moments in history – footage with Jagger, The Beatles, Bardot (I would have thought that he must have?). But crucially Johnny, the master impersonator, the shameless copycat, never played Elvis or Jimmy Dean, it seemed like in his own head he actually was Elvis or Jimmy Dean. He did it with such sincerity. The western world saw him as a clone. When you have Elvis you don't need Johnny. When you have Lennon or Jagger or Alvin Stardust or Michael Flatley… the list goes on. But France needed Johnny. And no Anglo-Saxon artist has had such an impact on the French population as a whole, appealing to young and old from every background.

Perhaps even more crucially, he nailed the live thing early on. His aunt knew Maurice Chevalier who, according to official legend, taught him to be a bit of a showman. By the seventies he was arriving on stage by helicopter, dangling on a rope. By the eighties he was looking like Siegfried and Roy's weird Gallic foreign exchange student and had upped his entrance to that of a heavyweight boxer. At one

strategy. Later in his career he was criticised for his role in enticing Disneyland to Paris and for presenting the *Médaille de la Chevalier* to Sylvester Stallone. His response? "One culture does not threaten another." He remained a popular figure until the end.

series of gigs at the *Parc des Princes*, such was his theatrical largesse, that he actually entered the sixty-thousand strong arena in that style, with a massive security force. He was mobbed, it took him over an hour to get to the stage. His response? "I will never do this again."

It is estimated that between a quarter and a third of the French population have seen him live. He is like a God in France.[213] Nobody dares to say they don't like him. He was a phenomenally powerful performer, like a big phallic, Gallic Cliff Richard. His gigs have got bigger and more epic as he has continued to grow into an almost exclusively stadium-based rocker. Even the left bank intellectuals recognise the social phenomenon of Johnny, but his core fans always remained the real working French people.

Johnny epitomises the French love–hate relationship with the States. Like how the cinematic *Nouvelle Vague* championed the American gangster flicks, so Johnny seemed obsessed by Americana, and in many ways he just copied it and made it in their language, just for them. Maybe it's the 'just for them' bit that is key. Yet he is also a long way from and a very different take on the archetype of French culture. And it is that stubbornness that makes him really French. He just chose not to sing in the English language. Unsurprisingly he has not exported well elsewhere.

The best bit? He's not even French, he's Belgian.

---

213 A couple of years later he was made a *Chévalier* (Knight) *de la Légion d'Honneur.* Definitely a step closer to God.

20 septembre

Fifteen Harley Davidsons came roaring up *La Route des Plages* at about 3 pm. They may as well have been riding horses. We knew because we took it in turns to get on the roof of the *Cabane* with binoculars. The paparazzi were surrounding the beach, trampling on sun loungers from all sides. They met most mornings at *Le Gorille* on the port for coffees and word would get up to the beaches in no time if there was an invasion planned. Romain was standing proud above the bar, hosing all the grabby lensmen he could with water to keep them at bay. Johnny is kind of a big deal.

As if arriving on stage at the *Parc des Princes, le Rocker National* was the last to appear through the bamboo curtain at the back of the beach. We had called in loads of security at the waterside of the beach as literally hundreds of holidaymakers had gotten wind of Johnny's imminent arrival and were packing it out. A helicopter circled overhead and boats all headed for *Cabane Bambou* to try and get a glimpse of The Legend. The gang assembled at the bar, some of the cooler clientele attempted to look non-plussed (they weren't) and all the other celebs had wisely stayed away to avoid humiliation on the starometer. Patrick and Bernard, who knew him from *Tabou* days, held court with them all at the bar, and after half an hour of drinking and smoking they made their way to their table, discreetly placed right in the middle of the restaurant. He looked pretty incredible considering he is 50-something. The French even do plastic surgery better. Johnny's young wife Laetitia was also in attendance and brought an element of femininity to the testosterone overload.

For their starters they ordered *les os*. I have never seen this on the menu before but then Johnny does not do menus. *Les os* is essentially 'bones' and involves scooping out the marrow from inside them. It looks foul, but certainly goes with the whole bandito bit they had going on.

After their main courses Bernard paid me the ultimate honour of my young career when he asked me to accompany him to the table where I had to take the dessert order.[214] Our in-house speciality of

---

214 This did not go down well with long-serving, yet occasionally very whiney, Sennet. He was a great guy at heart but didn't help himself in other ways. The fact that he was a massive rich kid didn't add much. But the biggest problem with Sennet was

une crêpe aux pommes caramalisées is a pancake made with caramalised apples and served with vanilla ice cream. People go cuckoo over it and all the staff are instructed to go on about the secret recipe at every given opportunity.

When you take an order for a sizeable table you generally take a pad, as most people are not Rain Man and also because you will make mistakes. In the excitement of it all I didn't take a pad and Bernard watched on vaguely aghast as I used an old teaching technique and asked my hard rockin' banditos to raise their hands if they wanted *une crêpe*, the rest I could remember. Johnny was being a particularly difficult child and his half-raised, half-not raised arm was making his dessert decision unclear. I politely asked him if his arm was up or down which brought a load of laughs at the table and a mock apologetic Monsieur Hallyday stood up and raised his arm like an eager child. He even put his arm round me, such was his *bonhomie*.

Bernard playfully cuffed me round the head backstage. Sennet would have gone for the uppercut.

Fuck it. I am having a FUCKING BALL.

.

that he was all substance and no style. And we were in St Tropez.

Salut, Pierrot

21 septembre

One of the best days.

Jean-Paul Belmondo was just sat at the bar. Patrick called me over. He was amazed that I knew anything of his films at all, let alone my extensive knowledge of *Pierrot le Fou*.[215] We chatted for about a minute and he was everything I wanted him to be. Laid-back, tanned and smiling he shook my hand when he left and I am going to go and ring all my mates again.[216]

215 Jean-Luc Godard's *Pierrot Le Fou* is a technicolour pop culture mash up, which for me epitomises everything that I love about the French sixties cinema we study. It is pop art. Released in 1965, starring Jean-Paul Belmondo and Anna Karina, it is a loopy road movie careering across France, starting in Paris and ending up in the south. Jean-Paul Belmondo is Ferdinand, who leaves his wife and kids for Karina's Marianne (yep, she represents France). Marianne calls him Pierrot throughout, there are loads of explosions, tomato ketchup gore, Algerian gangsters, piss-takes of the advertising industry and the best one liners in any French film.

216 This was rubbish, none of my mates had heard of him.

Three men and a little scooter

22 septembre

I can't believe it's almost over. I need to be home in ten days. It is the hardest work I have ever done but it is a brilliant feeling. Like how they say when you have finished an exam, the feeling of elation is never as good as you expect it to be. This one is. Everybody, as the end of the season draws closer, seems particularly pleased with themselves, just for getting through it, and this is the period when you get to enjoy it.

It's still really busy though. Pretty bewildering when the bookings board is full for the six hours of lunch service and it is only 8.30 am. But everyone has some grease on them and is faster. Now I have lasted the season I know so many people (albeit superficially) on the St. Tropez scene. We never pay to get in anywhere, let alone pay for drinks. Our beach is well-liked by locals so we get looked after pretty much everywhere we go, and forgetting to charge the odd round of drinks at the bar one night when the owner of the *Papagayo* club is amongst them never does you any harm.

23 septembre

Night off. Writing at the caravan, which is, weirdly, both empty and quiet.

The clubs in St. Tropez are not like the clubs in London. They are wall-to-wall with exceptionally beautiful (and largely unattainable) women and as long as the drinks are free we keep on frequenting. Most of them are open for dinner (weird) from ten or so and most stay open until six in the morning, later if you know where *le after* is being held. The *videur* rules and our best hope is normally either knowing someone on the door or getting sneaked in through the back or the kitchens by someone working there.

There are three main clubs on our radar; the *Papagayo*, *Le Bal* and

Les Caves du Roy. There is also *Studio Pirate, le Pigeonnier, Hysteria Bar, The Yeti* and *The Hilarios* but we aren't allowed in to those for lack of money. The oldest is the *Papagayo* which goes back to the sixties. The scene there is a bit too linen-trousers for us and we head more often to either *Le Bal* or, ridiculously *Les Caves du Roy.* Roy's Caves!!! I say ridiculously as it is the kind of place where rich property magnates go, hoping to see Jack Nicholson or Sacha Distel and not young hipsters like us, both cash and time poor. The reason we like it is because all the hot model-types get bored more quickly by the old grandads they are poncing from and we can sometimes get lucky with a snog or two. It is like high-class ambulance-chasing.

The DJ there has a 'calling card' whereby he shouts "Welcome back St. Tropez!" and they all go wild! Like they have been at a war or in prison. Another good one is announcing celebs' 'birthdays' thereby drawing attention to celebs who are there, although I think some people may have already noticed the 40-person entourage and feeding frenzy of girls in most cases.

24 septembre

Morning. Last night I was hugely overtired by about two in the morning at the caravan, and knew I started work in six hours. Adam came round and suggested we join his older brother at this mountain car racing scene in the hills behind Pampelonne. Some of the beachsellers have got really into it. Our other option was to drive the four miles to *Le Bal* on my scooter. We really love *Le Bal.* It is the only place I can force myself to go to. The music is the best in St. Tropez. Great banging Italian house anthems you can play piano in the sky to, with soaring vocals and helicopter sounds. A more accessible bunch of Eurotrash litters the club and the barmen know us.

I should never have gone but Adam had convinced me that the triple header of 1) Loads of Dutch girls he knew in attendance, 2) The fact that I could sleep plenty when I am dead (this almost proved particularly prescient) and 3) Free drink all night was too good to miss.

In the club I struggled with my conversation with the Dutch girls and I knew for a fact that it was simply not going to happen for me. I drank heavily to try and chase this demon away but I was never on to a winner. In a desperate attempt to get me to stay, Adam introduced me to a terrifying man who turned out to be the in-house dealer. He took me, along with two Russian girls, into a side room so that we could try his Provençal fare for free. He chopped out three massive lines on his credit card in the dark and pounding cupboard space we were all squeezed in to. My Trop credentials were not helped when I gave him back the card and thanked him and he pointed out to much giggling that I had snorted the raised Am Ex numbers.

I had to leave. Agreed to give Adam and another beachseller, Seb, a lift home back to the caravan. After the amount I had drunk driving back alone in a car would have been a dumb idea. The fact that I was driving a scooter made it even more so. Think how often, not in South East Asia, you have seen three people on a scooter. With one crash helmet.

We drove/veered up *La Route des Plages*, a notoriously treacherous stretch of badly-lit road. I vaguely remember losing complete control of the machine. We trundled (three blokes, going uphill on a scooter, we weren't troubling the 70km speed limit) almost pathetically over the edge of the road and fell into the ditch below, about three feet deep. I seem to recall us lying there laughing when the smell of burning suddenly caused blind panic. My trousers were pressed against the red-hot exhaust pipe, and Adam, (weirdly, looking back) wearing only jeans and shoes, was screaming that the engine was going to blow. We ran off, fearing an explosion. We finally wheeled the scooter home at about 6 am. Another quality night of rest. Ready for my 8 am start.

Afternoon.
Freud said, "There are no accidents." This is plainly misleading. Looking back it was the dumbest thing I have done all summer (and that's saying something). That road is an infamous death trap with the world's highest concentration of supercars,[217] plentiful alcohol and loads of dicks.

> "We were very tired, we were very merry,
> We had gone back and forth all night on the ferry."

217 Made-up, but probably true, statistic.

UN AN PLUS TARD: DES ACTIONS ET DES GESTES CHARMANTS DES GENS DU MIDI

- Inviting you to their house for dinner (food quality a given)
- Kissing you (women)
- Being complimentary about your French-speaking (men, women, some children, not so much the *videurs*)
- Saying good morning to you even if they don't know you
- Their innate insecurity about us Brits being out to get them, which, when dropped makes them very likeable
- Being incredibly romantic
- Repeatedly removing clothes in front of you as if very normal (females, preferably)
- Being comfortable at the beach with you and no clothes on (most French women)
- Serving bread for no extra charge with all food
- Offering you a cigarette if you appear not to have one handy (what comes around goes around)
- Being attentive and making you feel a million francs (waiters in other bars who had been served by you in your bar)
- Sticking up for you (everyone, once they trust you)

And in the end…

25 septembre

Synergy today. My first Tropezien boss, and still the finest of the Provençal human hairdryers (surely I am due another of them about now?), Mobby, walked into the bar at *Cabane* this evening. Dressed only in a pair of itsy-bitsy Speedos and rocking his Bali/White Bob Marley look he pulled up a seat at the bar and ordered some rosé. He seemed to be carrying the weight of the world on his narrow shoulders.

But it was nice that he came up, he said he had been meaning to all summer. I have seen him out a few times but for the first time in a while I sat and had a drink with him and we chatted, largely about him. He told me pretty much the entire beachseller rota and went through some of the sellers' worst performances in what seemed like real-time. Patrick kept serving him wine. He looked considerably less threatening now, sitting there in his little knickers, taking free drinks from my friend. Part of me hoped Patrick would give him an initiation ceremony. It seems like a lot longer than three months since he tore me a new asshole in front of a crowd of baying foot soldiers. I feel like I have changed a lot in that short period. But he is still Mobby.

He seemed like he wanted to ask me something but he never did.[218] I wonder whether he is too proud or whether he just doesn't know what he would be asking for.

As he left and I went back to the bar he turned round and tried to pull my shorts down in front of everyone. He is still a massive tosser.

---

218 I think he is looking for leads, he wanted to meet Patrick and Bernard who he had heard about, probably from Lee. I think he has gotten round to realising that he is doing a job for gap-year students and the disenfranchised, not particularly enjoying it, and drinking himself to death.

26 septembre

September is the best time to visit St.Tropez. It's still busy but the kids are gone and you can actually drive into town without adding three hours to your journey.

The football season is in flow and Tuesday, Friday and Saturday nights are part spent huddled round the radio rather than running ourselves into the red-hot sand.[219] *Thaï Bambou* is now only open in the evenings on the weekends and the beachseller crowd are beginning to drift off. Some are heading for a ski season.

Some hang around in the area for the massive *vendanges* – the grape harvest. The *vendangeurs* then sit around and drink the day's fruits.[220] No change there.

A return home is looming. I could head out to the Alpes where, based on the make-up of the St.Tropez crowd, I could be working in pretty much the same team, with snow replacing sand. Some are heading to St Barths, Martinique or Guadeloupe where they may even be working for the same beach, just shifted about 8,000 miles west. That's what I would love to do. Never been skiing.

The global seasonal worker scene is mental. Most of them don't seem to really miss England. But judging by the exaggerated allegiances pledged to the supporting of a football team I am not sure I believe them. I feel weird about going back to university. But I really need to slow down. But don't want to leave the south, I know I could happily live here.

27 septembre

My last night at *Cabane*.

It is a tradition to force the exiting waiter to take a hit from the sizeable kitchen bong every time he goes back there with an order. They are also deadly serious about the games they had planned. The 'games'

---

219 NB Your feet do get used to it quite quickly.

220 Grape-picking can be really hard work. Towards the end of your working day the bent over position of your back you've been holding all day can be excruciating. Even if you are doing the 'carrying' it can be pretty full-on (a full backbasket can weigh 50 kilograms). And it might still be well over thirty degrees for a chunk of the day.

included one in which I had to hold smoke in my lungs for 45 seconds and everyone else did things in an attempt to get me to choke. The incentive? If I could stand up I got to choose a 'slave' who must do what I said. Obviously I couldn't speak though. I chose Vanessa (it was an obvious choice) and instructed my ample-bosomed slave girl to "shock me". She led me into the bamboo bushes by the hand, removed her t-shirt and bra, gently put my head in between her breasts and then, her bare bosom still nestled against me, slipped her tongue into my mouth for one of the most sensuous kisses ever received. Swiftly returning me to the kitchen she smiled delectably and carried on with her work. This is a girl with a boyfriend!!!

Another one was one in which they all come up with a buzzword and then whoever says it first (obviously me as I was the only one who didn't know it) had their underwear removed publicly and thrown in the freezer, wet. That was it. The boundless imagination of the pro weed smoker.

About halfway through the night I could take no more and collapsed in the laundry basket. Then I was dragged naked into the Med, which is getting chillier by the day. I slept alone in the mattress shed that night, my self-satisfaction at a job completed accompanied by a spectacular storm of hot rain, which started falling heavily minutes after I went to sleep and stayed with me all through the night. Supine, stoned, completely monged I drifted off listening to giant raindrops and imagining myself in a marshmallow shower, Helena Christiansen giving me a head massage. I woke in the morning to a complete silence. I don't know if I have ever felt as cosy. For a few moments I lay supernal as if crucified across the white mattresses, 15 feet in the air. I did not have a clue where I was, who I was or why I was. I wondered if I had gone to heaven.

28 septembre

This morning I was summoned to Romain's bamboo office. He has generously supplied me (and all the other staff), with fags, food (essentially all my meals), booze (he could do nothing to control the Patrick freight train) and the odd bit of cash to spend throughout the entire season. As I am not declared for tax reasons I am paid in cash. I know that I was earning about 500 francs (fifty quid) a day if I do my standard double shift. It works out at about 75 days work, so around 37,000 francs. This equated to about £3,500 AKA an awful lot of money to me. The waiters all had a meeting a few weeks ago and agreed that the fairest system for tips was 20% to the house and the rest would go in to a pot for everyone to share come the end of the summer. I think I have just walked away with almost £5,500 all-in, in cash. Two grand in tips!!! Romain folded it all into a bumbag and offered me a job for the following season.[221] My Mum and Dad are going to be pretty chuffed that I am coming back from my year out, and before my final year, £5k plus.

Patrick dropped me back at my caravan and gave me a hug. Then he left, with only his passing words lingering,

"*Partir, pour revenir mieux.*"[222]

29 septembre

It is midday at the end of September. I have more money round my waist than I have ever seen in my life and in two hours my marathon beachseller leaving do is scheduled to begin. I have tidied up all my belongings, made a small flag to mark the spot, pulled out a wad of the 50 franc notes and buried the bumbag in the sand to the side of the tent. Then I have placed my bag over it and positioned my scooter over the bag. There is no way I am going anywhere near that money between now and leaving St. Tropez tomorrow afternoon.

Off to leaving do at the margarita bar. Scene of Mobby's infamous performance.

30 septembre

I think at some point we left that bar but after about nine everything blurred. I remember getting up to say a thank you speech. It was much like Cary Grant's speech when he belatedly won an Oscar.[223] Except I had no trousers on and I fell off the stage (table). Mobby brilliantly

221 Which I would take.
222 Leave, to come back better.
223 And said, "No greater honour could come to any man than the respect of his colleagues."

turned up at about 2 am and took me to one side. It is one of the last things I can remember. It sounds a bit gay but he gave me a silver hoop earring, WHICH I PUT IN!!!!! And gave me a hug which went on for ages. Then he left, totally sober as far as I could tell.

I also managed to pull the much-older-than-me woman who worked at the checkout in the Kon Tiki Beach Club supermarket at some point that night. Photos show her sitting on my lap. Never knew I was in with a shout. Have been served by her every day for months and she has never even smiled. Maybe it was because I was normally buying chocolate milk. A product aimed at five-year-olds.

Last night her companionship gave me a warm feeling of having come full-circle. Without sounding like a tosser she gave me an overwhelming sense of having completed a kind of personal journey.

1 octobre
And a particularly nasty dose of gonorrhea.

> "…The love you take
> Is equal to the love you make."

Hi Honey, I'm home!

2 octobre

I have to be back at Warwick in five days. I feel like that world is in a different galaxy. The drive back from St.Tropez to Cannes yesterday on a wrecked 50cc scooter with a massive bag on my back was not a swift one. For fear of overheating (the scooter) I had to constantly keep stopping at cafés in the Esterel mountains. I reckon that the scooter is probably worth less than my shorts. After the mountains I took a detour and drove through Mandelieu and onto the main road through La Bocca. I drove up to the school gates at Le Slab and could see lessons going on, kids in the playground, the general humdrum of normal life. My Tropezien experience has changed me and it feels almost unearthly and dreamy returning to the school. I keep thinking about the new assistant gearing up any day now to start. In my film-obsessed head I feel like I am returning from Vietnam, back in my old town, a changed and different soldier.[224]

Later

I am in a café in Cannes. Opposite the Palais. I drove (weirdly slowly) through the town centre and up towards Le Cannet where my stuff is. I agreed before I left France to sell my scooter to the school in Le Cannet who could offer it to my successor. Parking outside I realised quite how much has changed in the year since I first walked onto the grounds. Some kids from the music club strolled over, laughing at the length of my hair, my leather bracelets and my 'Red Indian' skin colouring. I caught a glimpse of myself in a mirrored door. I look like Mowgli. Monsieur Guy Rufin was in his office. He commented on my wayward look in a jovial, conservative uncle way. He looked less stately

---

224 St Tropez…Vietnam. Go with me here. It was all that bamboo.

and imposing now than he had before, I have grown up and changed a lot. But he is just as cool as he always was.

Left my bags at the school and walked down into the town centre with some cash. One goal. *Rue d'Antibes*. Boutique Lacoste. For the first time in my life I was able to buy a really expensive item of clothing. The 2000 francs did not dent my wealth. It is the only coat I will ever need again. Cary Grant would have bought this coat.[225]

I bought the mac. And I bought my Cannes–London Victoria coach ticket for the midnight departure tonight. I can still drop some cash on a slap-up fish supper with Jason Priestley in Brun before I go. It will then leave me with £5,200 to put in my bank account for my final year spending and living money at uni. I spoke to my Mum and Dad tonight and they sounded really chuffed with this news too as money is a shade tight at home.

On the way back I popped in to say goodbye to Madame Cocheteux. I felt less like a little boy around her his time and I swear she sensed that. She seemed to keep looking at me strangely as though she didn't think it was really me. God I adore her. I wonder what would have happened if I had just gone for it. Not really my style. Feel really weird.

The shop opposite has new owners with new opening hours. I popped in to buy a drink today at lunchtime. I told the new shopkeeper I used to live opposite, noted his Olympique Marseille postcard and we got chatting about football. He asked me where in France I was from. Where in France???? Amazing. This might be the moment I was waiting for. Linguistic acceptance.

2 octobre (overnight)

The coach ride home is about 29 hours and I am seven hours in. For most of it I have sat staring out of the window, listening endlessly to 'Exile on Main Street'. More film observations. I feel like Dustin Hoffman

---

225 Cary Grant said, "I'm reminded of a piece of advice my father gave me regarding shoes: it has stood me in good stead whenever my own finances were low. He said, 'It's better to buy one good pair of shoes than four cheap ones. One pair made of fine leather could outlast four inferior pairs and, if well cared for, would continue to proclaim your good judgement and taste no matter how old they become.'"

in just about every film he is ever in.[226] We hurtle along motorways and through spectacular mountain ranges but all I am seeing is the last sinuous 12 months of my life sped up and in a technicolour whirl. I have been reviewing everything, which has been before and it is leading to a revision of my future.

Certain things are dropping off my radar, others coming more into focus. I feel other-worldly and surreal, uncomfortably restless, yet at the same time joyously happy. I feel particularly emotional and keep wanting to cry. Like really, really ball it and sob. I don't even know if I am happy or sad. I feel homesickness for two places at the same time. Here and at home. How messed up is that?

I keep reading a quote I wrote down from *The Buddha of Suburbia*, "You must accept happiness when you can, not selfishly, but remember you are a part of the world, of others, not separate from them." I am accepting so much happiness that it is overwhelming me. Like before when I felt like the south of France's emotional punchbag, now it feels good. I almost feel embarrassed that it feels so good. I feel extremely different to the boy who left a year ago. Not because I have done anything particularly incredible. I haven't been to Africa or somewhere really that different to the western world I have been brought up in. Despite its relative proximity the Mediterranean is a world away from what I have known. I suppose for the first time in my life I have taken control of it. I can't believe I nearly jacked it all in when beachselling. The last few months have been everything I dreamt of.

But now what?

What do I do with all this?

I go back to uni, another mediocre middle class non-story. Having my life all mapped out again. I will run my club night, pull a bit cos I've got a tan. Work hard, get a 2:1. Get a job. I hope. Or do I? What will I do? I literally don't know what to do. I like loads of stuff but nothing so much more than anything else that I want to actually work in it.

Some people have started applying for jobs I have heard. I feel like a weird mixture of a man–child.

---

226 Exaggerated, but Dustin Hoffman always seems to be on a bus in films. Particularly at poignant moments. See *The Graduate* and *Midnight Cowboy*. Arguably *Rain Man*.

I feel overwhelmed again and just want to cry. I want to LET IT LOOSE. Like Jagger is telling me to.

But how? Why? What for?

Nothing will ever be the same again.

Particularly my engorged penis.

University of Warwick, Coventry, October 1995

October 4

Today I went on a bus in to Coventry with Sod. It was grey and pissing it down. Good job I had the Lacoste windsheeter.

October 6

A depressingly back-to-reality conversation with someone from my course, reported verbatim:

"So how was yours, Ben?"

"My what?"

"The year abroadingtons."

"Oh. Fine, it..."

"...Yeah? Awesome. Mine was pretty ok actually – Rennes better than I thought. Not a total shits-ville. Teaching really tough. Really testing. Pushed myself to the limit. Pulled a cracking girl though...You look different. Thin."

"Really?"

"You look like a refugee. You're so brown."

"Oh."

Uncomfortable pause

"Any bint action?"

"Nothing to write home about."

"So I assume you will be in your normal position then at the Ball tonight then? Sharking the pool of new nubile flesh, lining them up for a year of razzle?"

"I have to go."

October 7

Walk the walk.

I don't like listening to other people banging on about their year abroad. If you feel the need to talk about it as loudly as most people on my course seem to, then I don't believe you. If you are going to be as trite as to tell me that it was "life-changing" then it clearly wasn't.

Going to the pub for the first time in ten months. First pint in all that time.

I have run out of after-sun.

October 8, 1995, 11 pm

The pain in my groin is so excruciating that I feel like the only solution is to be castrated. Can they castrate your entire crotch? I desperately want to go to the union with everyone else but if I take on fluids I also have to let them out of my body and the normal passage for doing that is somewhat out of action. I think I am being punished. I would like to repent all my sins. I wish Madame Cocheteux was here.

I miss France.

November 18, 11 pm

Victoria Coach Station, London

I took the coach over to Paris three days ago, under the premise of seeing some friends there, but I have literally not stopped going on about Emilie for the last four weeks at uni. I have bought her a copy of 'Exile on Main Street' and despite the fact that I have only received one letter from her in response to my three, I knew she wanted me to hop onto a single decker bus and prove my love. I phoned from Paris and her distant voice instructed me how to get to her house. With the notion that I was about to begin the next phase of my life I took the train out to near Versailles, found her block and buzzed on the door. Emilie came down the stairs, far from bounding it has to be said, but still as gorgeous as ever. She looked incredibly different though, partly because she was wearing clothing, and also different in that weird way when you see a holiday romance for the first time in a different environment, dressed in normal clothes and *sans* tan.

But still gorgeous.

A rather embarrassing moment occurred when I thought she was beckoning me in but she was in fact coming out. I bumped into her quite forcefully. Her eyes all teary, I knew how much this moment meant to her too. I reassured her that it was OK now, I was here. Before I could get much more out, she told me that her boyfriend was upstairs and that she was sorry, this should never have happened.

Writing this now, I can still feel the sense of shock coursing through my body even though it happened over two days ago. I can barely hold the pen still.

In a few seconds it was over, she kissed me on the cheek, and, like a human spaniel, I gave her the CD. Then I left, trudging along, not able to compute what was happening.

It wasn't even raining, I remember it was a really nice evening, actually.

I got back to the flat whose floor I was dossing on for the weekend.[227] The radio had been set to a channel programmed only to play songs charged with emotionally crippling associations and references to carrying. It didn't help that my hostess is the only 21-year-old in the western world who is into the band Bread, furthermore that her favourite Bread track is 'It don't matter to me'.[228]

I did the only sensible thing and went out and bought a six-pack of 1664, a bottle of red wine and some chips nature. Booze and crisps combining again to save another meltdown. Six Kronenbourgs, half a litre of wine and one whole family size bag of crisps later, I decided in my alcoholic clarity that Emilie was only testing me and what she really wanted was for me to be a man and fight for her love. I couldn't let go. No Cary G, no Paul Newman, no Belmondo would just take this on the chin. This is France goddamn it! The home of love and sobbing men and crimes of passion! In my fit of drunken ardour, I rang up her house phone and left her a message in which I told her that I wouldn't give up on her and that I was coming for her and that she should be ready for me with bags packed.

Yesterday morning I called to make good on my boozy plan and the father of Emilie told me to never call their house again.

---

227 Sarah, a friend from Warwick, had a friend who had kindly let me stay.
228 A song with the soppy intensity of a rescued dog, a song so self-pitying and pathetic that it actually contains the lyrics; *"It don't matter to me, If you take up with, Someone who's better than me, 'Cause your happiness is all I want, For you to find, Peace ... your peace of mind."*

University of Warwick, Coventry, December 1995

December 8

Epic snowfall across the North and the Midlands.

I received a letter from Emilie today completely out of the blue. I have listed the best bits.

"*Notre séparation n'était pas des plus joyeuses, mais j'ai préféré tout arrêter.*"

Our separation was not the most joyous but I preferred to stop everything.

"*Je me suis mise dans une situation ambiguë.*"

I found myself in an ambiguous situation.

"*Rien ne servait de continuer mon jeu de cache-cache.*"

Nothing would be served by continuing my game of hidey-hidey.

"*Saches que tout ceci ne change rien au fait que tu es un mec très bien et que le très peu de temps que nous avons passé ensemble, je ne le regrette pas.*"

Know that all this doesn't change anything, in fact you are a great guy and that the very small amount of time we spent together, I don't regret it.

"*Je continuera cependant à t'écrire, même si tu me réponds jamais. Toujours ton Emilie.*"

I will however continue to write to you, even if you never respond. Always your Emilie.

Sod reckons I should get cache-cache tattooed on my arm.

Ah, la vie est peut-être triste, mais elle est toujours belle.

Outro

- Patrick and Bernard are in their twelfth year owning their own extremely successful private beach, *Cap 21 – Les Murenes*, exactly next door to *Club 55*. Patrick, Inès and Bernard have all visited London on many occasions and Patrick and Inès spend every Christmas at the apartment I share with my wife in London.
- Sod is still my best friend and has worked for the same major frozen food retailer for the last 15 years. He has had a hand in inventing some of the best straight-to-oven fish products available in the UK. He is married and has two children and was one of the two best men at my wedding.
- I visited Enzo in Nottingham in November 1995. We found that we had as much in common back home as we had on the Côte d'Azur. He is now an actor and producer living in Los Angeles, is married and has twins, one of whom is also my goddaughter. He was the other best man at my wedding. He's returned to Cannes only once since that summer, when a film he was in was in competition for the *Palme d'Or*. It didn't win.
- Taba married his childhood sweetheart and, after one reunion with Enzo and I in Camden, which was the night in both of our lives when we laughed the most, he got a cab home at 4 am and disappeared from our lives completely.
- Jason Priestley sent one card from Montpellier and then we lost contact. He is still MIA.
- Fabressa and I stayed in contact for about a year then we both started relationships, which killed that. Mine didn't last. I bet hers did.
- Alistair has a son and has been working for *The Economist* for fifteen years. He is still in a band, which gigs regularly in south London. He is still a good friend who I meet with regularly for beers. He is also

still friends with Enzo and recently visited him in Los Angeles.

- Pollyanna Peters split with Enzo after about a year and married a Mexican with whom she has two children. We are still in contact and with Alistair the three of us have dinner in a French restaurant about three times a year.
- I bumped into Charlotte at a really boozy house party in North London in about 2002. She was incredibly charming and I chatted to her in the kitchen for about two hours. I think we both considered having a snog but by then she was living with a boyfriend who may well have straightened her out a bit. And that was that. We didn't discuss Saffron or Hutchence.
- Monsieur Guy Rufin is no longer head teacher at Collège le Big Fun. He is probably the head of the UN or something. He certainly should be.
- The looser the grip, the tighter the hold... I literally never saw Alessandra again in my whole life after she got in to that Maserati.
- Lee became a trader in the city. We met once for a beer a couple of years later but seemed to have less in common without the Tropezien backdrop and the four pints we had were painfully slow for both of us.
- My leaving do was the last time I, or anyone else I knew, saw Mobby.
- On October 3rd, 1995, OJ was acquitted of the murder of Nicole Brown Simpson and Ronald Goldman.
- AS Cannes have slumped to the French third division. The only player of note they have produced recently is Gaël Clichy.
- Patrick Vieira enjoyed a reasonably successful career winning the World Cup and European Championships with France, who he captained. He won three league titles and four FA Cups with Arsenal, who he also captained. He won four league titles with Inter Milan, again, captain. He was awarded the *Légion d'Honneur* in 1998.
- I never saw Madame Cocheteux again although I did send her a postcard when I visited the Grand Canyon two years later and twice drove up to her house on later visits to Cannes to see if she was in. The second time the neighbour told me she thought they had moved to Switzerland.
- Two weeks after I left France the Mustang Adam's brother was racing in the hills behind Pampelonne, slid on a hairpin bend and

went over the side of a sheer fall. The driver, another beachseller, was killed outright and Adam's brother was airlifted to a hospital in Marseille where he spent the next four months. About eight years later I bumped into him by chance in a bar where he was working in London. He couldn't really walk properly and understandably had no interest in talking about St.Tropez, which he only referred to as "that fucking place".

- On February 5th, 1997 a civil jury unanimously found Simpson liable for the wrongful death of and battery against Goldman, and battery against Brown. Simpson was ordered to pay $33,500,000 in damages.
- After the December letter I never heard one word from Emilie "again".
- I had an amazing final year in terms of pulling women, 27 at last count, and got a 2:1 degree after working my nuts off. I also got a first for a massive essay on *Pierrot le Fou*. It helps when you are a close friend of the star of a film you are writing about.
- I returned to St.Tropez the following summer after graduating and worked an even longer season, until October.
- I then started a career working for an advertising agency, which was fun, but I grew tired of it after a few years.
- I set up my own marketing company after that, something I repeated in early 2011.
- I have continued to return to St.Tropez three or four times a year and always stay with Patrick and his daughter, Inès (now 18) in his beach cottage at the far western end, past the naturist beach and *Cabane Bambou*.
- I was married at Patrick and Bernard's Pampelonne beach/restaurant in 2012.
- I first drafted this book whilst staying with Patrick for four weeks in the summer of 2010, ostensibly to "sort my life out". Enzo and I have written and edited in Wimbledon, the British Library, Sherman Oaks, Bradford and New York. We finalised the draft in Toronto in November 2011, where his wife was filming an instalment of a movie based on a video game.
- I wang on about my time in France at every given opportunity.

Partir, pour revenir mieux.

3012100R00179

Printed in Great Britain
by Amazon.co.uk, Ltd.,
Marston Gate.